In Zoilum.
　Tentas Maklurii incassum discerpere nomen,
　Livide, praeclarum iam super astra volat

　　　　　　　　Pat. Sandaeus, 1630

In Search of Dr John MacLuire:

Pioneer Edinburgh Physician, Forgotten for over Three Hundred Years

Wellcome Unit for the History of Medicine
University of Glasgow
Publication No. 9
1997

Series Editor: Malcolm Nicolson

Previous Publications:

Wendy Alexander
First Ladies of Medicine 1987

Stephen Patterson
Finding Fife's Medical Records 1992

Robert Campbell Garry
Life in Physiology 1992

Alastair Tough
Medical Archives of Glasgow and Paisley 1993

Hamish Maxwell-Stewart, Alastair Tough, John Hope
McColl and Johanna Geyer-Kordesch
Selecting Clinical Records for Long-Term Preservation
1993

Helen Brock *Dr James Douglas's Papers and Drawings
in the Hunterian Collection, Glasgow University Library.*
1994

Charles J. Smith (with J.G. Collee) *Edinburgh's
Contribution to Medical Microbiology* 1994

Margot Mayes *The Stormy Petrel: A Life of Dr Kate
Fraser* 1995

In Search of Dr John MakLuire:

Pioneer Edinburgh Physician, Forgotten for over Three Hundred Years

James F. McHarg

With a Historical Introduction by Helen Dingwall

Wellcome Unit for the History of Medicine
University of Glasgow

Dr James F. McHarg, VRD, MD, FRCPEdin, FRCPsych, is a retired Consultant Psychiatrist whose ancestral roots are, with those of Dr John MakLuire, in Galloway.

This publication has been made possible by the financial support of the Wellcome Trust.

Published by Wellcome Unit for the History of Medicine
5 University Gardens
University of Glasgow
Glasgow, G12 8QQ

ISBN 0 9511765 8 7

Print Layout by Malcolm Nicolson and Francis McKee

The cover illustration is from S. Blankaart, *De Nieuw Hervromde Anatomie ofte ontleding des Menschen Lichaams*, Amsterdam, J. ten Hoorn, 1686. With thanks to the Iconography Department, Wellcome Institute of the History of Medicine

For Pippa Henderson, medical student, my grand-niece, with love.

Acknowledgements

I wish to thank, in the first place, Miss Joan Ferguson, FRCPEdin, formerly Librarian to the Royal College of Physicians of Edinburgh, for passing on to me her discovery of the existence of the three books written by Dr MakLuire, and in this way encouraging my first, hesitant, inclination to embark upon the daunting search for the identity of their author. I wish to thank especially, second, Mr Robert Smart, Keeper of the Muniments of the University of St Andrews, for his early help, for his subsequent advice on many occasions, and for his permission to reproduce the relevant manuscript matriculation and graduation lists. I cannot thank too much, third, Mr James J. Robertson, of the Law Faculty at the University of Dundee, for his kindness in offering to translate (a time-consuming and difficult task) Dr MakLuire's *Tractatus de Febre Pestilente*, argued here to be his MD thesis for the University of St Andrews and. perhaps, if so, the earliest MD thesis to be printed in Scotland.

Also, I must acknowledge, with thanks, the ever-relevant advice, from time to time, of Professor Emeritus Sir Ivor Batchelor. The fact that Dr W.H. Makey, formerly City Archivist, Edinburgh, and subsequently Mr A. T. Wilson, were unstinting in their help over the City records was a great encouragement. It was a privilege, furthermore, to have talked with the late Dr Gwenneth Whitteridge, at Cambridge, over her incomparable knowledge of the great William Harvey and about her translation of his *Exercitationes de Generatione Animalium*.

I owe a particularly personal debt of gratitude to Mrs G. Stone (née Delacherois) of the Manor House, Donaghadee, for allowing me unrestricted access to the early manuscript records of the first three Viscounts Montgomery of the Ards, and for the most kind hospitality of herself and of her sister, Mrs A. Day, during my search. Similarly, Mr William Montgomery of Grey Abbey, Co. Down, was most helpful over his family knowledge of Dr MakLuire's friend, Sir James Montgomery of Rosemount.

Others whose help I have greatly valued have been the Lord Dacre (Professor H. Trevor-Roper); Mr J. Imrie, formerly Keeper of the Records of Scotland; Mr D.J. McKitterick (Rare Books, Cambridge University Library); Mr R.D. McClure, Belfast; Dr J. Kappers, Amsterdam; Dr Jane Henderson, Paris; Dr R. Gillespie, Dublin; Dr D. Stevenson, formerly of Aberdeen University; Mr A.E. Truckle, formerly of The Museum, Dumfries; Sheriff A. Wilkinson formerly, and Professor I. Willocks presently, of the Faculty of Law, and Dr L.A. Williams, Department of Modern History, all of the University of Dundee; Mr M. Clancy, of the Law Society of Scotland, for permission to consult, and to quote from, his Master of Laws thesis; the Reverend J. Povey, parish minister at Mid Calder for his knowledge of his predecessor, Maister Hugh Kennedy; Mr Simpson, Librarian, New College, Edinburgh University; Mr Mark Kauffmann, Assistant Librarian, the Bodleian Library; Mr A.T. Wilson (formerly assistant archivist, Glasgow University); the Reverend Father T.G. Holt of the English Province of the Society of Jesus; the staffs of the Scottish Record Office, the Manuscript Department of the University of Edinburgh, the British Library and the Manuscript Department of the British Museum; and Mr William Ferguson, lately shepherd at Carminnows, Kirkcudbrightshire, and his successor Mr G.W. Carnochan.

I have to acknowledge, with thanks, the permission of Dr J. Shaw, Records Officer, Register House, Edinburgh, to have two entries of Edinburgh baptisms xeroxed, and the permission of the Secretary of the Board of Practice and Procedure of the General Assembly of the Church of Scotland to publish these. I have also to acknowledge, with thanks, the permission of the National Library of Scotland to reproduce part of the Gordon of Rothiemay aerial map of Edinburgh. Other acknowledgements are recorded in the text.

Finally, I am most grateful to Dr Helen Dingwall, medical historian, of Stirling University, for the honour she has done me in providing the scholarly account of the historical background to Dr MakLuire's life and work which her unique knowledge of history of medicine in Scotland during the first half of the seventeenth century has enabled.

Contents

Historical Introduction

Medicine and Surgery in Sixteenth- and Seventeenth-Century Scotland

Helen Dingwall

By the time that Dr John MakLuire submitted the physicians' petition to King Charles I in 1630, Scottish medicine had progressed somewhat from the days of medieval monastic medicine and surgery, though much remained primitive and impossible long after his lifetime. Medical training in the Highlands was rather different from that in the lowland areas, skills and knowledge being handed down from father to son in the classical Gaelic tradition, based primarily on translated manuscripts of Greek and Arabic medical treatises.[1] The end results for the patients, however, were probably very much the same as those in other parts of the country. The main focus of this brief introductory chapter will be on medical and surgical training and practice in the lowland areas, particularly Edinburgh. The capital was by far the largest burgh, contained the most physicians, surgeons and apothecaries, and was at the centre of the various attempts made by the physicians to establish a College; one of these attempts involved Dr MakLuire.[2]

In order to assess the background to Dr John MakLuire, his actions and those of his fellow-physicians, it is necessary to examine in some detail the progress and organisation of medicine and surgery in Scotland from the early sixteenth century onwards. The situation in Edinburgh was

---

[1] Full account of one of the most prominent Gaelic medical dynasties is given in J. Bannerman, *The Beaton: A Medical Kindred in the Classical Gaelic Tradition*, Edinburgh, 1986.

[2] General histories include J.D. Comrie, *History of Scottish Medicine*, 2 vols., London, 1932; D. Guthrie, *History of Medicine*, London, 1958; D. Hamilton, *The Healers: A History of Medicine in Scotland*, Edinburgh, 1981; also M. Nicolson, 'Medicine', in *Scotland: A Concise Cultural History*, ed. P.H. Scott, Edinburgh, 1993, pp. 327-42.

very different from that in London, for example, where the College of Physicians, founded in 1513, and later the Company of Apothecaries, incorporated a century later, in 1617, wielded considerable political power, often to the detriment of their surgical colleagues in the Company of Barber-Surgeons. The roles in Edinburgh were reversed, in that the surgeons had been organised and incorporated with royal and Town Council support since 1505, and they managed to block several attempts by the physicians to set up an organisation which would have had considerable powers of supervision and precedence over themselves and also over the unorganised, but medically important, apothecaries. Following the eventual achievement of collegiate status by the physicians of Edinburgh in 1681, peace did not come immediately, though, and a number of the ensuing quarrels between physicians and surgeons reached the highest courts in the land; the litigation consisted primarily of protracted and heated disputes over the supervision of the politically-weak apothecaries. MakLuire was long dead by 1681, and the difficulties were by no means fully resolved, despite the successful establishment of a College of Physicians.

The various attempts to set up a collegiate organisation for the physicians of Scotland took place during a period of organisational and institutional developments in a number of areas which would nowadays be readily accepted as professional or professionalising. The Court of Session was established by James V in 1532 (though it would be over a century before a similar central criminal court appeared, in 1672); the Faculty of Advocates and the Society of Writers to the Signet flourished; and attempts by successive monarchs to centralise administration meant that there was ample work for the numerous basic-grade writers who laboriously wrote out complex legal documents, many of which were several feet in length. The Advocates' Library opened its doors in 1681; and Dalrymple of Stair's famous and seminal *Institutions*,[3]

---

[3] Sir J. Dalrymple of Stair, *Institutions of the Law of Scotland*, Edinburgh, 1681.

also published in 1681 - an apparently vintage year for Scottish professional institutions - helped to establish the definitive articulation of Scots Law and its eventual incorporation into legal studies courses at Scottish universities. It was not until the 1750s, though, that advocates were required to pass an examination in Scots Law before being allowed to practise in the supreme courts. Most of these developments were centred on Edinburgh, not surprisingly, since the capital was the legal centre of the nation as well as the largest burgh. The effects were, however, widespread and significant for the whole country. Royal patronage was important during the whole period, and the physicians owed much to the support of the Duke of York, the future James VII, during their final attempt to achieve their aims.[4]

The Edinburgh surgeons were incorporated in 1505, strictly in the mould of the typical manual craft organisation. Skinners, hammermen, bakers, bonnetmakers and other groups obtained charters of incorporation in the late-fifteenth and early-sixteenth centuries, initially with religious and pastoral intent, but later concentrating on the training of apprentices and prevention of unauthorised work by untrained individuals. Ironically perhaps, it was this very craft-based structure which allowed the surgeons to begin to acquire a number of important elements of professionalisation during the course of the seventeenth century.[5]

In Glasgow the physicians and surgeons joined together in a corporate body, initially very few in number, in 1599,

---

[4] G. Ouston, 'York in Edinburgh: James VII and the patronage of learning in Scotland, 1673-1688', in *New Perspectives on the Politics and Culture of Early Modern Scotland*, eds. J. Dwyer, R.A. Mason and A. Murdoch, Edinburgh, 1982, pp. 133-55, illustrates the importance of royal patronage.

[5] It is not the purpose of this introductory chapter to offer a detailed account or analysis of professionalisation. Full discussion of this aspect of Edinburgh medical practitioners in H. M. Dingwall, *Physicians, Surgeons and Apothecaries: Medicine in Seventeenth-Century Edinburgh*, East Linton, 1995.

largely as a result of the efforts of Peter Lowe, a Scottish surgeon who had given lengthy service to the French monarch and armed forces, and was the author of an important surgical textbook, written in vernacular Scots and intended for the use of surgical students.[6] Because of the small numbers of practitioners involved, and the relative isolation of Glasgow from mainstream politics and the royal court, however, there was consequently less opportunity for the Glasgow physicians and surgeons, however sensibly united, to influence general medical or surgical politics to any great extent. Similarly, although the surgeons of Aberdeen had apparently been incorporated since the late fifteenth century, distance and small numbers effectively marginalised these practitioners, and those in Dundee, although in 1657 the latter town hosted a conference of Scottish physicians, who met there to discuss possible moves towards incorporation.[7]

In order to illustrate the progress of medical and surgical practice and training, it is necessary to look briefly at a number of factors, including the general social and economic background, the rise of Edinburgh, changing social structures, particularly in burghs, and also at medical and surgical philosophy, training and practice in Scotland in the sixteenth and early seventeenth centuries. Despite the small size of the country, its generally poor, rural aspect and relatively few legitimate medical or surgical practitioners even in the larger burghs, the situation was surprisingly complex and dependent on a number of interacting influences and external pressures, not the least of which was very necessary royal and political influence, patronage and favour. Although some of the more high-ranking physicians may have been less inclined to remain in Scotland after 1603 when many wealthy and influential patients followed James VI and his court to London, a fair

---

[6] P. Lowe, *A Discourse of the Whole Art of Chirurgerie*, London, 1634; first edition 1597. There is an account of his life and influence in D. Guthrie, 'The achievement of Peter Lowe and the unity of physician and surgeon', *Scottish Medical Journal*, **10**, 1965, pp. 271-8.

[7] Hamilton, *The Healers*, p. 27.

sprinkling of nobility and gentry still lived in and around Edinburgh and in other parts of Scotland. They required medical services, which they obtained either by direct consultation or by correspondence with as many practitioners as they chose to consult.

During the 'long sixteenth century', which lasted till around 1640, Scottish society and economy witnessed a series of changes and problems.[8] At the beginning of the century trade was poor, inflation rife, and the great majority of the population still lived in varying degrees of poverty in rural surroundings with limited or non-existent access to the services of even minimally-qualified medical practitioners. Virtually no useful medical education was available for Scottish students of medicine within the Scottish universities, although Dr MakLuire apparently gained his MD degree from St Andrews. A medical school had been suggested for that University by John Knox, but there was no separate medical school there in MakLuire's time.[9]

Similarly, a mediciner had been in post at the University of Aberdeen since its foundation in 1497,[10] but apart from a few zealous and conscientious individuals such as Gilbert Skene, (author of *Ane Breve Description of the Pest*, an early tract on the prevention and treatment of plague published in 1568), this post was something of a sinecure, and can be fairly easily disregarded as a legitimate or reputable source of training for Scottish physicians (even until the late eighteenth century, when medical degrees could still be obtained at Aberdeen on recommendation alone, without examination or any other form of assessment)[11].

---

[8] For a general account of Scotland in the period, see M. Lynch, *Scotland: A New History*, London, 1992.

[9] For an account of medical education at St Andrews in J.G.S. Blair, *History of Medicine in the University of St Andrews*, Edinburgh, 1987.

[10] There is a list of incumbent mediciners in Comrie, *History of Scottish Medicine*, p. 371.

[11] For accounts of medical training in Aberdeen, see G.A.G. Mitchell, 'The medical history of Aberdeen and its universities', *Aberdeen Uni-*

Most Scottish people lived in the country, and despite a 50 per cent increase in population over the course of the long century, by 1700 the proportion of people living in towns had reached only around one-tenth. In the 1640s the population of Edinburgh numbered around 25,000, and by the end of the seventeenth century some 45,000 souls inhabited the capital and its sprawling, rural suburbs of Leith, Canongate and West Kirk. It was not until the closing years of the seventeenth century that Glasgow began to make rapid economic and social progress, with a consequent increase in population and demand for more medical practitioners.[12]

In addition to this gradual process of slow urbanisation and rather more rapid general population increase, a number of new groups were beginning to emerge, which helped to mould and change the historic structure of Scottish society. In rural areas many lairds had benefited from the widespread feuing of church lands which had begun in the 1530s; in the burghs the growing numbers of lawyers, merchants, and others with middle-range incomes and a similar level of domestic comforts and increasing material aspirations heralded the emergence of the middling sort, a somewhat amorphous but yet vital group, which contained a fair number of surgeons, physicians and apothecaries within its ranks. Some members of these new groups provided medical services, and all of them required treatment for their own illnesses and injuries. During the early decades of the seventeenth century the wealthier merchants still dominated burgh society, economy and politics, but the organised craft incorporations in the larger

---

versity Review, 1958; A.A. Mclaren, 'Patronage and professionalism: the "forgotten middle class", 1760-1860', in *The Making of Scotland: Nation, Culture and Social Change*, eds. D. McCrone, S. Kendrick and P. Straw, Edinburgh, 1989, pp. 123-42.

[12] There is an analysis of population of Edinburgh in H.M. Dingwall, *Late-Seventeenth Century Edinburgh: A Demographic Study*, Aldershot, 1994, p. 14-21. Comparisons of burgh populations in M. Lynch, 'Urbanisation and urban networks in seventeenth-century Scotland: some further thoughts', *Scottish Economic and Social History*, **12**, 1992, pp. 24-41.

settlements were able to wield a degree of political influence, particularly following legislation in 1583 which allowed their permanent, though minority, representation on Town Councils.[13] The system established in Edinburgh was replicated in a number of other Scottish burghs, and would prove significant when the physicians began their several attempts to achieve an organisation, and drew up their various petitions for a royal charter. The Edinburgh surgeons were permanently represented on the Town Council after 1583, and because they had the ear and support of the Town Council, the physicians faced considerable opposition and obstacles. The changing socio-economic profile of Scotland and its major burghs, particularly Edinburgh, was of some significance for the progress of medicine.

Over the course of the seventeenth century a pattern of political manoeuvring began to take shape, resulting eventually in a situation where the Edinburgh surgeons and the Town Council were ranked in opposition against the physicians and the law courts. Questions of legal authority and precedence arose, a major issue being whether a decree of the Court of Session could supersede an act of the Town Council. This sort of legal conflict came to a head in the decades after 1681, but deeply-felt animosities between physicians and surgeons can be detected in most of the evidence which has survived relating to the various efforts made by the physicians to secure an organisation. Scots law itself was still in the process of exposition and formulation, and this added to the complexities of the debates. Most of the legal action took place after MakLuire's time, but the physicians' views on their own superiority and their perceived rights to dominate the apothecaries and surgeons are clear from

---

[13] *Extracts from the Records of the Burgh of Edinburgh 1528-1716,* 12 vols., eds. J.D. Marwick, M. Wood and H. Armet, Edinburgh, 1871-1967, 22 April, 1583.

Historical Introduction

the surviving documentation and colourful language of
their various petitions.[14]

All of these social, economic and political factors added
complexity to the situation in which the physicians - relatively few in number - found themselves. They may well
have enjoyed the advantages of higher social rank, with all
that this meant in terms of political influence and royal
favour, but other factors were in play also. By 1681, when
their campaign was finally successful, Scottish society had
changed. Edinburgh was, though, still dominant and by far
the most complex burgh, operating as the established
centre of the legal profession and other tertiary services,
and housing a fair number of physicians, surgeons and
apothecaries. The establishment of the physicians' College
was a further step along the difficult road taken by medical
men towards institutionalisation and professionalisation.
Much more rapid progress would take place during the
second half of the eighteenth century, in other Scottish
burghs as well as the capital, and the actions of Dr John
MakLuire and his colleagues, though initially unsuccessful, were of considerable importance when viewed over a
longer timescale. (The College of Physicians would play a
significant part in the foundation of the Medical School at
Edinburgh University in 1726, though its members had,
ironically, forfeited their own rights to teach medicine -
one of the concessions they were forced to make in 1681
in order to gain approval for their charter of incorporation.)

It is out of this background that the professional groups of
Scotland began to develop and evolve, and although the
early attempts to set up a corporate physicians' organisation may have been made from sentiments of a purely
protectionist, though apparently altruistic, nature, without
conscious thoughts of the long-term effects on the broader
professionalisation process, the result was a significant

---

[14] There are full accounts of these matters in W.S. Craig, *History of
the Royal College of Physicians of Edinburgh*, Oxford, 1976; and
Dingwall, *Physicians and Surgeons*.

and lasting contribution to the rise of the medical profession in Scotland. The pace of change quickened markedly during the Enlightenment period, but earlier events and individual actions must be accorded their rightful place in the longer term perspective.

Medical philosophy, training and practice in the sixteenth and seventeenth centuries

Fully-trained and qualified physicians in Scotland were few and mainly to be found in larger burghs, or attending the incumbent monarch, the royal court or the armed forces. Medical care for a large proportion of the population was obtained by self-treatment, or by consulting the local wise woman, minister or schoolteacher, together with the circulation of recipes obtained from printed 'poor man's guides' and publications such as MakLuire's *Buckler of Bodilie Health*. Extracts from these publications were often copied out in commonplace books compiled by the local minister or schoolmaster, who may have been the only literate individuals in the locality. Many of the recipes were outlandish, to say the least, but most of the vegetable, animal and mineral ingredients they contained were also to be found in some form in the prescriptions issued by qualified medical practitioners. A welcome surviving example of such a collection is 'Ane Gude Boke of Medicines', dated 1595, which by 1602 was apparently in the possession of David Wallace, son of Adam Wallace, minister at Crosbie Kirk.[15] This manuscript book contains 'The Treasure of Poor Men', a work by Thomas Petyt which was printed in four editions between 1539 and 1552. Among its multifarious contents are a recipe for *aqua vitae* and a number of curative and preventive measures. The most auspicious times of the year for prophylactic phlebotomy are noted; recipes are given for 'sax precyous waters yat Ipotras (apothecaries) maid & sent thame to ane quene yat sum tyme was into England'; while to 'make teith to fall by thame selfs' the patient is

---

[15] Edinburgh University Library, EUL, Dc.8.130; see also Comrie, *History of Scottish Medicine*, pp. 188-9.

advised to 'take ane water frogge and ane grene frogge & seith them togidder and gadder the greace and smeir their-with thy gumms about the teith'. Many current recipes included frogs, snails, millipedes and other livestock, and even at the end of the seventeenth century the eminent and notorious Edinburgh physician Archibald Pitcairne was not at all embarrassed to advise the application of live doves to the soles of a patient's feet as part of the prescribed treatment programme.[16]

In all of this, it is also essential to remember that the hand of God was believed to account for much disease and suffering, whether individual, endemic or epidemic. A confused mixture of sin, superstition, fear of witchcraft, divine providence, humoral imbalances and local pathology influenced the attitudes of the patient and the doctor towards disease and injury. Although physicians such as Gilbert Skene had published on prevention and cure of plague, and town councils tried to take preventive measures, outbreaks of such afflictions were still considered to be the judgement of God. In 1645, during the last major episode of plague in Scotland, Sir John Clerk of Penicuik received a letter from James Barnes, observing that 'both the distractions off this tyme and the lords hand yt hes beine upon us heir in this province of Lowdian and in spetiall in Edr and Leith qr yr is ane totall desolation but now the lords hand is stayt and the daithe is ceist'.[17] The medical practitioners - who may well have shared these beliefs and superstitions in varying degrees - had to develop their expertise and also separate themselves from the amateurs and from magical cures. MakLuire's published works were one means by which he could attempt to do this. It is interesting to note, though, that the contents lists of the *Buckler* confirm that matters of diet, constitution, climate and general behaviour were given due prominence, as they were in most poor man's guides and other medical publications.

---

[16] Hamilton, *The Healers*, p. 58.
[17] Scottish Record Office, SRO, GD18/2464, letter dated 22 October, 1645.

The boundaries between authorised, professional and amateur medical practice were blurred to a considerable extent, and the niceties of occupational designation were neither enforced nor clearly understood by the patients. In this period occupational nomenclature was generally very loosely applied, and in medicine the designation of 'apothecary' was used frequently by the patients as a generic term for any medical practitioner, so it is consequently difficult to assess from the surviving records just how many fully- or even partly-qualified practitioners of any particular branch of medicine served the bodily needs of the people of Scotland. It is fairly safe to assume, however, that the further away from an urbanised settlement, the less likely it was that the local physician, surgeon or apothecary had any qualifications at all, let alone a university degree or a full surgical apprenticeship training.

A clearer picture of the training and qualification of physicians is discernible from the early seventeenth century onwards, though Dr MakLuire's training seems to have been perhaps a little atypical. The aspirant physician (as MakLuire did), generally started the long road to qualification by taking an arts degree at a Scottish university, which he may have entered as early as twelve years of age. Following this, the student very often proceeded, either immediately or after a period of supervised 'apprenticeship' training, to a continental university to study medicine, there being little real opportunity to pursue such study at home. This continental drift is not surprising, given the very strong and long-standing contacts between Scotland and the mainland of Europe, particularly France and the Low Countries. The first recorded matriculation of a Scottish medical student at the University of Leiden, for example, was that of James Maculo, who commenced his studies there in 1602. Maculo matriculated at the relatively advanced age of twenty-eight years, but he did not enrol at Leiden in subsequent years, and did not take an MD degree of that university. It is not clear where, or if, Maculo obtained his MD degree, but he later served as physician to the royal household.[18] Leiden became a highly popular centre for Scottish medical students, though at the beginning of the seventeenth century Padua, Paris and Montpelier were among a variety of alternative teaching and examining centres chosen.

A three-year course of medical studies was normal before the student took his final examinations and was declared fit to practise medicine. However, unlike more modern arrangements, there was no requirement for the medical student to complete his studies, take final examinations and graduate at the same university. It became common practice for a student to matriculate and study for one or two years at one centre, then move to another to take his final examinations. It is not clear why the students chose to do this, but in this period the examinations were specifically a test of *knowledge.* There was no formal *curriculum* requirement; all that had to be demonstrated to the examiners was that the student had acquired the minimum level of knowledge deemed necessary for the practice of medicine. Consequently it was almost the exception rather than the rule for a medical student to graduate at the university where he had carried out most of his studies. Towards the end of the seventeenth century it became almost routine for Scottish medical students to matriculate and study in Leiden, but graduate from Reims. It may be that the latter centre had a reputation for easier examinations or was perhaps more open to bribery or other inducements, but whatever the reason, this became a fairly well-established pattern, though perhaps bringing into question the quality of some of the degrees gained.

No matter the chosen centre of education, final examinations (and eventually the entrance tests for the Edinburgh College of Physicians) generally took a similar format,

---

[18] Information on Leiden students was obtained from University of Leiden, Archief Senaat & Curatoren, and R.W. Innes-Smith, *English-Speaking Students of Medicine at the University of Leiden*, Edinburgh, 1926; National Library of Scotland, NLS, MS 5112/70, contains a prescription for a vomit and purge issued by Maculo for a member of the royal household.

consisting primarily in the exposition of one or more prescribed Hippocratic aphorisms, and the submission and public defence of a thesis or dissertation on a medical topic. The lectures at most teaching centres consisted of a detailed rehearsal of the writings of classical medical authors and the diagnosis and treatment of standard symptoms or symptom complexes, though within these general guidelines the constitution, diet and lifestyle of each patient had to be carefully assessed. Treatments were described on largely humoral lines, in accordance with the predominant medical philosophy, and this practice continued for most of the seventeenth century (though chemical medicines did begin to appear towards the turn of the eighteenth century). There was also some opportunity for the Scottish medical students to receive clinical instruction. Large centres such as Paris had long benefited from the presence of hospitals, and there was a small, but important hospital at Leiden, but current medical philosophy, teaching and prescribing practices did not require the medical students to have a great deal of 'hands on' experience. The persistence of humorally-based prescribing, even after iatro-mechanical and iatro-chemical theories were well known and widely debated, militated against progress in the techniques of physical examination or invasive investigations.

Medical education was descriptive, case histories were descriptive and examinations were little different. Surviving records at Leiden indicate the scope of the final tests, the aphorisms and the topics of some of the dissertations submitted by Scottish students who would in due course practise in Scotland what they had learned abroad. Among the aphorisms which were allocated to Scottish examination candidates were:

> In the beginning of diseases, if there appears any cause for moving of any thing, move it.

> In loosenesses and vomitings that happen spontaneously, if such things be purged as ought to be purged, they are profitable and easily endured, otherwise it falls out contrary.

People of an extream plight of body, are in a state of danger for they cannot continue in the same state, nor change into a better. It remains, therefore, that they must decline into a worse, so extream evacuations are dangerous, as also extream repletions.

Summer Quarta Feavers are for the most part short: but the Autumnal long, especially those which remain till Winter.

It is better that a Feaver should succeed a Convulsion than Convulsion a Feaver.

Whosoever having need of purging hath pains above the midriff, it is a sign that he must be purged upwards, but the pains which are under the same show a purging downwards to be needed.

Things evacuated and purged are not to be estimated by the multitude, but advisedly to be considered if these things be voided and sent forth which should and ought to be and if also the patient do easily endure it.[19]

These are typical of the aphorisms on which students were tested, and they clearly reflect the prevailing philosophical concerns with constitution, and the central pillars of treatment, which consisted of the administration of purges, enemas and vomits to rid the body of the malevolent humoral imbalance, followed by symptomatic treatments and tonics.

Once the student had cleared the first hurdle and successfully expounded on the required aphorisms, the final stage was the public examination and defence of his dissertation. Scottish students offered treatises on many topics, including:

de febre maligna

de lithiasi

---

[19] Text of aphorisms is taken from *The Aphorisms of Hippocrates and the Sentences of Celsus*, ed. C.J. Sprengell, London, 1708.

de vomitu

de apoplexia

de scorbuto

Fever, scurvy and apoplexy were among the conditions which would be frequently encountered by physicians (fever being the topic of MakLuire's own dissertation), while the thesis on vomiting is squarely based on the rationale of current treatment. Occasionally a candidate had the advantage of being allocated aphorisms which were very close to the subject of his thesis; consequently his qualification was based on a very narrow agenda, and its value perhaps called into question. What is indisputable, however, is that both aphorisms and dissertations were relevant to humoral medicine, which was practised in Scotland during MakLuire's time and long after. Although John MakLuire did not travel abroad for his medical training, there is little doubt that what he learned in Scotland would be very much the same as the knowledge gained by students who chose to - and could afford to - travel abroad. He did not, however, have the benefit of hospital training of any sort.

Because of the prevalence of humoral philosophy and current ideas as to the social context of the application of learning, medical students were not usually trained specifically in the techniques of physical examination or encouraged to do more than take a very detailed case history and assess the lifestyle and constitution of the patient. Although there is some evidence to suggest that medical students did avail themselves of the opportunity to attend hospitals in some of the major European centres during the course of their university studies, progress in clinical medicine was severely hampered by humoral practices, and so the student who had not attended at the bedside was not particularly disadvantaged when he began to consult and prescribe on his own account. Henry, for example, states that medical students 'were not stupid' and did make use of available hospital facilities.[20] The point is, however, that what took place at the bedside was mainly observation and description, not invasive or detailed physical examination. Medical education and practice involved theories and their application to the individual rather than a combination of theories and the acceptance of new knowledge, equipment or investigative techniques. Observation of urine and the condition of blood obtained at phlebotomy were perhaps the nearest the seventeenth-century physician came to clinical investigations.

Since so little changed over the course of the seventeenth century, it is reasonable to assume that case-histories taken from the later decades were typical of those from the early years, from which disappointingly little evidence survives. The two case histories which follow are typical of those extant, and clearly demonstrate the main pillars of humoral medicine. The first case concerns Lady Cassilis, and the physician's notes record that she had suffered a miscarriage in November 1670, when 'conceptione was irrevocably declyned and loos'd'. The remaining problem was 'gravell, waterie and melancholick humors in the whole mass of her blood'.[21] In addition to encouraging the patient to avoid 'meats of uneasye digestion', fish, cheese and fruit, the physician was of the opinion that:

> though the winter season forbids entering upon a course of medicine (except in case of need) and strengthening things are most proper for my Ladyes present conditione yet for taking away some parts of over-abounding and noxious humors, and for preparing of my Ladyes bodie to the more successfull use of restoratives, that all may be brought to the desyred temper it is

---

[20] J. Henry, 'Doctors and healers: popular culture and the medical profession', in *Science, Culture and Popular Belief in Renaissance Europe*, eds. S. Pumphrey, P.L. Rossi and M. Slawinski, Manchester, 1991, p. 195.

[21] SRO, GD25/9/44/7, document dated 22 November, 1670.

expedient that my Lady take a gently purgative medicine.

This case neatly encapsulates the holistic aspects of humoral medicine. The cure involved attention to diet and lifestyle as well as medicines, and the use of a purgative to remove the evil humors before the use of restoratives was entirely appropriate to this philosophy.

In the second case, the physician - no less a personage than Archibald Pitcairne - does not directly enunciate humoral philosophy, but his notes confirm that he was still practising very much according to humoral dictates. The patient is again female and of gentry rank:

She has never yet been 2 days free of her hyster-
ick vapours since the stubborn disease first took
her ... not a minute by night or day but she
complains of some symptom or other, frequently
a giddiness with a scotomia and sometymes a sort
of delirium but a perpetuall *sensus strangulat-*
ionis, a bad appetite yet necessitate every hour to
take some food *sub forma liquida* for she can
take nothing solide neither in dyet nor medicine;
her leggs swolled a little at night qch threattens a
relapse of the extraordinarie oedematous swel-
lings she had after her last chyldebearing some 6
or 8 months ago for which she was forced to
undergo a course of purging physic. She is but
feeble and thin, yet not so weak and lean as I
have seen her since she took this disease. She is
easily terrified, very apprehensive and thinks that
every paroxisme will kill her as is ordinarie with
others in lyke cases.[22]

This is again a typical account, though admittedly from sources of limited scope. The general condition of the patient and her multiple symptomatology are noted. There is no mention of any physical examination, and no central diagnosis is offered. Pitcairne prescribed two different

[22] EUL, Dc. 1.62, *Praxeos Pitcarnianae*, 29 August, 1702.

vomits followed by a purge (these despite the observation that the patient was 'but feeble and thin'), together with several strengthening or tonic drinks. Mercury was not advised at that stage, though it may well have been offered at a subsequent consultation, as it was used to treat many conditions, ranging from madness to gout and gonorrhoea. Symptoms were related to humoral imbalances rather than to localised causes, and treatment was offered on this basis. In order to effect a cure, it was necessary to rid the body of evil matters or humors by means of purges, enemas, vomits, and bloodletting, and then restore the balance with strengthening drinks and additional Galenical palliatives for each individual symptom. This is exactly what happened to the patients referred to above and doubt-less to their ancestors for most of the sixteenth and seventeenth centuries.

Medicine at this time was perfectly easily practised at a distance; there was no particular need to see or examine the patient in order to arrive at a diagnosis. Even the taking of the pulse was not regarded as essential, though it did become more acceptable later in the period. Thermometers also began to appear in the early years of the eighteenth century. Since diagnosis and treatment were matters of principle and detailed individual account of symptoms, a considerable amount of the physician's work could be, and was, carried out by correspondence. In the cases described, the physicians had seen the patients, but the limited surviving records indicate that many consultations were carried out unseen. Treatment was axiomatic and symptomatic, and a carefully-written letter served just as well as a consultation in many cases. This would be the reality at least until new classifications and causations of disease were introduced by William Cullen and others in the later eighteenth century during the intellectual stimulation of the Scottish Enlightenment period. The rival iatro-mechanical and iatro-chemical philosophies caused much debate and controversy, and produced a split within the membership of the Edinburgh College of Physicians, but as Henry states, these beliefs did not affect treatments because 'new theories did not dictate new practices'.[23]

During the course of the sixteenth and seventeenth centuries the prescriptions issued by Scottish physicians became more and more complex, and by the end of the seventeenth century were bordering on the ludicrous. It was not unknown for a prescription to contain fifty or sixty ingredients, most of which were herbs and vegetable substances. Mercury was frequently offered, its side-effects of excessive salivation and mouth ulcers also requiring prolonged symptomatic treatment. Chemical substances seem to have been slower to appear in Scotland than in England, but by the end of the period items such as oil of tartar or spirit of sulphur can be found occasionally in treatment programmes. It has been claimed that the increasing complexity of physicians' prescriptions was in part an attempt to outdo the apothecaries, who were themselves offering treatment unofficially.[24] Whatever the case, the first few editions of the *Edinburgh Pharmacopoeia* (first published in 1699) contained most of these numerous and sometimes exotic substances; it was not till the middle of the eighteenth century that the publication was purged of its most bizarre offerings.

Much of the surviving material on consultations and treatments concerns patients drawn from upper social ranks, but there is evidence that while individuals of lesser social status and financial means might well consult more amateur practitioners before reaching the qualified physician (many of whom offered some free treatments to the poor themselves as an altruistic or Christian duty), the medicines and advice offered to these patients were similar. Evidence from treatments given free to the poorest inhabitants of Edinburgh, for example, confirms that the advice and prescriptions offered to these people were very much the same as those supplied with greater frequency to the better-off. Suggestions to move to the country or visit

[23] Henry, 'Doctors and healers', p. 213.
[24] Hamilton, *The Healers*, p. 31.

Bath or Aix-la-Chapelle in order to take the curative waters, however, had no place in the treatment of the poor.

It seems clear from the available records that physicians' training and their subsequent medical practice in Scotland changed but little over the course of the sixteenth and seventeenth centuries, despite the increasing awareness of new theories and philosophies of disease. Changes in treatments lagged far behind any new explanation or classification of disease, and it is, therefore, more than likely that the case histories taken by Dr MakLuire and his colleagues and the treatments they prescribed in the early years of the turbulent seventeenth century were very similar to those offered by Archibald Pitcairne and his fellow members of the College of Physicians at the end of the century.

Apothecaries and their role in medicine

Apothecaries played an important part in the general provision of medicine and medical treatment, again particularly in the burghs, and they deserve separate consideration at this point. Although often missed out in analyses of medical practitioners, the apothecaries carried out many functions and offered an important and pivotal service to physicians and surgeons, and also directly to the public. Evidence as to their apprenticeship training and examinations is fragmentary; the Edinburgh apothecaries (who numbered around twenty by the end of the seventeenth century) enjoyed only a very brief period of corporate organisation, in stark contrast to their London counterparts, who wielded considerable political power and belonged to a strong organisation. Apothecaries were also to be found in most of the larger burghs, including Glasgow, Dundee and Aberdeen, but were few in number. Despite the lack of political power or corporate strength, Scottish apothecaries offered a comprehensive medical service in a number of areas.

Following a period of apprenticeship training and subsequent testing, either by their colleagues or the Town Council, the apothecary was free to set up shop and hang out an appropriate sign to advertise his services. Surviving testamentary evidence for a small number of Edinburgh apothecaries indicates that in the capital, and probably in other burghs, their shops were specialist in nature from an early date.

The testament of Thomas Davidson is particularly informative in this regard.[25] Davidson died in October 1574, having offered his services in Edinburgh for several decades previously. The inventory of his shop stock is carefully recorded in his testament, and this gives welcome insight into the substances he bought in, compounded and sold to his customers. Among the many vegetable ingredients to be found on the shelves were tamarind and cardamom seeds, almonds, roses, cloves, mint, opium and myrrh, while animal and mineral products included beetles, millipedes, arsenic, borax and mercury. Medicinal glass and earthenware containers were also available. What is perhaps more surprising, however, is the apparently wide range of ready-prepared compounds available for immediate sale. Over seventy of these were listed, including some of the items which appeared most frequently on the surviving prescriptions issued by later medical practitioners, doubtless including Dr MakLuire and his colleagues. An apothecary's bill dated June 1630, the very year of MakLuire's petition, contained charges for mercury sublimate and almond oil.[26] Among the ready-prepared compounds available from Thomas Davidson were *unguentum apostolorum*, so named because of the twelve ingredients it usually contained; *unguentum de althea*, an ointment containing extracts from the marshmallow plant; and *emplastrum diachylon*, a commonly used lead plaster applied as a strengthener to the limbs or torso. Given the precarious nature of some of the compounds and presumably brief shelf-life before decay set in, Davidson's comprehensive stock would appear to confirm that his was a fairly active business and that he

---

[25] SRO, CC8/8, Register of Testaments, 18 June, 1575.

[26] NLS, Adv. Ms. 80.2.5, f175r, account sent to the Earl of Dundas by apothecary John Hamilton. Payment was received on 5 July, 1630.

was confident that he could dispose of both the raw ingredients and the compounded items. An account due by Dundas to John Hamilton in 1629 included 'materials for fomentation to his briest', together with a pectoral ointment, a purgative electuary and a vomiting potion, confirming that both unmixed ingredients and prepared compounds were supplied.[27]

The recorded stock of Davidson's and the (admittedly few) other surviving inventories confirms that, in the Edinburgh shops at least, all of the contents were directly related to the apothecary's trade. Work on English apothecaries in the period has suggested that many of these individuals owned shops which were rather more in the nature of general grocery stores as well as specialist dispensaries.[28] This is perhaps not surprising, as the London apothecaries, and probably those in regional centres, had been members of the Grocers Company before they achieved incorporated status in 1617. The Edinburgh (and other Scottish) apothecaries had no long-standing organisation, but seem to have become specialists in the larger towns. It is very likely that in the more rural areas the general supply aspect would increase, and this is confirmed from the surviving account book of an apothecary supplying Dumfries and the surrounding area.[29]

The apothecary made up prescriptions 'at direction' (of a physician), or sold the individual raw ingredients to the physician or direct to the patient. Mail-order business was also carried out. The widespread practice of circulating recipes for cures, either derived from folk-medicine or originating in doctors' prescriptions, meant that the dispensing apothecary was a vital element in the general

---

[27] *Ibid.*, f174r, 17 July 1629.

[28] J.G.L. Burnby, *A Study of the English Apothecary from 1660-1760*, London, 1983, is mainly concerned with provincial apothecaries.

[29] Royal College of Physicians of Edinburgh, 'Ane Doctors Account Book, c1682-93'. Besides the usual medical goods, this individual sold baskets, rope and other general hardware items. Despite its title, this book is clearly that of an apothecary, not a physician.

provision of medical care. In remoter areas the shops were much less specialised, and in very distant parts there were none, but the influence of these shops and their proprietors was great, and perhaps under-reported hitherto. The apothecary also consulted and prescribed independently, though against the wishes of physicians and surgeons, and he must therefore be given due status in the hierarchy of Scottish medicine. It is probably precisely because of their medical importance and economic success that they became the political football of Edinburgh medicine during the 1680s and onwards.[30] There is little doubt that physicians such as MakLuire would be familiar with the more well-known apothecaries and may well have directed their patients to obtain their cures from their shops. Physicians and surgeons may have been the main players on the stage of Scottish medical politics, but in terms of medicine and its provision to the patients, the apothecary was no less important.

Surgeons and surgical training in the sixteenth and seventeenth centuries

Scottish surgeons achieved their qualifications very differently from the physicians, though arguably more appropriately. Training was by apprenticeship, in line with the methods used by all craft organisations, which sought to achieve occupational exclusivity, maintain standards and prevent unauthorised individuals from carrying out the same work. These were precisely the objectives of the physicians and surgeons, and also of most groups which are nowadays recognised as professions. Most of the early surviving records concern the Edinburgh surgeons, and these give welcome insight into the running of an incorporation as well as surgical training and organisation. In most other parts of Scotland the numbers of surgeons were too small to allow viable incorporations in the early six-

---

[30] There is a fuller account of Edinburgh apothecaries in H.M. Dingwall, 'Making up the medicine: apothecaries in sixteenth- and seventeenth-century Edinburgh', *Caduceus*, **10**, 1994, pp. 121-30; also Dingwall, *Physicians, Surgeons and Apothecaries.*

teenth century. In Glasgow a combined organisation initially comprising two physicians, six surgeons and one apothecary was established in 1599; this was a unique situation and one which has lasted to this day (though a separate surgical incorporation linked to the Town Council was established in the mid-seventeenth century).[31] Around thirty individuals have been identified as being medical practitioners in Dundee during the course of the sixteenth century; numbers at any point must, therefore, have been small. A surgical incorporation also existed in Aberdeen, but again had few members.[32] It may be assumed, though, that where apprenticeship training was available, the experiences of the apprentices and their relationships with the masters were similar in most areas. Edinburgh apprentices enjoyed the academic advantages of a library, museum collection and dissection theatre by the end of the seventeenth century, but facilities of this type were only possible in larger settlements with substantial numbers of masters and apprentices.

As noted, the Edinburgh surgeons were incorporated in 1505, their charter, or Seal of Cause, being ratified the following year by James IV, a monarch fortuitously interested in all matters of a scientific and medical nature.[33] In addition to organisational features common to all craft incorporations, such as the annual election of a deacon and other office-bearers and attempts to regulate behaviour, this charter contained three elements which helped to elevate the Edinburgh surgeons above other crafts and which had an impact on training and practice. Firstly, it was stipulated that no apprentice could be indentured unless he could read and write, and later evidence

---

[31] For account of developments in Glasgow, see A. Duncan, *Memorials of the Faculty of Physicians and Surgeons of Glasgow,* Glasgow, 1896.

[32] E. Bain, *Merchant and Craft Guilds: A History of the Aberdeen Incorporated Trades*, Aberdeen, 1887.

[33] Full text of Seal of Cause is in *Edinburgh Records*, 1 July, 1505; account of Incorporation in C.H. Cresswell, *The Royal College of Surgeons of Edinburgh*, Edinburgh, 1926.

confirms that they were tested in Latin as well as in vernacular Scots, a number being sent away to improve their grammar before their indentures could be concluded. (The Barber-Surgeons of London brought in a similar regulation in 1556, but cancelled it within a month, while the charter of the Glasgow Faculty does not contain specific rules on literacy.)[34] Every Edinburgh apprentice should, therefore, have been able to read the vital works of Vesalius, Harvey or Peter Lowe. By 1700 the Incorporation had built up an academic lending library containing around 120 texts together with a collection of curiosities and a supply of surgical instruments available for hire.

Secondly, well-supervised apprenticeship training was ordered, since 'every man ought to know the nature and substance of everything he works, or ellis he is negligent'. Anatomy was particularly emphasised (some forty years before Vesalius' *De Fabrica Corporis Humani* was published), as was detailed knowledge of the venous system for bloodletting purposes, and also of the astrological signs, the latter perhaps of slightly more importance in 1505 than in 1700. Close study of anatomy meant that what little surgery was possible was carried out as well as it could be. This combination of academic study and practical apprenticeship was unique among the craft organisations, and surely a sign of early professionalisation.

Thirdly, properly organised and rigorous examinations were to be undertaken, as every surgeon should be 'diligently and avisitly examinit and provit' before admission to the Incorporation. The examination syllabus was formalised in 1647, and included sessions on general anatomy, operative procedures and bandaging (the latter delightfully referred to as 'proper apparell'). Tests on botany and *materia medica* were added in the early eighteenth century in response to an attempt by the College of Physicians to become involved in the instruction of surgical apprentices. These regulations, enforced from the start, ensured that the

---

[34] Company of Barber-Surgeons of London, Court Minute Books, 22 July, 1556 and 26 August, 1556.

aims of the surgeons were correct; undoubtedly some apprentices were less well treated and received inferior training, but at least the basis was established early upon which the profession of surgery would be built in succeeding centuries.

These three factors were of particular importance for the subsequent practice of surgery, even in the limited form in which it was possible, and it is likely that similar training, but without some of the academic trappings, was available elsewhere in Scotland. In social terms, it is likely that the high standards of literacy and testing imposed were in part responsible for the relatively higher social rank attainable by Scottish surgeons in comparison to their English colleagues. There was, and is, a deeply-held regard for learning and broad-based education in Scotland, and this combination of academic study and practical experience was appropriate and accepted, whereas for physicians this type of practical training was as yet deemed inappropriate as well as being inappropriate to learned medical practice.

The ways in which surgical training affected surgical practice were perhaps a little different from the situation with the physicians. Surgeons were, naturally, obliged to touch the patients, and in turn the patients could hardly refuse, although again the patient could choose to change surgeons midway through a course of post-operative treatment and could also refuse to take medicines or undergo medical treatments advised by surgeons. One of the less worthy aspects of the Edinburgh Incorporation was that on a number of occasions members were disciplined for poaching patients from their colleagues, despite having sworn an oath not to do so; these patients, not surprisingly, were generally of high social rank. Because of the turbulent state of sixteenth- and seventeenth-century Scotland, with civil wars, factional disputes and high levels of background violence, the surgeons gained wide experience in the routine treatment of wounds, fractures, dislocations, gunshot wounds and head injuries. However primitive, treatment had progressed somewhat from the days of the weapon-salve. In 1567, only two months before she was deposed from the throne, Mary, Queen of Scots granted the Edinburgh surgeons permanent exemption from bearing arms and from jury service, and in return the surgeons offered treatment to the wounded 'behind the lines'. Royal and military service was a prominent feature of the surgeons' work, though the surgeons who attended the Scottish royal house did not have the same influence over their colleagues as did the French royal surgeon in the period. Their reputation was such that, for example, in 1617 a patient who had been shot and wounded in Moscow thought it prudent to make the lengthy and hazardous journey to Edinburgh to have the musket ball removed from his left femur, in which it had been 'stuck and fixit'. The offending object was removed and the wound finally healed after eleven weeks of treatment (a not untypical length of time).[35]

As with the physicians, where distance reduced the patient's access to the services of a legitimate practitioner, the further away the patient was from a large settlement, the less likely it was that treatment could be obtained from a qualified surgeon. In rural areas amateur surgery was performed of necessity, but in Edinburgh and later Glasgow, the beginnings of professional training were evident; the effects would ultimately reach most parts of Scotland. Despite good training, however, it was rarely possible to offer complex surgical procedures because of the lack of effective anaesthetic and antiseptic agents. Qualified surgeons avoided operating for the stone, for example, this procedure mostly being left to itinerant, usually unqualified, lithotomists, although a resident stone-cutter was appointed in Glasgow in the mid-seventeenth century.

But there is evidence that good training could yield positive results, even in the case of a socially-disadvantaged patient. The accounts submitted to the Edinburgh Town Council in 1710 by Thomas Gibson, the surgeon appointed to treat the poor at the town's expense, contain the case of Jean Beaton. She was initially treated with various applications and mercury ointment in April of that year,

---

[35] Edinburgh City Archive, ECA, Burgh Court Books, 17 April, 1617.

following which her leg was amputated at a cost of £40 Scots (£12 Scots = £1 sterling in the period). The significant point, however, is that fully six months later the town was charged a further £3 for fitting her with a wooden leg.[36] This was a patient in receipt of town charity, whose living conditions and level of nutrition cannot have been remotely favourable to survival of such a heroic procedure. Amputation technique was frequently chosen as an examination topic, and on occasion the results were good.

Much of the surgeons' work was concerned with the often prolonged treatment of deep-seated infections and ulcers caused by injuries and by the less than favourable conditions in which the patients were treated. These problems often required many months of attendance and dressing, and it is in this area that another reality of early-modern medical practice appears. Considerable effort was made by surgeons and physicians to delineate and enforce their respective demarcation zones. Conditions of an internal origin were supposed to be solely the province of physicians, those of external cause the surgeons, but in many cases it might not have been entirely clear whether an ulcer or infection was caused by a particular incident or by an underlying chronic condition. Examination of cases taken to arbitration at the bench of the Edinburgh Burgh Court because of non-payment of bills (similar cases were noted in Dundee)[37] confirms that surgeons were openly treating cases of all sorts. In 1606, for example, Edinburgh surgeon James Brown sued a merchant for payment of the account due to Brown for his services in curing 'twa heavie and greit impostumations in his richte arme', the cure having involved daily visits for six weeks, and continued attendance for a further six weeks.[38] James Kinloch attended Christian Kennedy for no less than

---

[36] ECA, Accompt of Medicaments & Drugs furnish'd to the Poor of Edinburgh by Thomas Gibson from January 1710 to January 1711.

[37] Several cases are noted in Hamilton, *The Healers*, pp. 31-2.

[38] ECA, Burgh Court Books, 3 May, 1606.

thirty-eight weeks in 1618 as she was 'greatlie diseasit in her body';[39] while a more obviously surgical case involved Henry Aikman, who had treated and cured a casualty of 'ane greit wound in his heid and in his right hand being almost strucken away'.[40]

Demarcation disputes among physicians, surgeons and apothecaries were often heated and matters carried to the ridiculous extent that on one occasion an apothecary was prosecuted by the surgeons for 'taking some water out of the belly of a woman his relation that had died. of a hydropsy that she might be put the more easily in her coffin'.[41] While each of main branches of medical practice loudly protested its rights and privileges, the reality was that, at least to some extent, everyone did everything. Surviving bills for treatments show that surgeons were regularly treating scurvy, dropsy and chest complaints in addition to their more legitimate concerns. In an age of almost wholly private medicine, the patient had far greater input, and there was considerable cross-over among practitioners, although the physicians, naturally, had little inclination to perform surgical procedures.

Despite the difficulties, the widespread amateur practice, self-diagnosis, popular medication, and the lack of hospitals, there is, none the less, evidence that the surgeons were consolidating their organisational structures, where these existed. They promoted proper education and training, they attempted to provide academic facilities to enable good practice, and they performed operations to the limits imposed by the ability of the patient to survive surgery without anaesthetic or recover from serious infection or post-operative shock. There is evidence from the

---

[39] *Ibid.*, 6 January, 1618.

[40] *Ibid.*, 29 April, 1620. The injury had been sustained in 1611, giving some indication of the delay in payment in some cases.

[41] This case is recounted in a highly vitriolic document written by William Eccles, President of the Royal College of Physicians, in 1707. W. Eccles, *An Historical Account of the Rights and Privileges of the Royal College of Physicians and of the Incorporation of Chirurgeons of Edinburgh*, Edinburgh, 1707, p. 11.

later eighteenth century that very soon after surgical procedures had been first described elsewhere, they appeared as examination topics for candidates for surgical qualification in Edinburgh. Complex operations such as forequarter amputation or repair of hare lip began to be tested alongside the usual topics of trepanning, leg amputation and cataract surgery, many of the latter techniques having been derived initially from the works of Ambroise Paré or from Peter Lowe's *Discourse of the Whole Art of Chirurgerie.*

Medical practice and the role of the patient

A further, and very important, aspect of early-modern medical practice was the role of the patient and his or her relatives and friends, particularly those from the upper social ranks. Scottish society had long been stratified in a series of ranks or stations, some of which required certain modes of conduct or even dress (there is the oft-quoted example of the Edinburgh skinner's wife, who was informed by the Town Council that since her husband had become a burgess it would no longer be acceptable for her to wear an apron in the street).[42] Medical practice was entirely private - apart from free treatment of the most deserving poor - and it was open to the patient to summon medical assistance and take multiple opinions at will, from all sorts of practitioners. By the turn of the eighteenth century medicine was becoming a little more practical, but some higher-rank patients may well have felt unable to submit themselves to the physical ministrations of those perhaps slightly lower down the social ladder (though the widespread use and acceptance of enemas as treatment perhaps contradicts this view). Whereas nowadays most individuals and their relatives will generally accept a physician's advice as to diagnosis and treatment without question, the sixteenth- or seventeenth-century patient and his or her family had far greater control over which doctors to consult, how much examination to tolerate and

---

[42] Quoted in T. C. Smout, *A History of the Scottish People*, London, 1969, p. 160.

which medicines to accept. In his own turn, the physician may have felt on occasion that it was beneath the conventions of his social rank to touch certain patients, as well as being philosophically unnecessary. Matters would begin to change slowly once hospitals became established in the larger burghs. These had the important effect of separating and isolating the patient from the influences of household and family, and eventually the balance between the roles of doctor and patient was changed. In Dr MakLuire's time, though, the physician did not enjoy complete clinical freedom.

The general mechanics of consultation in the period are less than clear and the evidence fragmentary. What seems to have been usual practice was that when a patient became ill or sustained an injury, a physician or surgeon (or both, or several) was summoned, and after initial assessment an informal, unwritten contract was entered into, the practitioner(s) undertaking to carry out treatment and the family agreeing on the fee to be paid, either in instalments or in full at the conclusion of treatment. These agreements were made in the presence of witnesses where possible, and non-payment of fees, or non-attendance by the practitioner resulted in complaints being brought to court for settlement.[43] While surgeons charged specific amounts for attendance as well as for treatment and prescriptions, it was a matter of some pride to the physicians that they did not claim a specific fee for attendance, but left the patient to decide what remuneration he should receive for his professional services. Eccles claimed that while 'the patient may pay his physician what he thinks fit', surgeons charged exorbitant fees and 'pay it the poor patient must'.[44]

---

[43] There is an account of routine practice in Edinburgh in H.M. Dingwall, '"General practice" in seventeenth-century Edinburgh: evidence from the burgh court', *Social History of Medicine*, 6, 1993, pp. 125-42.

[44] Eccles, *Historical Account*, p. 9.

Multiple consultation and prescription by correspondence were widespread, so that there was no real sense of doctors or surgeons practising only in defined areas of the country or in particular burghs. The more well-known physicians and surgeons were called to visit gentry patients at considerable distances and also offered advice by correspondence. Country doctors also sought second opinions from established burgh physicians, and there was consequently a complex network of consultation and treatment in operation, in which the patient, not the doctor, was often the leading influence. Further down the social ladder matters were a little different. Multiple consultation may well have taken place, but the 'practitioners' involved were in all probability mostly unqualified, the more expensive, qualified doctors and surgeons being consulted as a last resort. As Pelling neatly states, 'the critical consumer of the early-modern period absorbed enormous quantities of medical care of all kinds'.[45] What was consumed varied according to rank and means, but there is little doubt that health mattered greatly to everyone.

Summary

In summary, the medicine that Dr MakLuire practised seems to have been typical of his time and for some considerable time after he had ceased to practise his art in Scotland. He is notable for many things: his well-connected acquaintances, his apparently wholly Scottish medical training, his publications and his role in the presentation of the 1630 petition to King Charles I, not to mention his possible meeting with Harvey. In many other ways, though, he was no different from his less well-known colleagues in other parts of Scotland. The organisational basis of medicine and surgery was changing relatively slowly, the physicians not achieving their aims until long after MakLuire's death; elements of professionalisation were beginning to appear in the actions and

---

[45] M. Pelling, 'Medical practice in early-modern England: trade or profession?', in *Professions in Early-Modern England*, ed. W. Prest, New York, 1987, p. 101.

organisation of the Edinburgh surgeons and the Glasgow Faculty of Physicians and Surgeons; and anatomical knowledge was steadily increasing, although it would take many decades for the anatomical nomenclature of the modern *nomina anatomica* to be finalised,[46] with significant contributions from Scottish anatomists, such as Alexander Monro *secundus*, whose name denotes the foramen between the ventricles of the brain.

The experiences of MakLuire's patients would have been little different from those of patients all over Scotland, and indeed most of Europe. Humoral philosophy predominated, and treatments were given on this basis. Surgery was severely hampered, not by lack of anatomical knowledge, but because the means to anaesthetise the patient or treat infection and post-operative shock were not available. There seems little doubt, however, that most physicians and surgeons did the best they could (with the exception of unscrupulous practitioners who appear in all periods); they carefully assessed each patient either directly or by correspondence, and offered treatment in line with the best practice of the day. With the benefit - or, perhaps, disadvantage - of historical hindsight, what early physicians and surgeons did seems crude and based on a primitive and seemingly naive philosophy. This is, however, to do the early medical practitioners an injustice. This was a period in which the legitimate medical men were gaining a substantial amount of new knowledge and experience vital to professionalisation, but it was also one of transition, when new treatments were slow to appear and when much of what they did was also done by amateurs from all walks of life. It is this complex set of interfaces, between old and new knowledge and between professional and amateur practice, that makes this period arguably the most important in the evolution of the Scottish medical profession,

---

[46] As late as 1719, for example, one Edinburgh surgical student was asked to describe the anatomy of the brain and its eleven pairs of nerves; modern anatomy describes twelve pairs of cranial nerves. Royal College of Surgeons of Edinburgh, Minute Books, 10 September, 1719.

despite the more tangible effects of late-eighteenth and nineteenth-century advances in knowledge and treatment.

Introduction

The 'Maister John MakLuire, Doctor in Physick' of this study had first come to the attention of the author in the nineteen seventies while the latter was investigating his own McClure ancestry. The chance discovery had been made that the petitioner to Charles I in the 1630 attempt (itself well-known) to establish the Royal College of Physicians in Edinburgh had been (as had hitherto been unknown) a 'Doctor Makcleuir'. This discovery of the identity of the petitioner in that pioneer attempt had been announced at the historical symposium held on the occasion of the tercentenary of the College in 1981. A subsequent conclusion had been that the petitioner had been the same person as the 'Dr MakLuire' who had written, and had had published, in Edinburgh (in 1634), what had appeared to have been the first textbook on general medicine by a Scottish author to have been printed and published in Scotland. In this also it had seemed that his pioneer status had escaped recognition.

Understandably, therefore, the questions had become intriguing as to who this Dr MakLuire had been; what his relevance may have been in the context of the medicine of Scotland in the first half of the seventeenth century; and why he had been, already in his own century, overlooked, and then completely forgotten about for more than three hundred years.

One early conjecture about Dr MakLuire of particular interest for the history of medicine in Scotland had been of a hitherto unsuspected meeting he may have had in Edinburgh, in November, 1641, with the great William Harvey. This would have been on the occasion (in itself medically celebrated) of the visit paid to the Court of Charles I by the young Hugh Montgomery, son of a nobleman from the Ards in Ulster, during which a remarkable cavity in the chest wall of the young man, dating from a childhood injury, and exposing his beating heart both to view and to touch, had been examined by Harvey and demonstrated to the King in person. The two-fold novelty of the conjecture had been, first, that the young man's visit would, most probably, have been (as had never previously been suggested) while the Court had been in Edinburgh and, second, that Dr MakLuire and his wife, Mareon Greir, known to have been resident in Edinburgh at the time, would have been the un-named 'creditable' persons present on that occasion with whom Harvey says that he consulted about the early history of the case.

These conjectures had first been voiced at the 1981 historical symposium. They had depended, however, upon what, at that time, had itself been no more than a further intriguing conjecture. This had been that both Dr MakLuire and his wife had had personal knowledge of the young Hugh Montgomery's case from the time of the young man's childhood. This would have been knowledge which (if the conjecture were true) would have led them both to extend a personal welcome to the young Hugh on the latter's appearance in Edinburgh, and also to be only too pleased to share their knowledge of the early, clinical, history of the young man's condition with Harvey.

A major task, therefore, after the historical symposium, had appeared to be to throw light, if possible, on the truth or otherwise of these two conjectures. Here, the intuition had been that it would be the discovery of the full identity, and pre-marriage background, of the Mareon Greir, already found to have been spouse to Dr MakLuire (but about whom nothing more had been found at the time) which might do this.

Meanwhile, the broad search for the identity of Dr John MakLuire himself, which had been resumed and intensified after the tercentenary symposium, had expanded into the biographical enquiry, the results of which are presented here. These have shown that the Mareon Greir, who was to become his second wife, had - although born in Kirkcudbrightshire - been taken, during her childhood, to Ulster, when her father emigrated there in 1626/7 and, as a Montgomery tenant, would have probably been living close to the young Hugh Montgomery's home at Comber.

2

The results of the search have led to the conclusion that Dr MakLuire had, since student days, and probably from childhood, continued to be in touch with the Montgomery household of the 1st Viscount (father of Dr MakLuire's student friend, Sir James Montgomery) at Newtown House, Newtownards, and probably also with that of the Viscount's oldest son and heir, Hugh (and his son, the medically famous young Hugh), at Mount Alexander House, at nearby Comber. His continued contact with them would have ensured that he would have had personal, and probably clinical, knowledge of the young Hugh Montgomery's case, dating probably from the time (in 1630) when the boy, at Comber, would have been aged six or seven, but with virtual certainty from the time (in 1634) of Dr MakLuire's presumed sojourn in Co. Down, close to Comber, at the time of his marriage, there, to Mareon Greir. In that year the young Hugh Montgomery would have been aged ten or eleven. If this conclusion is correct, Dr MakLuire and his wife (whose father had been a tenant of the Montgomerys since the young Hugh had been aged four) would surely have indeed been the 'creditable' persons who were later, in Edinburgh, consulted by Harvey about the early history of the case.

The results of the search have also shown that Dr John MakLuire had been an earlier contributor to British midwifery than Dr William Harvey (hitherto thought to be the first) and the first contributor to Scottish, and perhaps to British, paediatrics. Also his MD thesis, the *Tractatus de febre pestilente* (and not, as hitherto supposed, that of William Broad of Aberdeen), would appear to have been the earliest Scottish MD thesis to be printed.

The frequency may be noted with which, in the course of the search for 'Maister John MakLuire, Doctor in Physick', the pattern for the naming of children which predominated in those days, has been invoked. It should be emphasised, however, that that pattern was always subject to all kinds of exception and modification and that the fruitful resort to it has been, throughout, heuristic rather than evidential in intention.

Chapter One - Early Findings and Conjectures

The initial discoveries

The author, while pursuing, in the Scottish Record Office, his own McCluire ancestry, had come across an index which referred to a 'Doctor Makcleuir'. It had therefore been the possibility of discovering a hitherto unsuspected medical ancestor that had at first been most intriguing. But the reference had turned out to be more interesting than expected. It was to a copy-letter, in the (manuscript) register of royal letters kept by Sir William Alexander, Principal Secretary for Scotland, dated 2 October 1630, from Charles I (then at Hampton Court) to his Privy Council in Scotland, commending the petition of this 'Doctor Makcleuir' to establish a College of Physicians (see Chapter 9, fig. 3).[1] No less intriguing, therefore, was the leading role which this 'Doctor Makcleuir' obviously had played in the 1630 attempt to establish the Royal College of Physicians of Edinburgh.

In following up this matter, it was soon realised that, although success in establishing the College had not been achieved until 1681 under Charles II, the 1630 attempt, and the support given to it by Charles I, had been well known. But it had been discovered, also, that the leading role of 'Doctor Makcleuir' in that attempt, unrecorded in Sir Robert Sibbald's unfinished manuscript history, of the early 1700s[2], had been still unknown to the anonymous author of the *Historical Sketch* of the College of 1925.[3]

---

[1] SRO SP1/6, Sir William Alexander, Register of Royal Letters 1626-1631, p. 533.

[2] Sir Robert Sibbald, 'Account of the Original Institution of the Royal College of Physicians' - an unfinished manuscript published as *Sir Robert Sibbald's Memoirs of the Royal College of Physicians at Edinburgh: A Fragment*, Edinburgh: Stevenson, 1837, p. 6.

[3] Anonymous, *Historical Sketch and Laws of the Royal College of Physicians*, Edinburgh, 1925.

It had been in this way that, naturally, curiosity had been
aroused as to who this 'Doctor Makcleuir' had been and
why he had been so completely overlooked. The beginnings of the search for his identity, in the wider literature of
the history of medicine in Scotland, had resulted, however,
in the discovery, only, of two references to a 'Doctor
McCluir' who could, possibly, have been the 1630 petitioner. Both of these references had been, merely, to brief
extracts from contemporaneous records - the one recording
the engagement, at a time of plague, of a 'Doctor McCluir'
by the burgh of Glasgow 'to attend the visitatioune of the
toun'[4], and the other recording the appointment of the
latter as a burgess there.[5] Indeed, it had only been when
Miss Joan Ferguson, Librarian to the Royal College of
Physicians of Edinburgh, had passed on a reference she
had chanced to come across to three seventeenth-century
medical books by a 'Mr John MakLuire, Doctor in Medicine', that the search had begun to make significant
progress.

The three books thus brought to attention, and clearly of
great importance to Scottish medicine (if only because of
their early dates) had been *The Buckler of Bodilie Health*,
*Sanitatis Semita: Cum tractatu de febre pestilente prae-
fixo*, and *The Generall Practise of Medecine*. The first two
of these had been published in 1630 (the same year as the
petition), while the third, under the pseudonym
'φιλιατρευσ', and the initials 'I.M.'(surely standing for
'Ioannes Makluireus'), had been published in 1634, all
three books having been printed in Edinburgh, by John
Wreittoun. A copy of *The Generall Practise of Medecine*
had been found in the Library of the University of Aberdeen, bound together with a number of other, unrelated,
works. The copy had originally been in the library of a Dr
Alexander Reid - a native of Banchory Ternan, but

[4] J.D. Comrie, *History of Scottish Medicine*, 2nd edition, I, p. 220. See
also Sir James D. Marwick, ed., *Extracts from the Records of the
Burgh of Glasgow 1630-1662*, 2 vols., Edinburgh: Burgh Records
Society, 1881, II, p. 119.

[5] J.R. Anderson, ed., *Burgesses and Guild Brethren of Glasgow 1573-
1750*, Edinburgh: Scottish Record Society, Old Series, 56, 1925.

practising in London - and had been left, on his death in 1680, to Marischal College. It had seemed that this book - dealing, as it does, with the principles of diagnosis, prognosis and treatment - quite probably has indeed the distinction of having been the earliest textbook of general medicine to have been written and printed in Scotland. It had appeared that, with this exception, however, no copies of Dr MakLuire's books had survived in their country of origin, although examples of the first and third were reported to be available in the British Library, and of the second, at the Library of the University of Cambridge.

Consulting next, therefore, at the British Library, *The Buckler of Bodilie Health*, it had been found that it had included a complaint to the same Privy Council of Scotland to which the King's commendation of the petition of 'Doctor Makcleuir' had, in the same year, been addressed. The complaint had been about unqualified practitioners - 'old ignorant ruffians, practised Man-slayers' - who alone, the author had claimed, were being accorded the reputation of being 'worthie' physicians. To this complaint had been added an appeal for that Council's help on behalf of the victims of such practitioners, in the following terms :-

> To you be it said my Lords of his majesties Counsell and Session, and on you be laide the blood of these poore innocents, dayly precipitate to their graves. By this neglect GOD is bereft of his servants, and the King of his subjects; helpe this my Lords, and let not this old science, commanded of GOD, followed by Kings and Princes, imbraced of all ... decay among you.[6]

The King's commendation to the Council of the petition of 'Doctor Makcleuir'[7], had then seemed so to echo the tone and wording of the above appeal, that there could be little doubt that the 'Doctor Makcleuir' of the petition had been

---

[6] J. MakLuire, *The Buckler of Bodilie Health*, Edinburgh: Wreittoun, 1630, pp. vii-viii.

[7] SRO SP1/6, Sir William Alexander, Register of Royal Letters 1626-1631, p.533.

the same person as the 'Mr (Maister) John MakLuire, Doctor in Medicine', of the three books.

Conjectures at the College tercentenary

In the paper read at the 1981 symposium such little factual information about Dr MakLuire's life and background as had, at that early stage, been ascertained, had been put forward.[8] However, beyond the factual outline a number of suggestions and conjectures had been advanced as appropriate for further enquiry. These had provided the growing points for the wider search (for the identity of Dr MakLuire) which was embarked upon after the symposium, the results of which are reported here. The growing points had been mainly in relation to connections, which had come to light, of Dr MakLuire with various historic persons.

Prominent among these, illustrating his social and professional contacts, had been Sir John Wedderburn, trusted physician to Charles I, who, presumably taking his first steps in his career in medicine, had transferred from divinity at St Mary's College, St Andrews, to philosophy at St Leonard's College, becoming Regent there at a time when Dr MakLuire, as a second year Arts student at the same College, had already embarked upon the writing of his medical book *The Buckler of Bodilie Health*; Dr George Sibbald, an older-generation supporter of Dr MakLuire, and uncle of the future Sir Robert Sibbald who was to be the virtual founder of the Royal College of Physicians of Edinburgh; Sir William Alexander, later to become 1st Earl of Stirling, through whom, as Master of Requests for Scotland, Dr MakLuire's petition would have been submitted to the King and into whose hand the King's commendation of it certainly came; and Sir James Montgomery, second son of the 1st Viscount Montgomery of the Ards in Ulster, courtier to James VI and I, Charles I and Charles II, for whom Dr MakLuire certainly entertained a deep

---

[8] J.F. McHarg, *Dr Johnne MakLuire and the 1630 Attempt to Establish the College*, Proceedings of the Royal College of Physicians of Edinburgh, 1982, Publication No 6, pp. 44-98.

devotion, at least from the age of about fifteen at St Andrews University, where they were fellow-students, but more probably, as will be argued, from a shared childhood in the Ards in Ulster.

A further two probable connections, which had seemed potentially of special interest for the history of medicine in Scotland, had been raised at the time of the 1981 symposium. One of these had been with the great William Harvey, and the other with one of the latter's medically most famous patients, the young Hugh Montgomery, son and heir of the 2nd Viscount Montgomery, grandson of Sir William Alexander, and nephew of Dr MakLuire's student friend, Sir James Montgomery. In respect of the first of these, it had been suggested that Dr MakLuire would at least have met with Harvey during one or both of the latter's two visits to Edinburgh with the King, in 1633 and 1641 respectively. But beyond this, the suggestion had been made that it might well have been with Dr MakLuire that Harvey's reported clinical consultation had been (in the latter year, and in Edinburgh) over the early history of the remarkable cardiac condition affecting the young Hugh Montgomery - *viz.*, the cavity in his chest wall, which had resulted from a serious chest injury in childhood, and through which one could both see and touch his beating heart.

Chapter Two - Origins in Kirkcudbrightshire

His birth probably between 1600 and 1603

The year of birth, parentage, family background and place of origin of Dr John MakLuire had seemed nowhere to have been documented. Nevertheless, it was noted that Dr MakLuire, in the dedication of his 1630 book, *The Buckler of Bodilie Health*, to his friend from student days, Sir James Montgomery, second son of the 1st Viscount Montgomery of the Ards in Ulster, had stated that the book had been 'hatched in the University of St Androws (sic) eleven years since'[1] - which would have been in 1619. Next, confirmation had been found that he, and the young James Montgomery, had indeed been fellow students at St Andrews in that year. This confirmation had lain in a manuscript book at that University, where their signatures ('Jacobus Montgomerius' and 'Joannes McCluire') appear on a list, dated 22 February 1619, of twenty-seven students at St Leonard's College, taking the academic oath, who would have matriculated for the first time in October of the previous year, *viz.*, in 1618.[2]

Now, according to Mr Robert Smart, Keeper of the Muniments of St Andrews University, most of those students would have been aged about fifteen at their first matriculation. However, as he also explained, St Andrews students in those days matriculated as primars, secundars or ternars, according to social class and, according to Mr Smart, some of the ternars could have been a year or two older than fifteen. Also, while James Montgomery's signature appeared high on the list, betokening him to have been a primar, that of John MakLuire was low down, betokening him to have been a ternar. As such, John MakLuire could have been a year or two older than fifteen.

---

[1] J. MakLuire, *The Buckler of Bodilie Health*, Edinburgh: Wreittoun, 1630, p. iv.

[2] Mss. UY 305 3, p. 125, Muniments of the University of St Andrews.

In this way it had been possible reliably to deduce that Dr MakLuire's birth had probably been between 1601 and 1603 - but possibly as early as the later months of 1600.

Thomas McCluire in Kirkoswald parish excluded as his father

It could further be concluded, according to Mr Smart, from the fact that Dr MakLuire's matriculation at St Andrews was as a ternar, that his father was of the artisan or tenant farmer class. A first provisional supposition, therefore, that his father may have been an urban artisan, and in the Edinburgh where Dr MakLuire was subsequently to be resident, called for a search for evidence of his birth and parentage in the Edinburgh baptismal registers for the years 1600-1603.[3] No such evidence was found. A similar search in the registers for Glasgow, where eventually he had been elected as a burgess, was also negative.[4] A second provisional supposition was therefore entertained - *viz.*, that Dr MakLuire's father may have been a rural artisan or, more probably, a tenant farmer. Now, baptismal registers for rural parishes at the beginning of the 1600s do not, for the most part, exist, and so the search turned to a survey of potentially relevant McCluire testaments from the commissariat records.

Only one of these McCluire testaments was found, in the survey, to call for detailed study. This was the testament, dated April 1616, of a tenant farmer, Thomas McCluire in Airds, in the parish of Kirkoswald, Ayrshire.[5] This man's testament showed that, of his seven children, all of them 'bairns', the oldest of them had indeed been called 'Jon'. Moreover, it had been possible to deduce that the year of birth of that 'Jon' McCluire would have been between 1602 and 1611 and therefore compatible with him having been the future Dr John MakLuire. Furthermore, at that stage of the inquiry, the first evidence of Dr MakLuire

---

[3] SRO OPR 685 1/1, Edinburgh (Greyfriars) Register of Baptisms.

[4] SRO OPR 644/1, Glasgow Register of Baptisms.

[5] SRO CC9/7/11, Testament Thomas McClure in Airds, 1616.

having had issue had just come to light - *viz.*, the baptism, in Edinburgh, of a son called 'Thomas'.[6] It had been realised that if this 'Thomas' was Dr MakLuire's eldest son, and named, according to custom, after his paternal grandfather, the Thomas McCluire in the parish of Kirkoswald might indeed have been his father. The facts thus far, therefore, were beguilingly consistent with the Kirkoswald 'Jon' McCluire having been the future Dr John MakLuire - the variant spelling of the surname being, of course, of little significance.

A subsequent systematic search of baptismal registers, established, however, that the nine children of Dr Mak-Luire had been named, successively, John, Helen, Alison, William, James, Thomas, Hew, John, and John (fig. 1).[7] From this, it had become clear that the first-discovered son of Dr MakLuire, Thomas, had not been the first-born son, and also that Dr MakLuire had not named either of his two daughters 'Jonet'. He surely would have done so had he been son of the Kirkoswald Thomas McCluire, because, as the Kirkoswald testament showed, a Jonet Graham had been the mother of the 'bairns' of the Thomas McCluire of that parish. These two facts, taken together, had alone made it almost certain that Dr MakLuire's father could not, after all, have been that Thomas McCluire.

His parents 'John MakLuire in Carmonoch' and 'Alison Denholme'?

The failure of these two approaches to the identity of Dr MakLuire's parents (through baptismal registers and testaments respectively) obliged a change to a provisional approach through the naming patterns which, in the 1600s, were dominant. Here, the above-mentioned elucidation of the full naming-pattern of Dr MakLuire's children prov-ided grounds for two provisional suppositions. The first of these was that, in naming his first son 'John', Dr Mak-Luire, following custom, would have been naming him

---

[6] SRO OPR 685 1/5, Edinburgh (Greyfriars) Register of Baptisms.

[7] SRO OPR 685 1/4, Edinburgh (Greyfriars) Register of Baptisms, and SRO OPR 694/1, Mid Calder Register of Baptisms.

after the paternal grandfather - in which case, Dr Mak-
Luire's father would himself have been called 'John
MakLuire'. The probability that this was in fact the case
was strengthened by the apparent determination of Dr
MakLuire (presumably because of the deaths of two
'Johns' in childhood) that not only a second son, but also a
third, should be named 'John'. The second supposition
was that while, in accordance with the same custom, his
first daughter, Helen, would have been named after the
maternal grandmother (to be discussed further below), it
would have been his second daughter, Alison, who would
have been named after the paternal grandmother - in which
case Dr MakLuire's own mother would have borne the
Christian name 'Alison'.

These two suppositions thus led to a search for evidence
for the historical existence, at the time of Dr MakLuire's
birth about 1600-1603, of a married couple called 'John
MakLuire' and 'Alison *******'. The search was at first
felt to be somewhat forlorn - if only because of the virtual
absence of marriage records for that era. Nevertheless,
while no evidence of such a married couple bearing these
names was found, attention happened almost by chance,
and quite early in the search, to fall upon the record of a
couple, just so named - but whose relationship was alle-
gedly adulterous.

The first-noticed historical record of that couple had been
in the officially transcribed, abbreviated, and printed version of the *Register of the Great Seal of Scotland.*[8] The
record had been of a 'Joannes McLuir in Carmonoch',
who, on 28 August 1622, had been granted, by James VI
& I, a remission for the alleged crime of adultery with an
'Alison,' whose surname was given as 'Donnane'. Check-
ing with the manuscript itself of the *Register* had at first
suggested that the correct transcription of the surname
(fig. 2 - line 12) might have been 'Doncane' (i.e. 'Dun-

---

[8] *Register of the Great Seal of Scotland (1620-1633),* No 364, Edinburgh, 1984, p. 123.

can').[9] However, later manuscript material relating to the case showed that, elsewhere, the name, presumably correct, had been given as 'Denholme' and thus that the official, printed, transcription should be changed to 'Dennane' - an acceptable variant of 'Denholme'.[10]

However, for this couple, 'John MakLuire in Carmonoch' and 'Alison Denholme', to have indeed been the lawful parents of Dr John MakLuire, their marriage, some time later than the alleged adultery between them - presumably not until the death or divorce of the lawful spouse of one of them had seemed to them to allow them to marry - would have had to have been before the latter's birth between 1600 and 1603. The inevitable conclusion that the alleged adultery between them had been in the 1590s, or even earlier, had implied, however, the very long time-interval of two or three decades between the alleged adultery and the royal remission for it. Such a long time-interval had seemed, at first consideration, improbable and even fanciful.

The archaic legal procedure of a royal remission before trial

The very unexpectedness of having succeeded at least in identifying a couple with the distinctive, sought-for, names 'John MakLuire' and 'Alison *******', was alone felt to be sufficient to justify, nevertheless, further investigation of the very possibility of a satisfactory explanation being found for the two or three decades of delay between the alleged crime of adultery by 'John MakLuire in Carmonoch' with 'Alison Denholme', some time in the 1590s, and the royal remission for that alleged crime obtained on 28 August 1622.

The investigation into this specific possibility was launched under the understandable assumption that the remission would have been preceded by a trial and conviction for

---

[9] SRO C3/2, Manuscript Register of the Great Seal of Scotland, No 210.

[10] SRO JC 2/6, Justiciary Court, p. 98.

that crime. However, precisely because perusal of the Justiciary Court records had been confined to those of trials prior to the date of the remission, it had not been until a considerably later stage in the investigation that it had been found, from the records, that 'John MakLuire in Carmonoch' had indeed appeared for trial but, surprisingly, that this had not been until some ten weeks after his alleged crime had been pardoned by the King.

The record of this post-remission trial shows that this 'John MakLuire', there specified more precisely as 'in Nether Carmonoch', had, on 8 November 1622, at the Court of Justiciary in Edinburgh, been dilated of his 'admitted' crime of adultery; had alleged that he could not be 'put to an assise' because the King had granted him a remission; had had his remission admitted by the Justice; and had 'askit instrumentis' - i.e. had asked for a written statement of the finding of the Court. That a certain finality to the case had been generally assumed, had seemed to be suggested by the fact that the jurymen (or witnesses?) summoned to the hearing also 'tuik instrumentis of their compeirance & ptestit that tha nor nane of thame be charget upon this assise in tyme cu'ing'.[11]

Now, even the general significance of resort to this strange legal procedure was by no means apparent. However, light seemed to be thrown on the matter by the authority on Scots Law, David Hume. Hume says that royal remission could be either before or after conviction but that, while it seemed doubtful whether a remission after conviction so thoroughly took away the conviction as to relieve from the state of infamy attached to it, a remission before conviction maintained the accused person in all respects in his state and condition, as at the time of the pardon'.[12] It had appeared, moreover, that when resorting to this procedure, the mere admission of guilt, which itself did not constitute proof of guilt, would often have been made solely for the purpose of obtaining a remission for the alleged crime -

---

[11] Ibid., p. 99.

[12] D. Hume, *Commentaries on the Law of Scotland Respecting Crimes*, Edinburgh: Bell and Bradfute, 1844, I, p. 501.

even, perhaps, in circumstances in which a credible defence may have been available - but in the confidence that the remission would end the case; lead to the permanent discharge of potentially incriminating witnesses; and thus to the protection, effectively for ever, from the hazard of an actual finding of guilt. Hume mentions, indeed, that Mackenzie had observed that men, on betaking themselves of this sort of protection, 'redeemed themselves rather from hazard, than from guilt'.

The more particular significance of this procedure - *viz.*, in cases of adultery - and the nature of the specific hazard from which men would most usually have sought to redeem themselves by resorting to it, was also by no means immediately apparent. Here again Hume seemed to throw light. He pointed out that a statute (*Statute 1600 c20*) had been passed in 1600 which had declared that the marriage of adulterous parties would be 'null and unlawfull' and the issue of such marriages incapable of succession.[13] More recently, Clancy, enquiring into the effects of the Reformation in Scotland upon the law of husband and wife, examined the ambiguities in the minds of the Reformers, which persisted to the very end of the Reformation century, about the idea of adultery as a 'diriment impediment' to marriage. In particular, he recorded that even during the 1590s (the decade during which it had seemed most likely that the alleged adultery of Dr MakLuire's father had taken place) an Act, in 1592, which had narrated that 'By occasion whereof the crime of Adultery dayly increased ... the marriage of Paramours is ... contrary to the Law of God and Public Honestie', had still not gone so far as to declare such marriages, although 'contrary to the Law of God', to be null and void.[14]

---

[13] Ibid., p. 455.

[14] M.P.A. Clancy, 'The effects of the Reformation in Scotland upon the Law of Husband and Wife with particular attention paid to the Constitution and Dissolution of Marriage during the period 1560 to 1690', unpublished Master of Laws thesis, University of Glasgow, 1984, pp. 248-53.

It had appeared probable, from all this, that, in the decades prior to the passing of the statute of 1600, which had crystallised the legal situation, there would have been, in Scotland, certain marriages, otherwise without impediment, between persons for whom, with its passing, there would immediately have sprung into being the hazard of their marriage being challenged as null and unlawful, and of their issue being found to be illegitimate and incapable of succession. It had also seemed that such a hazard would most usually have become an actual threat in the context of a family dispute, or uncertainty, about legitimacy, primogeniture and inheritance. Furthermore, if it was not at the time of the marriage itself that such a threat arose (from a challenge to the validity of the marriage), or at the time of the birth of an heir apparent, the most likely time would have been the approaching majority of that heir apparent, or of a counter-claimant.

It had seemed, in this way, that resort to the legal procedure of obtaining a royal remission prior to trial, as the appropriate measure to be adopted in such a case, may well have not been put into effect until between two and three decades after the alleged pre-marriage adultery. It had been in this way, also, that it had begun to seem not nearly so improbable, after all, that the identified couple under consideration - John MakLuire in Nether Carmonoch and Alison Denholme - could have been the parents of the future Dr John MakLuire.

Now, the petition of the older of the two 'John MakLuires' for the remission granted to him on 28 August 1622, would presumably have been submitted either earlier that same month or, perhaps more probably, in the previous month - *viz.*, in July 1622. Here, it had been noted that this would have been the very month in which the graduation, as Master of Arts, at St Andrews University, in that year, of the younger of the two 'John MakLuires', would have taken place. Admittedly, the coincidence of the two events could have been mere chance, but it had seemed to be strongly suggestive that the graduation of the younger 'John MakLuire' (as well, perhaps, as the approach of his majority, or of that of a rival claimant to primogeniture), may have precipitated the submission of the petition for a royal pardon by the older 'John MakLuire'.

If so, it would have indicated that the two 'John Mak-Luires' had, indeed, been father and son and that the pardon had been sought in order to establish, in the face of a potential challenge, the young graduand's legitimacy, primogeniture, and right to succeed. It will be seen, below, that this believed filial relationship of Dr John MakLuire to the John MakLuire who was tenant (certainly in 1622) in Nether Carmonoch will be further borne out by the discovery that Mareon Greir, Dr MakLuire's future spouse, was the daughter of that John Greir who, in 1643, was to be retoured heir to the lands which included the farm of Nether Carmonoch.

Thus, the presumed marriage between John MakLuire (later to be the tenant in Nether Carmonoch) and Alison Denholme, subsequent to their alleged pre-marriage adultery and (being prior to the statute of 1600) seeming to be legal, would have been in the 1590s and prior to the birth of Dr MakLuire in 1600/3.

The site of Nether Carmonoch (in ruins) discovered

The location of the unspecified 'Carmonoch' mentioned in the 1622 royal remission recorded in the *Register of the Great Seal*, although it was obviously somewhere in Scotland, had remained mysterious after the first discovery of its mention in that Register. Combing through the writings of Dr MakLuire himself, the only possible, and still very speculative, clue as to his geographical roots, and thus to the location of 'Carmonoch', had appeared to be his mention of 'Kyle and Galloway', whose 'mourish men', he had written, would be unlikely to agree with his advice that cheese was 'not to be much used'.[15] The term 'moor men' or 'moors-men', had been a widely used term in the 1600s to distinguish the hill-farmers from the 'low-country' people - mainly of Galloway - and Dr MakLuire's comment would suggest that at least he had personal

---

[15] MakLuire, *The Buckler of Bodilie Health*, p. 49.

knowledge of the dietary predilections of the hill-farmers of Galloway, even if the tone of his comment suggested a certain distancing of himself from them. Indeed, it was to Galloway that the first firm clue to the true location of 'Carmonoch' pointed.

It had been when studying the Justiciary Court record of the trial of 'John MakLuire in Nether Carmonoch' (when it had emerged that the addresses of the ten jurymen who had been summoned to attend the assise in Edinburgh had all been living in the adjacent parishes of Kells and Dalry) that it had seemed that it would indeed be in Galloway, and specifically within these two parishes, that 'Carmonoch' should be sought. Even so, no 'Nether Carmonoch' could be identified on modern maps covering these parishes.

The next real clue had been the discovery of the signature 'James Makcleuir Kermonoch' on the 1637 petition from the presbytery of Kirkcudbright against the Service Book of Charles I.[16] Close to this signature, on the vellum of the original petition itself, there had been several place-names which were recognisable as the names of farms shown on modern maps as close to the Water of Deugh. Concentrating, therefore, on this geographical region, it had then begun to seem very probable that the present-day farm known as 'Carminnows' (in the plural) may have been so named from three Carmonochs - Over (or Upper), Mid and Nether. Turning to the same geographical region as it is represented on the Blaeu map of the *'Praefectura Kirkcubriensis'*, based upon the drawings made by Timothy Pont towards the end of the 1500s, it was found that there were indeed three relevant farms, each represented by a small circle close to the Water of Deugh - one labelled 'O. Karmunnow' ('Over Karmunnow') and two sharing a common label 'Karmunnow' (fig. 3a). Ordnance Survey maps of 1853 and 1894 were then found to show 'Upper Carminnow (in ruins)', (Mid) 'Carminnow' and 'Nether Carminnow (in ruins)' (fig. 3c and d).

---

[16] SRO PC 11/6B, Petition from the Presbytery of Kirkcudbright against the Service Book of Charles I, 1637.

Eventually, a visit to the site in 1985, armed with modern maps on to which the position of the original 'Nether Carmonoch' had been transposed (fig. 3e), located it about half a mile to the east of Polquhanity bridge, which is on the A713 road from New Galloway to Ayr. The foundations, and most of the walls, of the original buildings were still clearly to be seen - together with the remains of a corn-kiln (plate I).

'John MakLuire in Castelmaddie' his grandfather

The discovery of the location of Nether Carmonoch, which had followed from the deduction that Dr MakLuire's father had been the John MakLuire who had been the tenant, there, in 1622, had, however, been no indication that Dr MakLuire's place of birth had also been found. Here, it had been felt that before attempting to draw any conclusions as to Dr MakLuire's place of birth search should be made for other relatives, both on the paternal (MakLuire) side and the maternal (Denholme) side, in the hope that their places of abode might throw light on where Dr MakLuire himself had been born about 1600/3.

The search had started amongst the invaluable collection of transcribed manuscript material held at the Ewart Library, Dumfries. Here, a suspicion had arisen quite early that there might indeed be evidence, awaiting discovery and evaluation, for there having existed yet a third 'John MakLuire', earlier than, and senior to, the John MakLuire who had been Dr MakLuire's father - but a tenant, like him, of the same laird 'Gilbert Greirson of Castelmaddie' - and very probably, therefore, a relative.[17] This suspicion had arisen while reading R. C. Reid's transcription of the 'Register of Hornings and Inhibitions for Kirkcudbrightshire' and from then going on to study the manuscript register itself.[18]

---

[17] SRO C22/6, Retour, Gilbert Greirson of Castelmaddie, 1615, fol. 73.

[18] 'Register of Hornings and Inhibitions for Kirkcudbrightshire. Vol. I, 1614-1621', transcribed by R.C. Reid, Dumfries and Galloway Collection, Dumfries Library.

Gilbert Greirson, laird of Castelmaddie and the three Carmonochs (fig. 3b), had been alleged, on 11 March 1617 (mistakenly, as it was to turn out) to have failed to 'deliver up' the testament of one who had died in that year. For this, he had been 'put to the horn' on 28 April 1618 - the deceased person being designated, in the Register, as 'Jonet McClane in Castelmaddie'. An appeal against horning had been rejected by the Privy Council on 19 August 1618. However, shortly afterwards, Gilbert Greirson had successfully proved to the King that he ought not to have been put to the horn and, on 23 November 1618, letters of 'relaxing' from the horning had been registered. Now, in the record of the 'relaxing', the name of the deceased had been 'corrected' to 'John McCleune in Castelmaddie'. But a crucial palaeographic study of the handwriting in the Register (see Appendix A) was able to demonstrate a consistent quirk whereby the writer regularly mis-wrote terminal letters undoubtedly intended as 're' as 'ne'. As a result, it became clear that the person who had died in 1617 had been a 'John McCleure in Castelmaddie'.

The relevance of the exposure of this hand-writing quirk lay in the fact that it had seemed almost certain that if Dr John MakLuire, son of the John MakLuire who had been tenant in Nether Carmonoche in 1622, had indeed been the latter's oldest son and heir - as was suggested by the circumstances of the royal remission and of the trial of that year - he would have been given his Christian name, 'John', from his paternal grandfather whose name, therefore, would have been 'John MakLuire'. It had thus become difficult to escape the conclusion that the 'John McCleure in Castelmaddie' who had died in 1617, had been Dr MakLuire's grandfather.

Presumably, it was after the death of 'John MakLuire in Castelmaddie' in 1617, that his son and heir, John Mak-Luire, Dr MakLuire's father who, as will be discussed below, had emigrated to Ulster, returned from there to take up the 'kindly' tenancy with Gilbert Greirson of Castelmaddie which he had thereby inherited - although at

Nether Carmonoch rather than Castelmaddie, where the laird was himself living.

Unfortunately, this discovery of the identity of Dr Mak-Luire's grandfather, and of the fact that grandfather and father had been 'kindly', hereditary, tenants of the laird of Castelmaddie and the Carmonochs, threw no light on where Dr John MakLuire would himself have been born.

'James Makcluir Kermonoch' his brother

The next person to be considered as a probable relative of Dr MakLuire had been the 'James Makcluir' whose signature, 'James Makcluir Kermonoch', on the 1637 petition from the presbytery of Kirkcudbright against the Service Book of Charles I (see fig. 4), had been the first firm clue to Dr MakLuire's origins in Galloway.[19]

The association of the place-name 'Kermonoch' with the personal name 'James Makcluir' had signified at least that the latter had been living on the lands of Gilbert Greirson of Castelmaddie, whose signature (see fig. 4) also appears on the 1637 petition), *viz.*, at one of the three Carmonochs - Over, Mid or Nether. It had been noted, here, that there were, on the same petition, two further signatures associated with the Carmonochs - *viz.*, that of a 'David McKill in Carmonow' and that of a 'Johnne Milligane in Cairnmonow' (see fig. 4). The identification of precisely two such further signatures had suggested that each of the three individuals had been living, respectively, in 1637, in one of the three Carmonochs. Nevertheless, the question had remained, in which of the three this 'James Makcluir' had been living. Here, it had seemed, because he must surely have been adult at the time of the 1637 petition, that he would at least have been already alive, fifteen years earlier, in 1622, when John MakLuire, Dr MakLuire's father, is known to have been living in Nether Carmonoch. It had then seemed very probable that it would have been together with Dr MakLuire's father, at Nether Carmonoch

---

[19] SRO PC 11/6B, Petition from the Presbytery of Kirkcudbright against the Service Book of Charles I, 1637.

(rather than at either Over or Mid Carmonoch) that 'James Makcluir' would have been living in 1622, and that it would have been at Nether Carmonoch that he would still have been living in 1637.

Now, while the word 'in' in the signatures of David McKill and John Milligan had indicated that they had been lawful tenants (presumably in Upper and Mid Carmonoch), the absence of that word from the signature of 'James Makcluir' had indicated that he was not the current lawful tenant in the Nether Carmonoch where he was living. Also, it had been noted that John MakLuire, Dr MakLuire's father, the tenant in 1622, was not a signatory to the 1637 petition. The explanation first coming to mind had been that the latter may have died. However, at least it had been clear that 'James Makcluir', not being a lawful tenant, had not been the son and heir of Dr MakLuire's father, who had simply stepped into a 'kindly' or 'few-ferm' tenancy vacated by the death of the latter.[20] It will be argued, below, indeed, that Dr MakLuire's father had not died, and that his absence from Nether Carmonoch at the time of the 1637 petition would have been due to him having emigrated, for a second time, to Ulster.

What had remained uncertain had been the relationship of this 'James Makcluir' to Dr MakLuire's father, and thus to Dr MakLuire himself. The most probable relationship, nevertheless, had been that he had been a son of the same parents as the future Dr MakLuire. He may, indeed, have been an older son but, unlike his younger brother, inherently incapable of legitimation and of succeeding to such a tenancy, by reason of having been the product of his parents' pre-marriage adultery and of having been born (unlike the future Dr John MakLuire) before they had been in a position legally, as would have appeared to them, to marry. Furthermore, if so, it may indeed have been a claim of primogeniture which this 'James Makcluir' would otherwise have had, which had precipitated his father's petition for the royal remission of 1622. Also, finally,

---

[20] M. Perceval-Maxwell, *The Scottish Migration to Ulster in the Reign of James I*, London, 1973, p. 32.

adequate provision by his father for the protection of a 'natural bairn's rights', and the provision of an acceptable livelihood at Nether Carmonoch, may have been the requirement under the law before the King would have granted the royal remission of 1622.[21] Presumably, Dr MakLuire's father, while in Ulster, remained the lawful tenant of Gilbert Greirson of Castelmaddie, but delegated the running of Nether Carmonoch to his oldest, but illegitimate, son, James.

Unfortunately, again, the location of James MakLuire at Nether Carmonoch threw no light upon the place of birth of Dr MakLuire.

His birth in the parish of Dalry - perhaps in Blauquhairn

In view of the lack of light thrown upon the probable birth-place of Dr MakLuire by these enquiries into the above MakLuire relatives, attention had turned to an interesting fact about the 1622 trial for pre-marriage adultery of Dr MakLuire's parents, 'John MakLuire in Nether Carmonoch' and 'Alison Denholme'. This was that those individuals summoned to Edinburgh to 'pas' on the case seemed to have been selected by virtue of having been the immediate neighbours of the two accused at the time of their alleged adultery in the 1590s.

The case, heard on 8th November, 1622, had been the second of two cases, both of alleged adultery and both specified as '*ad remissionem*', which had been taken together. The first of the two cases had been that of a James Finlay in Garrerie and a Mareon Schaw at Craiginbae - neighbours in the parish of Kells (see fig. 5).

Now, the meaning of the Scots expression 'to pas', 'to pais' or 'to pass' (in relation to proceedings in court) is given, in the *Concise Scots Dictionary*, as 'to serve or sit

---

[21] Hume, *Commentaries on the Law of Scotland Respecting Crimes*, I, p. 499.

on a jury, inquest, etc.'.[22] However, in these two cases, only ten, and not the usual fifteen, individuals were called so 'to pas'. Also, the selection, by reason of being immediate neighbours to the accused, had seemed to be contrary to usual principles of jury-selection and more appropriate for the summoning of witnesses. It had seemed, however, that (whether summoned as jurors or as witnesses) the locations of the homes of the individuals so summoned might throw light on where John MakLuire and Alison Denholme (only later to be 'in Nether Carmonoch') had been living at the time of their alleged pre-marriage adultery.

The ten who had been summoned from Kirkcudbrightshire to the Court in Edinburgh to 'pas' on the two cases, had been specified, in the court records, as follows:

> Compeirit Jon Newall in St Johnes Clauchane Rot McDowell yr Jon Inglis in Craigschy'nie Jon McMyllen in Craigneill Quintene McMyllane yr Andro Finlay in Gait Jon Finlay yr Johnne Edzer in Clauchane Rot Scott in Grennan Johnne Aha'- nay in Garroche and declairit yai war su'mond to pas upone the assyse of ye saids James Finlay and Johnne McClure for ye crymes foursaids[23]

This list shows that there had been some duplication in the representation of families and that, when this was taken into account, the ten individuals were seen to have come from eight homes - four in the parish of Kells and four in the parish of Dalry, forming two, equal, non-contiguous, groups (see fig. 5) as follows:

Parish of Kells

1. Craigschynnie - Jon Inglis
2. Craigneill - Jon and Quintene McMyllane
3. Gait - Andro and Jon Finlay

---

[22] M. Robinson, ed., *The Concise Scots Dictionary*, Aberdeen, 1985, p. 476.

[23] SRO JC 2/6, Justiciary Court, p. 99.

4.   Garroch - Johnne Ahannay

Parish of Dalry

1.   St John's Clauchane - Jon Newall
2.   St John's Clauchane - Rot McDowell
3.   St John's Clauchane - Johnne Edzer
4.   Grennan - Rot Scott

Now, as the four homes in the parish of Kells group were indeed immediate neighbours of the two defendants in the first case (*viz.*, James Finlay in Garrerie and Mareon Schaw at Craiginbae), it had seemed that the individuals from those four homes had been selected precisely because they were immediate neighbours of the accused parties in Case 1. It had then seemed, if this was so, that the individuals from the non-contiguous group of four adjacent homes in the parish of Dalry would indeed have been similarly selected by reason of having been immediate neighbours of John MakLuire and of Alison Denholme at the time of their alleged adultery (see fig. 5).

In this way it had seemed certain that both the accused parties, in the case of John MakLuire and Alison Denholme, at the time of their alleged adultery (and presumably, also, at the time of their subsequent marriage and of the birth of their son, the future Dr John MakLuire), had been living in the parish of Dalry and probably either in the clauchan itself of St John's Town of Dalry or in a farm very close to it.

Finally, as one such farm is Blauquhairn and, as it is recorded in the Kirkcudbrightshire Petition against the Service Book of Charles I, that an Adam Denholme was the tenant there in 1637 and, fourteen years earlier, in 1623, a David MakLuire, it had seemed possible that, only two decades earlier still, Denholmes (see Appendix B) and/or MakLuires (including, perhaps, Dr MakLuire's parents, John MakLuire and Alison Denholme) may have been either tenants, or living, there and that Blauquhairn may, therefore, have been the birth-place of Dr MakLuire (see fig. 6).[24]

---

[24] See SRO PC 11/6B, Petition from the Presbytery of Kirkcudbright against the Service Book of Charles I, 1637, and *Register of the Privy Council of Scotland*, Series 1, XIII (1622-1625), p. 217.

Figure 1

The nine children of Dr MakLuire and Mareon Greir.

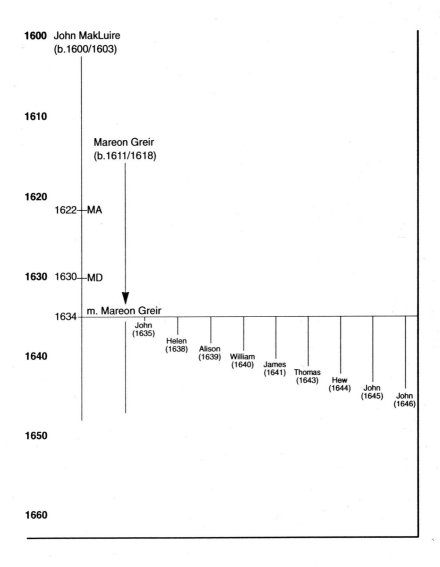

Figure 2

'Remissio Joannis McLuir in Carmonoch'.

A royal remission granted by James VI, on 28th August, 1622, to Dr MakLuire's father, John MakLuire in Nether Carmonoch, for the alleged crime of adultery with 'Alisona Dennane'.

<u>Lines 11 and 12.</u>

pro detestabili est turpe crimine adulterii per nosterii Joannem McLuir cum Alisona Dennane filia quond … Dennane in … vilo

(N.B. 'Dennane' ('Denholme'), not 'Donnane')

Ref: (Manuscript) Register of the Great Seal of Scotland, SRO C3/2 No. 210.

Reproduced by permission of the Keeper of the Records of Scotland with the agreement of the Controller of Her Majesty's Stationery Office.

Figure 3

The discovery of Nether Carmonoch.

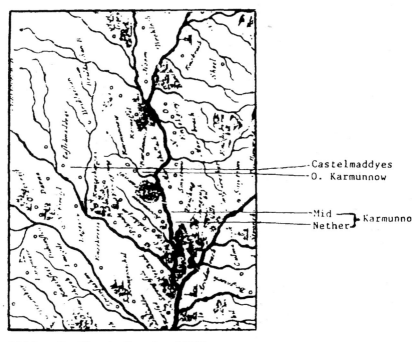

(a) Map after Timothy Pont, late 1500's.

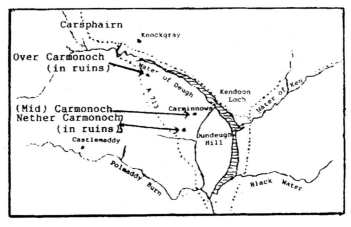

(b) Modern map, after hydro-electric modifications.

Figure 3

The discovery of Nether Carmonoch.

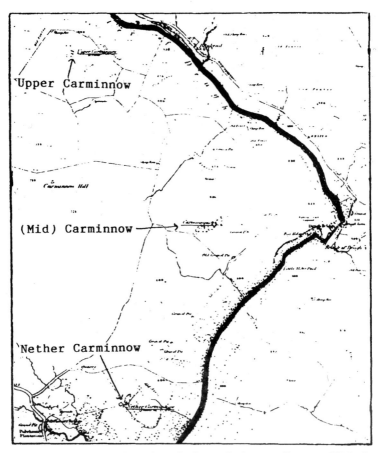

(c) Map, reproduced (reduced) from Ordnance Survey, Kirkud-brightshire, Sheet 9, 6", 1853: Showing Upper, ('Mid') and Nether 'Carminnow' (Carmonoch), the Water of Deugh, Deugh Linn and Deugh Bridge, prior to hydro-electric developments.

With acknowledgement to the trustees of the National Library of Scotland.

Figure 3

The discovery of Nether Carmonoch.

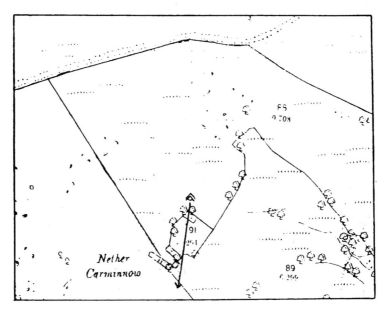

(d) Map, reproduced from Ordnance Survey, Kirkcudbrightshire, Sheet XIII-1, 25", 1:2500, 1894: Showing Nether Carminnow (Nether Carmonoch).

With acknowledgement to the Trustees of the National Library of Scotland.

Figure 3

The discovery of Nether Carmonoch.

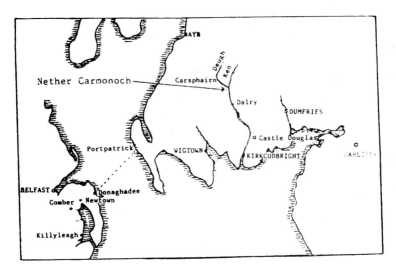

(e) Nether Carmonoch, the southernmost of three farms, Over, Mid and Nether Carmonoch, close to the Water of Deugh, in Kirkcudbrightshire, of which only Mid Carmonoch, as 'Carminnows' now survives.

Figure 4

Some relevant signatures

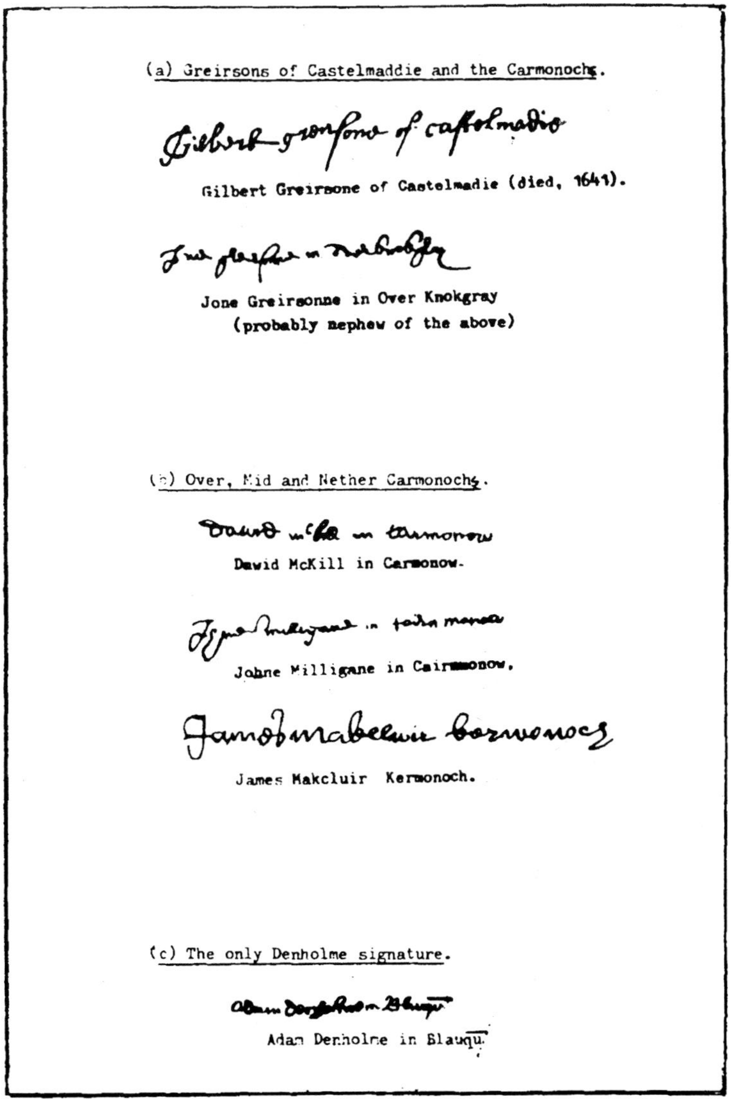

(a) Greirsons of Castelmaddie and the Carmonochs.

[signature]

Gilbert Greirsone of Castelmadie (died, 1641).

[signature]

Jone Greirsonne in Over Knokgray
(probably nephew of the above)

(b) Over, Mid and Nether Carmonochs.

[signature]

Dawid McKill in Carmonow.

[signature]

Johne Milligane in Cairmonow.

[signature]

James Makcluir Kermonoch.

(c) The only Denholme signature.

[signature]

Adam Denholme in Blauqu.

Tracings (reduced) of some of the 559 signatures on the 1637 petition from the presbytery of Kirkcudbright against the Service Book of Charles I.

Figure 5

The four Dalry homes of jurymen in the 1622 trial of Dr MakLuire's father.

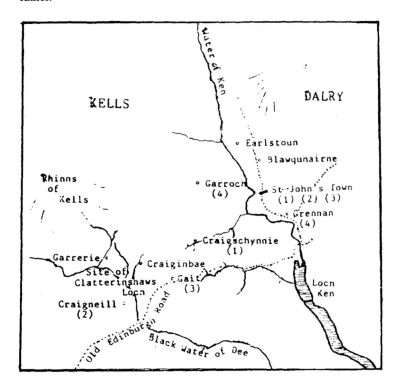

Case 1 – against James Finlay in Garrerie and Mareon Schaw at Craiginbae, (Kells).

Four homes of jurymen:
(1) Craigschynnie
(2) Craigneill
(3) Gait
(4) Garroch

Case 2 – against John MakLuire and Alison Denholme, (Dalry).

Four homes of Jurymen:
(1) St John's Town
(2) St John's Town
(3) St John's Town
(4) Grennan

Figure 6

Dr MakLuire's probable place of birth.

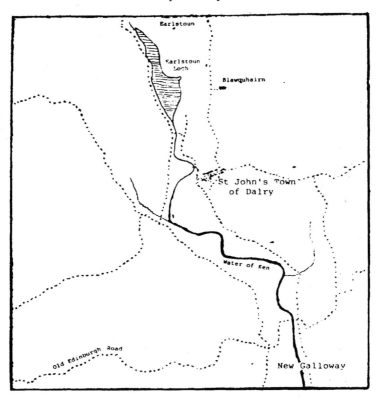

Dr John MakLuire born, probably, in, or close to, St John's Town of Dalry, and perhaps in the farm of Blawquhairn.

Chapter Three - Childhood in Ulster

Infancy in the parish of Dalry

It had seemed reasonable to assume that at least the early infancy of the future Dr John MakLuire, from the time of his birth in 1600/3, had been spent in the place where he had been born - in the parish of Dalry, probably either in the clauchan of St John's Town of Dalry itself, or in a farm very close to it, and perhaps in the farm of Blawquhairn.

It had to be admitted, however, that no firm evidence had come to light of where the young John MakLuire and his parents would have spent the years of his childhood between infancy and the time (itself initially obscure) of his father's first occupancy of the tenancy of Nether Carmonoch from Gilbert Greirson of Castelmaddie - the tenancy which, however, he was known to have been holding by 1622, the year in which he obtained his royal remission.

However, the identification of the 'John MakLuire in Castelmaddie' as Dr MakLuire's paternal grandfather, holding a tenancy from the same Gilbert Greirson of Castelmaddie from whom his son and heir, Dr MakLuire's father, would also come to hold a tenancy (in Nether Carmonoch), had suggested strongly that this would have been a tenancy of the heritable type - 'kindly' or 'fewferm'. If so, John MakLuire, Dr MakLuire's father, would have been aware, at the beginning of the century, when his son, the future Dr MakLuire, was still an infant, of his presumptive entitlement to the hereditary tenancy from the Greirsons which would eventually fall to him - but not until the death of his father in Castelmaddie.

Meanwhile, however, the father of the future Dr John MakLuire may well have been without adequate means of support for himself and for a wife and young family.

His removal to Ulster in early childhood

One obvious solution for a young married man so placed, and living in the south-west of Scotland during the first decade of the 1600s, would have been to join up with the rather large number who became emigrants to the Ards in County Down at the time of the historic settlement organised in 1606 by the then Sir Hugh Montgomery, of Braidstane Castle in the parish of Beith, Ayrshire (see fig.).[1]

Now, many of those so emigrating had been recruited by Sir Hugh from places in the parish of Beith itself, in the immediate neighbourhood of Braidstane Castle. One possibility had been that Dr MakLuire's father had, before 1606, moved, whether from Dalry parish, or from Castelmaddie in the parish of Kells, to the parish of Beith. This possibility had arisen, as a conjecture, when it was discovered that an Agnes Maxwell had been living in the parish of Beith - *viz.*, at Threepwood, not far from Braidstane Castle - certainly in 1609 at the time of the death of her husband, James Hamilton of Threepwood (fig.).[2] The conjecture had been that she might have been the Agnes Maxwell, widow of the Gilbert Greirson of Castelmaddie and the Carmonochs who had died in 1598 and that she had remarried and taken her two bairns, Gilbert (the under-age new laird of Castelmaddie and the Carmonochs) and John, with her to the parish of Beith. This conjecture, if true, would raise the possibility that Dr MakLuire's father, son of the John MakLuire staying behind in charge of Castelmaddie, may have accompanied them in some sort of family serving capacity to the under-age Gilbert and his mother, and have been recruited there.

But this had indeed been a highly speculative possibility. More certainly, it had been known that others, coming from farther afield than the parish of Beith, had been included in Sir Hugh Montgomery's emigration. One such had been a Patrick Moore, believed to have been one of the Moores of Milltoun (fig.), in the parish of Beith, who nevertheless had been, himself, the proprietor of Deugh Linn, and thus a close neighbour to John MakLuire in Castelmaddie, tenant of the Greirsons, because Deugh Linn faced, immediately, the latters' lands of Castelmaddie

---

[1] W. Montgomery, *The Montgomery Manuscripts 1603-1706*, ed. Revd. G. Hill, Belfast: Cleeland, 1869, p. 51.

[2] J. Paterson, *History of the County of Ayr*, Vol I., Ayr, 1847, p. 271.

and the Carmonochs from the opposite bank of the Water of Deugh (Chapter 2, fig. 3c).[3] Here, it had been hoped that the extensive manuscript material concerning the early Viscounts Montgomery of the Ards held at the Manor House, Donaghadee, might have shown a connection between Patrick Moore and John MakLuire, Dr MakLuire's father, and whether they might have moved together to become early tenants in the Ards of the then Sir Hugh Montgomery. Unfortunately, the tenantry records did not extend quite so far back.

The strongest argument for Dr MakLuire's father having indeed joined himself to those recruited by Sir Hugh Montgomery for the 1606 emigration to the Ards (whatever may have been the precise circumstances leading to his recruitment) had seemed, however, to have been the fact that the friendship at St Andrews University of the young John MakLuire, a mere 'ternar', with the young James Montgomery (a 'primar'), second son to Sir Hugh Montgomery - by then the 1st Viscount Montgomery of the Ards - had been already so close, even in their first year, as to have made it unlikely that it had not been already established, still earlier, during a shared childhood - which would have been in the Ards.

The young James Montgomery had been born at Braidstane Castle in 1600 and would have been aged about six when taken to the Ards in 1606.[4] It had seemed probable that the young John MakLuire if, as the son of one of the recruited tenants emigrating there, he also was taken to the Ards at the same time, may well have begun his known friendship with the young James Montgomery then. He would have been of the same age as, or a very little younger than him.

---

[3] Montgomery, *The Montgomery Manuscripts 1603-1706*, p. 54.

[4] *Lodge's Irish Peerage*, London: 1754, p. 365.

His parents' lives in the Ards in the early 1600s

An indication of the kind of life obtaining for the 1606 emigrants to the Ards can be found in Stevenson's *Two Centuries of Life in Down 1600-1800*. Stevenson says that:

> The men who came with Hamilton and Montgomery had lived through Elizabeth's reign - even the illiterate of them had heard of the travels of Raleigh, and the deeds of Hawkins Drake and Dudley and Cumberland in the seas and lands of the golden West. Movement and change were everywhere, the crowns of England and Scotland had been joined, and great events were happening in Ireland. There the Scots found within a few hours from their shores an America of new land, where for roaming Red Indian lurked the Wild Irish in woods and morasses ... they saw themselves in the glow of a hot modernity.

> The spring of 1606 witnessed the beginning of the Settlements, and the work proceeded apace. At enmity with each other, the planters did not allow their quarrel to interfere with their land surveying and allotment - perhaps by reason of it they worked with the greater strenuousness ...

> Montgomery made his headquarters at Newtownards, where he roughly repaired portions of an old Castle to provide for himself and friends. [He brought many who] were given large tracts of land in freehold, and other holdings by lease, laying the foundation for the status of minor gentry of the county in the centuries to come. In turn the grantees let their lands, some times in very small parcels of two, three, or four acres at the rent of a boll of barley per acre ... Montgomery's undertenants and those of their friends were certainly of better character and standing than the bulk of small occupiers in later settled Ulster counties ...

> New settlements have more than their share of the adventure-seeking violent and godless ... But

from the beginning there were spare-living, God-fearing folk, and the good harvests of a few years later brought many of good character and men of property ... On the poor lands some of the Irish remained as Canaanites to be thorns in the side of the Scottish Israel. The Montgomery historian [William Montgomery of Rosemount, grandson of the 1st Viscount] speaks of them as Gibeonites, hewers of wood and drawers of water. Some of the settlers made terms with natives who preferred any service to leaving their place of birth, but they did not learn to love their masters ...

While the larger holders ... proceeded to build stone houses as fast as possible, the poorer men in a wild and houseless land had, perforce, to adopt the Irish fashion and construct wattled booths. The material for construction was all at hand. A frame of trees or large branches was set up - through the beams was woven underwood - outside, and against this were built sods, - the roof was thatched with rushes. In such rude shelters did many of the settlers live their days in the new America. No doubt the hardships of these days were endured the more cheerfully because of the nearness of friends in Scotland. By 1607 it was not uncommon for Scotch folk in days of favouring weather to ride, carrying wares for sale from Stranraer to Portpatrick, leave their horses there, cross the Channel, hire horses at Donaghadee, ride to Newtownards, sell their produce, and, reversing the journey, reach homes round Loch Ryan by bedtime ...

It was a wild country in which the settlers raised their first shelters. In the great woods deer were numerous, the wild boar saw the century waning before it disappeared, the author of the Montgomery MSS mentions wolves in the list of animals hunted by the first Viscount Montgomery, who, soldier-like, 'delighted little in soft recreations' and sought his pleasure in the field with horse and hawk and hound.[5]

The 1st Viscount Montgomery was greatly supported by his first wife, Elizabeth Shaw. Of her labours, the Montgomery historian has to say:

This ... gave occasion to Sir Hugh's Lady to build water-mills in all the parishes, to the great advantage of her house, which was numerous in servants, of whom she stood in need, in working about her gardens, carriages etc. having then no duty day's works from tenants, or very few as exacted, they being sufficiently employed in their proper labour and the publique. The millers also prevented the necessity of bringing meal from Scotland, and grinding with quairn stones (as the Irish did to make their graddon) both which inconveniencys the people, at their first coming, were forced to undergo ...

Her ladyship had also her farms at Greyabbey and [Comber] as well as at Newtown, both to supply the new-comers and her house; and she easily got men for plough and barn, for many came over who had not stocks to plant and take leases of land, but had brought a cow or two and a few sheep, for which she gave them grass and so much grain per annum, and an house and garden-plot to live on, and some land for flax and potatoes, as they agreed on for doing their work, and there be at this day many such poor labourers amongst us; and this was but part of her good management, for she set up and encouraged linen and woolen manufactory, which soon brougt down the prices of ye breakens [i.e. tartan plaids, from Ayrshire] ...

Now everybody minded their trades, and the ploughs, and the spade, building, and setting fruit

---

[5] J. Stevenson, *Two Centuries of Life in Down*, Belfast: Linenhall Press, 1920, p. 44.

trees, etc. in orchards and gardens, and by ditching in their grounds. The old women spun, and the young girls plyed their nimble fingers at knitting, and everybody was innocently busy. Now the Golden peacable age renewed, no strife, contention, querulous lawyers, or Scottish or Irish feuds, between clanns and families, and sirnames, disturbing the tranquility of those times; and the towns and temples were erected, with other great works.

The precise standing of the parents of the future Dr MakLuire amongst these early emigrants to the Ards is not certain. They would appear, however, to have been of the tenant farmer class but marrying (as will be shown) into that of the 'bonnet laird' - i.e. the proprietors of small estates all, or parts, of which they would farm themselves.

His schooling at Newtownards

Something can be gleaned also about the preliminary childhood education of the young John MakLuire and his friend James Montgomery. Stevenson says that exactly how many schoolmasters the 1st Viscount Montgomery 'planted' is not known but that we have a few details of what was doubtless the principal school - that close to his own great house at Newtownards.[6]

Stevenson says that while the 1st Viscount's record may show self-aggrandisement to have been the ruling motive of his actions, it is clear that, with pride in newly attained rank, he had a desire to exhibit a grand style in his house and appointments, and the school which was to rank as the first on his estates. Stevenson quotes from *The Montgomery Manuscripts* where the writer says that the 1st Viscount:

> built a great school at Newtown, endowing it, as I am credibly told, with twenty pounds yearly salary for a Master of Arts to teach Latin, Greek,

---

[6] Stevenson, *Two Centuries of Life in Down*, p. 204.

and Logycks, allowing the scholars a green for recreation at golf, football and archery, declaring that if he lived some few years longer, he would convert his priory houses into a College for Philosophy; and further paid small stipends to a master to teach Orthography and Arithmatic, and to a Music-master who should also be precentor to the church, so that both sexes should learn all those three arts; the several masters ... having over and beside what I have mentioned, wages from every scholar under their charge

Stevenson, here, does not continue the quotation, but inserts his own statement, claiming a Presbyterian basis for the schooling, which runs as follows:

It is probable that all the masters of these early school foundations were Presbyterians, as were the ministers placed in charge of the Scottish settlers by Hamilton and Montgomery.

However, continuation of the quotation would have asserted, on the contrary, an Episcopalian ethos, and loyalty, of the schoolmasters, prevailing from the time of the plantation in 1606 at least until the coming of the Scots army nearly forty years later - in 1642. The school was next to the restored priory church and:

The scholars of the great school also came in order, following the master, and seated themselves in the next form in the loft or gallery, behind the Provost, who had his Burgesses on each hand of them.

But, alas! this beautiful order, appointed and settled by his Lordship, lasted no longer than till the Scottish army came over and put their Chaplains in our churches; who, having power, regarded not law, equity or right to back or countenance them; they turned out all the legal loyal Clergy, who would not desert Episcopacy and the service book, and take the Covenant, a very bitter pill, indeed, to honest men[7]

Whether the erection of this school would have been in time to benefit Hugh Montgomery, the Viscount's eldest son and heir, Hugh, who would already have been of about nine years of age when taken to the Ards, is not certain. But his younger brother, James, only about six years of age at the time, would surely have been a beneficiary - and have shared the benefit with the young John MakLuire. The 'beautiful order' lasted, in fact, for more than thirty years - and thus long after the time of the education of the future Dr John MakLuire there.

The latter, recognised by the Viscount, in due course, both as a friend of his son (the young James Montgomery), and as a 'lad o' pairts', would probably have been chosen at that time by the Viscount as a protégé to be encouraged in scholarly pursuits; to be a reliable student-companion to the young James; and to accompany the latter to the university in 1618 both as a fellow student and, possibly, as a personal servant.

Finally, if the conjecture was correct that the 'James Makcleuir Kermonoch' who, thirty years later than the emigration, was, in 1637, to sign the Kirkcudbright petition against the Charles I Service Book of that year, had been an older, but not legitimable, brother of the future Dr John MakLuire, he would presumably have shared in that education. That possibility would at least help to explain the confident clarity and style of his signature - for which the teacher of Orthography was, perhaps, partly to be congratulated (see Chapter 2, fig. 4).

Return to Kirkcudbrightshire

The end of the future Dr John MakLuire's schooldays in 1618 would appear to have been at the time of the return of his father from Ulster to Kirkcudbrightshire to take up the heritable tenancy of Nether Carmonoch which had fallen

---

[7] Montgomery, *The Montgomery Manuscripts 1603-1706*, p. 127.

to him with the death of his father in Castelmaddie in 1617. It would appear that the heritable tenancy with the Greirsons was transferred from Castelmaddie to that at Nether Carmonoch because the young laird of Castelmaddie and the Carmonochs, Gilbert Greirson, had chosen to live, himself, at Castelmaddie.

Precisely when Dr MakLuire's father would have actually taken up the tenancy of Nether Carmonoch, which fell due to him, is not known. However, it is known that the 'giving up' of the testament of John MakLuire in Castelmaddie ought to have been carried out promptly after the death of the testator, in 1617, by his son, John MakLuire, Dr MakLuire's father. It is also known, however, that the testament had not been 'given up' in 1617, or even by 28 April, 1618, the date on which Gilbert Greirson of Castelmaddie had been (erroneously) 'put to the horn' for failing to do this. This had seemed to indicate that the reason why John MakLuire, Dr MakLuire's father, had not 'given up' the testament promptly would have been because he had not returned immediately to Kirkcudbrightshire from Ulster to take up the tenancy, even by 28 April, 1618. Presumably, therefore, the date of his return would have been still later in 1618. This was, in fact, the year in which his son had first matriculated at St Andrews.

Possibly, therefore, the young John MakLuire, in the summer of 1618, may have been able to live for only a brief period with his father at Nether Carmonoch, while waiting to go up to St Andrews, and have been able to help with the harvest that summer. But, subsequently, as a student, he may well have returned home, during the university vacations, for the same purpose.

Now, John Greirson, the younger brother of the laird, would probably have been living - not in Castelmaddie, with his older brother, Gilbert - but in Mid Carmonoch, where the two brothers, in the past, had stayed with their father. Also, this John Greirson, unlike his brother, had followed the example of the family Chief, Sir Robert Greir of Lag, and modified his name to John Greir. Furthermore, as was later to be deduced (see below), it had been he who had been the father of the young John MakLuire's future wife, Mareon Greir.

Thus, it would probably have been during the young John MakLuire's visits to Nether Carmonoch to help on the farm during the vacations that he may have noticed, for the first time, the little girl of between four and eight who lived in the neighbouring farm of Mid Carmonoch and who was to be his future wife - Mareon Greir.

Chapter Four - St Andrews University

His first matriculation in October 1618

It had been seen that it had not been known for certain whether the young John MakLuire would have come to St Andrews University in 1618 directly from the Ards, in Ulster, together with the young James Montgomery, or from his father's newly acquired tenancy of the farm at Nether Carmonoch.

Certainly, however, the young John MakLuire's first matriculation, at St Leonard's College, was in October of that year, as was established by the finding of his signature ('Joannes McCluire') on the page recording those taking the academic oath on 22 February 1619, during the second term of their first year (see fig. 1).[1] Certainly, also, he had subsequently engaged in four years of study for the degree of Master of Arts.

His early studies

The four-year course of the young John MakLuire for the degree of Master of Arts would still have started, no doubt, with the trivium, the three-fold programme which had characterised the first stage of the curriculum of the mediaeval undergraduate. This would have comprised the three arts of grammar, rhetoric and logic - arts which, as the distinguished neurologist, Sir Francis Walshe, has pointed out, may be superficially summed up as the skilled use of language, some working knowledge of which is the indispensable condition of the maintenance of medicine still in our time.

Walshe, in contemplating the many proposals for a reform of medical education, had perceived little more than superficial and uncoordinated attempts to grapple with the problems. None, he had found, had been informed by an adequate appreciation of those intellectual instruments and methods by which alone the confused data of the exper-

---

[1] MSS UY 305 3, Muniments of the University of St Andrews, p. 125.

ience of physicians can be transmuted into a more or less coherent body of ordered knowledge. In his Harveian Oration, Walshe said:

> These instruments and methods are not awaiting discovery. On the contrary, they were forged and brought to a high of refinement by our mediaeval ancestors. Unhappily, when, at the Renaissance, we rejected the appeal to authority in our study of nature, and installed observation on its empty throne, we also abandoned the study of those liberal arts by which only can the fruits of observation be expressed in a grammar of science, rhetorically expanded and logically interpreted. I refer to the arts of grammar, rhetoric, and logic, the trivium of the mediaeval undergraduate's curriculum. These arts may be superficially summed up as the skilled use of language, but to be content to say, as we do so often and so glibly, that a command of English is an indispensable instrument for the formulation and communication of ideas is to pay lip service to a notion that we have neglected fully to explore. How many Masters of Arts in our day know what are the arts of which they are the titular masters?

> I am therefore proposing that some working knowledge of these liberal arts is the indispensable condition of the maintenance of medicine in our time on the level of a true branch of learning. For all phenomena have to be translated into language, into a grammar, before we can assimilate them into science. Symbolic thought is our instrument to this end, and it is surely imperative that we should know its laws and use it expertly.[2]

> Every complex of presenting phenomena is a text to be read, translated into the grammar of science, rhetorically expanded and interpreted.[3]

---

[2] Sir Francis M. Walshe, *Further Critical Studies in Neurology and Other Essays and Addresses*, Edinburgh, 1965, p. 223.

[3] Ibid., p. 231.

If, as is probable, the study of these liberal arts - the trivium of grammar, rhetoric, and logic - had not already been
abandoned at St Andrews in 1618, the young John
MakLuire may have had as sound a preliminary basis for
his study of medicine as the average medical student of
today - perhaps even better. Less certain is which of the
quadrivium (of arithmetic, geometry, music and astronomy) he may have gone on to study. Here, arithmetic and
geometry may perhaps be taken for granted. As for the
astronomy taught to the young John MakLuire, it would
have been that of Copernicus rather than Ptolemy - but not
yet that of Galileo, whose findings were not to be published until 1632.

His implied musical education and skills

A later '*carmen*' in the praise of Dr John MakLuire, by Dr
George Sibbald, uncle of the renowned Sir Robert Sibbald,
suggests that, as well as Apollo's healing skills, He had
acquired the latter's legendary musical skill at the lyre:

In IOAN. MAKLVIREUM (sive lyradem)
Aonidem pater est, idem est Asclepii, Apollo;
Illius inventum est ars metrica & medica.
Verum Asclepiadis citharamque & Paeonis artem,
Musarum vt famulis tradidit Aoniam.
Pteridum nato simul atque Epidaurii alumno
Phoebus avus Lyrada donat vtramque lyram,
Macte lyra vtravis, canones dignate modosque
Tradere Paeonios, ludere & Aonios.

Ludebat G. Sibbaldus.[4]

Translation

For John MakLuire (otherwise the muse of the
lute). Apollo is his father, as also of Asclepius;
He who found the worthy art of medicine.
Indeed, he taught the Asclepian followers the art

---

[4] J. MakLuire, *The Buckler of Bodilie Health*, Edinburgh: Wreittoun,
1630, p. ix.

of the lute and of the healing god as he taught the
servants of the Aonian Muses. Winged forefather
Phoebus at the same time gives the lute both to
Epidaurus' born pupil and to the Lyradan stars.
Good fortune be to both, the lute and being
worthy to hand down the Asclepian rules and
ways, and playing the muses.

G. Sibbald was the composer.[5]

Perhaps, even at school at Newtownards, the young John
MakLuire had already benefited from teaching by the
stipendiary 'Musick Masters' provided for by the 1st
Viscount Montgomery and, at St Andrews, had been given
the opportunity to improve upon his musical talent.

His undergraduate instruction in medicine

It had appeared that the young John MakLuire's inclination towards medicine had been present from an early
age. This is shown by the record of his early start, in 1619,
during his first year as an Arts student (when he would
have been aged only, most probably, about sixteen), on his
medical book, *The Buckler of Bodilie Health*. But his
undergraduate studies in medicine would not have been
started merely upon his own initiative. There can be no
doubt that he would also have been taught medicine.

Blair points out that over the whole of the Reformation
and Post-Reformation periods there was medical teaching
in St Andrews. He says that the reason why medicine has
traditionally been held up as the subject which was never
taught at St Andrews was the undoubted failure of the
teachers of the later eighteenth and earlier nineteenth
centuries to do so - as a result of which it had come to be
generally assumed that this had always been the case.[6]

---

[5] Translated by Mr James J. Robertson, of the Faculty of Law at the
University of Dundee.

[6] J.S.G. Blair, *History of Medicine in the University of St Andrews*,
Edinburgh, 1987, p. 10.

It seems that, already in 1579, almost forty years earlier than the matriculation of John MakLuire, a visitation ordered by the young James VI had proposed that Master James Martine, Provost of St Salvator's College (and also parish minister at Cults, near Aberdeen) who was described as the 'Principall Professor of Medicin thairin' - presumably in the general, occupational, sense - was then to be the 'Professor of Medicine', presumably in the official sense. He was to teach four times a week on Monday, Tuesday, Wednesday and Friday 'at the hours to be appointed by the electors and maisters of the universitie'. As 'Maister' James Martine is described as having been (already) 'principal' professor of medicine before his official appointment, this had seemed to imply that there had also (already) been others at the university who 'professed' (and taught) medicine. A later report recorded that Master James Martine had said that he taught medicine, since 1590, twice a week, although Blair says that this was denied by certain of the other masters.

The nature and extent of the undergraduate instruction in medicine at St Andrews University, specifically at the time when the young John MakLuire would have been a student there, has been discussed by Blair. He pointed out that, in 1600, the duty of teaching medicine had fallen to the second master of St Salvator's. This may, therefore, have still been the situation in 1618. Blair also mentions that after various private benefactors had been encouraged to pass their private collections of books to St Andrews, and the King himself had donated 200 volumes, a library collection did exist by 1612. This had included a few medical books, which would have been available to John MakLuire in 1618 - specifically works by Aetius, Almansor, Celsus, Dioscorides, Galen, Mesue, Albertus Magnus and Geber.[7]

Closer still to the young MakLuire's 1618 matriculation (specifically in 1616) there had been presented, at St Andrews, as the fifth of 'Certane Articillis gevine to be

---

[7] Ibid., p. 9.

advysit upone', and listed under the heading 'Thingis to be Reformit w'in the Universitie, 1616', the recommendation 'That ther be wirthie men socht and gotting for the professione of Medicen and Lawis, without quhom our Universitie, quilk suld be ane moder (mother) of all knawlege, is ane Universitie only in name; and so mony men may be appointed as is abill sufficientlie to do that turne'.[8]

It had seemed probable, in particular, that Master John Wedderburn (not yet with a doctorate but later to become Charles I's trusted physician, and to be knighted), who transferred from Divinity at St Mary's College to 'Philosophy' at St Leonard's in 1620, had been one of these 'wirthie men socht' to teach medicine.[9] Clearly, however, his arrival at St Leonard's College had been at a time when the young John MakLuire had already started on his book. Master John Wedderburn would, perhaps, have nevertheless supplemented the teaching already being given by James Martine (by then having graduated as 'Doctor' - presumably at St Andrews itself) who, in fact, because it is known that he supervised the administration of the academic oath to the young John MakLuire in 1619 (see fig. 1), must, although ageing, have still been active.

What medicine the young John MakLuire would have been taught would have been the writings, regarded as authoritative, of the classical medical authors of antiquity - in particular those listed above - and no importance would have been attached to the clinical experience which could only come later, with apprenticeship to an established physician. Nevertheless, the teaching which the young John MakLuire would have received would have been an encouragement to him to progress, in due course, to his post-graduate medical apprenticeship.

---

[8] *Evidence, oral and documentary, taken by the Commissioners appointed by King George IV, for visiting the Universities of Scotland*, 4 vols., London, 1837, III, pp. 200-1.

[9] *Dictionary of National Biography*, Oxford, 1917, XX, p. 1049.

The social-class distribution of his fellow students

The list of the young John MakLuire's fellow students, matriculating in October, 1618, and taking the academic oath (as administered by the Rector, Dr James Martine, Provost of St Salvator's College on 22nd February, 1619), is shown in fig. 1.[10] An attempt was made to identify, from this, as many as possible of the young John MakLuire's fellow students, and to find out whether they had been of relevance to him in his subsequent life.

Here, it had been recognised, as has already been mentioned, that students at St Andrews University in those days were classified, according to social class, as primars (sons of nobility), secundars (sons of land-owners or merchants) or ternars (sons of artisans or tenant farmers). The list for the matriculation of 1618 is not explicit, however, as to where the dividing lines are to be drawn between the social classes - except for the cross against the name 'David Scrymgeure' (who was an undoubted primar) and which, therefore, may have been meant to indicate the last of the primars.

Understandably, the primars were found to be the most easily identified. The first five on the matriculation list proved to be persons who were historically identifiable, by reason of coming from noble families, and were thus, undoubtedly, primars. They were:

> 1. 'Jacobus Montgomerius', primar by reason of being second son of the 1st Viscount Montgomery of the Ards.

> 2. 'Franciscus Fraser', primar by reason of being grandson of the Earl of Buchan and son of the future 1st Lord Fraser.

> 3. 'Alexander Lindesius', primar by reason of being son of the future 13th Earl of Crawford.

---

[10] MSS UY 305 3, Muniments of the University of St Andrews, p. 125.

4. 'Gulielmus Douglasius', primar by reason of being second son of the 1st Earl of Queensberry.

5. 'David Scrymgeure', primar by reason of being third son of the future Viscount Dudhope.

The status of the sixth on the list - Andrew Hume - had been uncertain. No one of that name, of appropriate age, and coming from the noble families either of Hume or Home had been identified and he had therefore been presumed to have been either an unidentified primar or the first of the secundars.

The secundars and ternars proved to be the most difficult to differentiate but, no doubt, the ternars, of whom John MakLuire, as a son of a tenant farmer, clearly was one, were the lowest on the list - which ends, it would seem (but see below), with the first two of the right-hand column.

Some specific fellow students

'Jacobus Montgomerius' - The fellow student clearly of the greatest relevance to Dr MakLuire was James Montgomery, the first of the primars. He was, of course, the James Montgomery who had been the second son of Sir Hugh Montgomery of Braidstane Castle, in the parish of Beith, Ayrshire, by then the 1st Viscount Montgomery of the Ards in Ulster - and he was a primar for that reason.

James Montgomery had been born at Braidstane in 1600 and would thus have been of the same age as, or perhaps a little older than, John MakLuire.[11] If the latter was not only a companion fellow student but acting also as a personal servant to James Montgomery, one may wonder whether James Montgomery may have attended the races at Cupar - which was only permitted to primars - but have taken John MakLuire with him in the latter's capacity as a servant!

James Montgomery, after graduating, became a life-long courtier with three monarchs - James VI and I, Charles I

---

[11] *Lodge's Irish Peerage*, London, 1754, p. 365.

and Charles II - and, although a Scot by birth, was given an English knighthood. His adventuresome life, as Sir James Montgomery, and the relationship between him and Dr John MakLuire dating, certainly from their first year together at St Andrews, but more probably from a shared childhood in Ulster, and continuing throughout the lives of both of them, will be discussed further below.

'Jacobus Scotus' - The James Scott who matriculated, apparently as a secundar, with John MakLuire at St Leonard's College in 1618 and who took the academic oath in 1619 (signing himself as 'Jacobus Scotus') did not graduate with John MakLuire at St Andrews in 1622. However, he was probably the James Scott who graduated at Edinburgh University in that year.[12] Also, he would surely have been the 'Mr James Scott, merchant' who was, later in 1639, a witness of the baptism of Dr MakLuire's second daughter, Alison.[13]

During a baptismal search, the baptism in Edinburgh of a James Scott, son of a James Scott, writer, on 8th June, 1601 - and therefore of about the same age as John MakLuire - was found.[14] It had thus seemed that this James Scott from Edinburgh was most likely to have been the fellow student of 1618. He would seem to have been related to Sir James Scott of Abbotshall, knight, who was one of the witnesses at his baptism.

That James Scott, because of his father's social class as a writer, would indeed, in 1618, have been a secundar. Also, it had been possible, but by no means certain, that he would have been the 'Mr James Scott, merchant' who, on 31st December, of the same year as the baptism of Dr MakLuire's child (1639), and as the only 'Mr James Scott,

---

[12] Edinburgh University, Manuscript Roll of Edinburgh Graduates, MA degree, James Scott, 1622.

[13] SRO OPR 685 1/4, Edinburgh (Greyfriars) Register of Baptisms, 29th July, 1639.

[14] SRO OPR OPR 685 1/1, Edinburgh (Greyfriars) Register of Baptisms, 8th June, 1601.

merchant' on the Edinburgh Marriage Register of those days, had married a Mary Cowen.[15]

'Joannes Kynnere' - This 'John Kynnere', presumably a secundar, would surely have been the 'Mr John Kinneir' who, later (with a Mr Alexander Kinneir), clearly was sufficiently close to Dr MakLuire to be invited to be witness at the baptism, in Edinburgh, of the latter's first daughter, Helen, on 4th July, 1638.[16]

'Aex^{r}ander Caledonis.' - This somewhat cryptic two-worded signature calls for closer examination.

It cannot be doubted that a second letter, an 'l', is missing, by reason of having been condensed into the downward right-hand stroke of the initial capital 'A' (fig. 2a). Also, as there would appear to be a suprascriptal 'r' immediately following the first four letters 'Alex' - giving 'Alex^r', the conventional contraction of 'Alexander' - it would appear that this 'Alex^r' has been similarly condensed into the surname 'Alexander', to represent 'Alexander Alexander' as the full name.

Now, an authoritative calling in question of this inter-pretation has been voiced. This would appear to be based on the view that, in those days, a person of the name 'Alexander Alexander' simply would not, when signing his name, have condensed his Christian name within his surname in that manner. This calling in question would appear to include, also, the assumption that the suprascrip-tal mark following the first four letters 'Alex' cannot be interpreted as the suprascriptal 'r' which it appears to be, and must, simply, be ignored, as a meaningless mark.

An answer to this sceptical questioning would seem to lie, however, on the same page, in two of the signatures on the postgraduate list - signatures of two Masters of Arts who also matriculated, as postgraduates, in October, 1618.

---

[15] H. Paton, ed., *Register of Marriages, Parish of Edinburgh 1595-1700*, Edinburgh: Scottish Record Society, 1905, 31 December 1639.

[16] SRO OPR 685 1/4, Edinburgh (Greyfriars) Register of Baptisms, 4 July 1638.

The one of these two signatures, the fifth on the post-graduate list, a single-worded signature, appears to give 'Johnston' as the surname (fig. 2b). Now, although no one of that surname had graduated as Master of Arts at St Andrews earlier, in July 1618[17], a 'Joannes Johnstoune' had graduated MA at Edinburgh University that very year - on 25 July 1618.[18] It is probable, therefore, that it was that 'John Johnston' who, three months after graduating at Edinburgh, matriculated as a postgraduate student at St Andrews in October 1618, and signed the academic oath in February 1619.[19] If so, his signature would seem to exemplify a condensation of the very same kind as has been suggested in the case of 'Alexander Alexander'. It would appear to be a condensation of the Christian name 'John' within the latinised surname 'Johnstonus' - signifying (after taking into account, also, a capital 'A', created by a cross-bar inserted into the condensation 'GJ', and a suprascriptal 'r') a full signature of 'M^{r}AG (Magister) John Johnstonus'.

The other of these two signatures, the second on the post-graduate list, is two-worded. The second of the two words, 'Abred.', being the abbreviation for 'Aberdeen', must surely be a territorial qualification and not the surname. The surname would therefore appear to be 'Ros' but (together with a condensation into it of 'MR', for 'Magister') there must surely also be at least some indication within the signature of the signatory's Christian name. What the Christian name may be, presumably condensed, here, is, admittedly, less clear. However, in view of the firm cross-bar which creates a capital 'A' within the condensation JMR, it would seem to be 'JAs' (see fig. 2c). Now, while no person of the name 'James Ros' is recorded as having graduated at Aberdeen - either

[17] MSS UY 305 3, Muniments of the University of St Andrews, p. 334.

[18] *A Catalogue of the Graduates in the Arts Divinity and Law: University of Edinburgh,* Edinburgh: Neill & Co., 1858, p. 32.

[19] MSS UY 305 3, Muniments of the University of St Andrews, p. 336.

at King's College[20] or Marischal College, in July 1618[21] - the name 'Jacobus Ross' was entered as that of a graduate at St Andrews itself in July 1618.[22] It is probable, therefore, that it was he (presumably a native of Aberdeen) who matriculated again, at St Andrews, as a postgraduate student, three months later, in October 1618, and signed the academic oath in February 1619.[23]

The interpretation which is offered of the 'Alexander Alexander Caledonis' signature obviates, as with the 'Mr (JAs) Ros Abred.' signature, the necessity for attempting to interpret the second word of this signature as a surname. In view of the latinisation of the signature, the interpretation offered would see it certainly not as 'Caledonius' (from which it would have to be assumed that the letter 'n' has been, accidentally, omitted), but as the 'Caledonis' which it more plainly appears to be - the genitive of 'Caledon'. The right-hand dot, of the three dots above the word, would appear to be the dot of an 'i' - the other two being fortuitous marks.

Now, while no 'Caledon' (as distinct from 'Caledonia') has been identified in Scotland, there is a Caledon in Co. Tyrone, Ulster, which is best known as the place where the Irish Rebellion of 1641 first broke out. The significance of this Caledon in Co. Tyrone for this signature, however, is surely as a territorial qualification of the name. Moreover, a V-shaped insertion into the capital 'A', additional to the flowing cross-bar already present, suggests yet a further condensation. This is of a capital 'M' which, in association with the suggested suprascriptal 'r', further along, suggests 'Mr', meaning 'Magister'. This would represent a claim by the signatory to be, not a 'Master of Arts', but 'Master of Caledon'. It would represent a claim

---

[20] C. Innes, ed., *Fasti Aberdonensis 1494-1854*, Aberdeen: Spalding Club, 1854, p. 455.

[21] P. J. Anderson, ed., *Fasti Academiae Mariscallanae Aberdonensis*, Aberdeen: New Spalding Club, 1889, Vol II, p. 191.

[22] MSS UY 305 3, Muniments of the University of St Andrews, p. 334.

[23] Ibid., p. 167.

to be the son and heir of the proprietor of the lands of Caledon. These are lands known to have been escheated following the famous flight of the Earl of Tyrone (together with the Earl of Tyrconnel) in 1607, and planted in 1610.

The further question which had arisen from this interpretation of the signature had been the identity of this 'Alexander Alexander (?Master) of Caledon'. Now, an enquiry based upon the comprehensive genealogical work, *Memorials of the Earl of Stirling and of the House of Alexander*, by Rogers, found only one 'Alexander Alexander', out of the very many of that name indexed in that work, whose dates were compatible with him having matriculated as a student at St Andrews University in 1618.[24] This individual's name is recorded in the chapter devoted to Alexanders 'of Edinburgh and Leith'.[25] Nevertheless, although this Alexander Alexander had certainly died in Edinburgh, no evidence is given of an Edinburgh or Leith birth or parentage. The Alexander Alexander specified in that chapter is stated, simply, to have been long employed as the servitor or principal amanuensis to Sir William Alexander, the Earl of Stirling. Rogers' other two-volume book, *The Earl of Stirling's Register of Royal Letters 1615-1635*, goes further, however, and states that Alexander Alexander, the amanuensis, had been a relative of Lord Stirling.[26] If so, he (and the signatory below him) could have been 'primars' - and not the last on the list of ternars.

A connection of the signatory 'Alexander Alexander' with Caledon in Co. Tyrone raises further questions. The present-day Alexander family, who are Earls of Caledon, trace their ancestry, according to *The Scottish Nation*, to 'a junior branch of the Stirling family' - i.e. that of Sir Will-

[24] C. Rogers, *Memorials of the Earl of Stirling and of the House of Alexander*, 2 vols., Edinburgh: Paterson, 1877.

[25] Ibid., II, Chaps 12, 13.

[26] C. Rogers, *The Earl of Stirling's Register of Royal Letters 1615-1635*, 2 vols., Edinburgh: privately printed, 1885, I, p. lxi.

iam Alexander, 1st Earl of Stirling.[27] Now, a Robert Alexander, son of a Christopher Alexander, burgess and baillie of Stirling, is recorded as having been on the third list, dated 4th August, of the 1609 Scottish Applicants for land in Ulster for the 1610 plantation.[28] Whether or not the land given to him was that at Caledon in Tyrone; whether or not that Christopher Alexander of Stirling, the father of Robert, was of a junior branch of the Alexanders of Menstrie (Sir William's family); whether or not his son, Robert, having emigrated to Ulster, was the ancestor of the present Earls of Caledon; and whether or not the 'Alexander Alexander, Master of Caledon' of the signature was the son and heir of that Robert Alexander (presumably not himself living there), are questions which have resisted clarification.

However, in order to check the suggestion that Alexander Alexander, the 1619 student, was Alexander Alexander the relative, servitor and principal amanuensis to Sir William Alexander, 1st Earl of Stirling, of later years, a signature of the amanuensis, for comparison with that of the matriculating student, was sought - although without success. Nevertheless, in one of the six volumes (Rogers seems to recognise only the three which are deposited in Scotland) of Sir William's (manuscript) 'Register of Royal Letters', one entry, in the hand of this amanuensis himself (concerning the intended grant, to him, of a place of masery at the Court of Session) was found in which he writes (not signs) his own name.[29] A comparison of writings of the name 'Alexander' in 1632 by the amanuensis, with the university signature '(?M^r) Alexander Alexander Caledonis' of thirteen years earlier, in 1619, (see fig. 3), shows resemblances in favour of them having indeed been written by the same person. In

---

[27] W. Anderson, *The Scottish Nation*, Edinburgh: Fullarton, 1865, p. 106.

[28] M. Perceval-Maxwell, *The Scottish Migration to Ulster in the Reign of James I*, London, 1973, p. 322.

[29] BM Add MS 23111, Sir William Alexander. Vol II, Untitled 1630-1635, p. 147.

particular, in both examples of the word 'Alexander', the first of the two letters 'e' is written in the modern way (e) while the second is written in the older manner (ε). Moreover, this is the case both in the 1619 and the 1632 examples - surely evidence that the two writings are by the same individual.

This Alexander Alexander, fellow student with the young John MakLuire, if the future amanuensis at the Court, after an uncertain length of time, after matriculating in October, 1618, and signing the academic oath in February 1619, and studying at St Andrews University, seems not to have graduated. He seems to have served Sir William in Edinburgh from 26 January 1626 to 3 July 1627; and at the Court in England, from 3 July 1627 to 20 December 1630.[30] Thus, he would not have been in Edinburgh in September 1630, at the time of Dr MakLuire's petition to the King to establish a Royal College of Physicians in Edinburgh, or (as a friend of Dr MakLuire), have been an intermediary passing on the petition to his master Sir William - who was himself in Edinburgh at the time as the King's plenipotentiary and Master of Requests for Scotland.

Nevertheless, as Alexander Alexander was serving with the King at Hampton Court at the time of receipt of Dr MakLuire's petition there, it is of interest to note that he had indeed been the writer of one of the four copies extant of the King's letter of 2 October 1630, to his Privy Council in Edinburgh, commending Dr MakLuire's petition.[31] This had been the copy made at source, at Hampton Court (see fig. 1, Chapter 9), as distinct from the three made at the point of reception, *viz.*, in Edinburgh.[32]

---

[30] See C. Rogers, *The Earl of Stirling's Register of Royal Letters 1615-1635*, I, p. lxi; and *A Catalogue of the Graduates in the Arts Divinity Law: University of Edinburgh,* Edinburgh: Neill & Co., 1858, p. 32.

[31] BM Add MSS 23111, Sir William Alexander, Vol II, Untitled 1630-1635, p. 24.

[32] See SRO SP1/6; 533, Sir William Alexander, Register of Royal Letters 1626-1631; NLS Adv MSS 34.2.12, Sir William Alexander,

Finally, Alexander Alexander's death, in Edinburgh, had been in April, 1645.[33] Now, plague had broken out in Edinburgh in the first weeks of that year and had continued for the rest of it, the University of Edinburgh having to be closed in the April.[34] This was the very month of Alexander Alexander's death and it may well be, therefore, that he died from plague. It is also possible that Dr MakLuire, with his recognised expertise in dealing with plague, attended his old class-mate, Alexander Alexander, in his last illness.

John MakLuire's graduation as Master of Arts in 1622

The undergraduate studies of the young John MakLuire culminated in his graduation as Master of Arts in 1622 - probably in July of that year and the list of those graduating with him in 1622, after four years of study, is shown in fig. 4.

This list includes only thirteen of the twenty-eight who had matriculated with him in 1618. Twenty-four others seem to have, meanwhile, joined him as fellow students (some, perhaps, from other universities) and to have graduated with him. One of these, John Arnot, had not matriculated with John MakLuire in 1618. He was probably the future Dr Arnot who, with Dr MakLuire and a Dr Kinkead, was instructed to examine Sir John Hay in 1641 over the latter's medical fitness to go to prison in Edinburgh Castle.[35] A Stephan May on the list had been the only student specified as English ('Anglus').[36]

Vol. I, Earl of Stirling's Register 1626-1635, 2nd October, 1630; and SRO PC 1/33, Manuscript Register of the Privy Council for Scotland, f265v-266r.

[33] SRO CC8/8/62, Testament, Alexander Alexander, 7th April, 1646.

[34] J. Ritchie, 'A History of the Plague in Scotland', manuscript, Royal College of Physicians of Edinburgh, 1955.

[35] J. Balfour, *The Historical works of Sir James Balfour*, 4 vols., Edinburgh: Aitchison, 1824, III, p. 47.

[36] MSS UY 305 3, Muniments of the University of St Andrews, p. 342.

It had been of interest to note that not one of the primars who had matriculated with John MakLuire, nor any primar who might have later joined him, had appeared with him on the graduation list. However, despite the fact that the name of the primar, James Montgomery, is not recorded on the graduation list on which that of John MakLuire appears, the former is known to have graduated at St Andrews, from the statement of his son, William Montgomery of Rosemount, that he had seen, and shown to others, his father's degree diploma, with the seal of the university attached.[37] It is therefore possible that some of the other primars (perhaps even all of them) had similarly graduated.

The name of John MakLuire appears high up (fourth) on the graduation list (see fig. 4). This is clearly not an indication of social class and is probably an indication of merit.

---

[37] W. Montgomery, *The Montgomery Manuscripts 1603-1706*, ed. Revd. G. Hill, Belfast: Cleeland, 1869, p. 91.

Figure

Braidstone Castle, Threepwood and Milltoun in the parish of Beith; and Dalry, Deugh Linn, Castelmaddie and the Carmonochs; at the time of the emigration to the Ards, in Ulster, organised by Sir Hugh Montgomery in 1606.

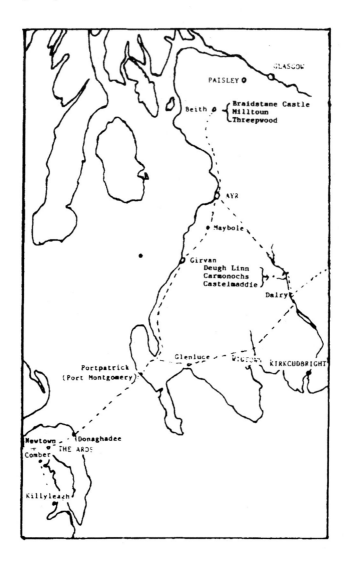

Figure 1

Matriculations, St Andrews University, October 1618.

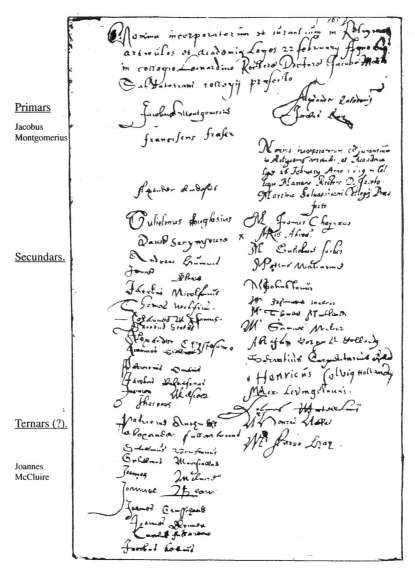

Primars

Jacobus
Montgomerius

Secundars.

Ternars (?).

Joannes
McCluire

Left-hand column, and first two of right-hand column.
Undergraduates taking the oath on 22nd February, 1619.

Remainder of right-hand column. Post-graduates, on 26th February,
mostly designated 'Mr' (i.e. 'Magister'), sometimes with place of origin.

Figure 2

Analysis of Condensed Signatures.

(a) (?Mr) Alex^r Alexander Caledonis

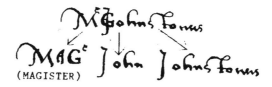

(b) probably the 'John Johnston' who graduated at Edinburgh in July, 1618, and three months later matriculated, as a postgraduate student, at St Andrews.

(c) probably the 'James Ross' who graduated at St Andrews in July, 1618, and three months later matriculated, as a postgraduate student.

Figure 3

'Alexander Alexander': The signature by the 1619 student, compared with the writing of the same words by the 1632 amanuensis.

1619

1632

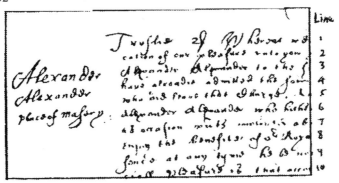

From a copy letter from Charles I to the Session in Edinburgh about a grant of masery to Alexander Alexander, principal amanuensis to Sir William Alexander, Secretary for Scotland – in the hand of Alexander Alexander himself.

Ref: Sir William Alexander. Vol II (Untitled) 1630-1635. BM Add MS 23111; 147.

By permission of the British Library.

Comment – The large loop introducing the capital 'A' of the 1619 **signature** is, perhaps, recognisable in all the capital 'A's of the six **writings**, in 1632, of the word 'Alexander'.

More significant is the different way of writing the two letters 'e' in the word 'Alexander' – consistent for all seven examples. The first 'e' is always written in the modern way (*e*) while the second 'e' is always written in the older way (*ℓ*).

These observations strongly suggest the 1619 and the 1632 writers to be the same person.

Figure 4

Graduations, St Andrews University, July, 1622

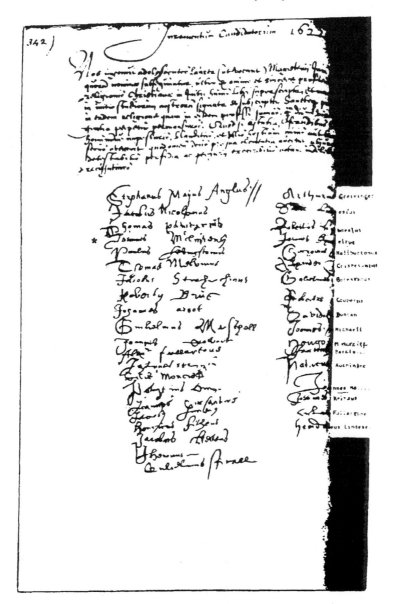

* 'Joannes McCluireus', fourth on the list.

Chapter Five - Apprenticeship in Edinburgh

A probable eight years of medical apprenticeship

John MakLuire, having graduated as Master of Arts at St Andrews University in 1622, would have achieved already, as an undergraduate, sufficient mastery of the skilled use of language, particularly of the Latin and Greek tongues, for the effective furtherance of a medical career. He would also have benefited from the instruction he would have received in the theoretical basis of medicine, as understood in those days. Thus, by 1622, Maister John MakLuire would have been in a position to embark upon the period of postgraduate, clinical, apprenticeship and study which would have been required for the degree of Doctor of Medicine.

How long this required period of training and preparation would have been is not known. However, as Blair has pointed out, the medieval requirement for a doctorate had been at least eight years, and there had seemed no reason to think that there would, in the 1600s, have been any departure from that norm.[1] The earliest date for him being granted his doctorate would, if so, have been in the year 1630.

The postgraduate preparation for Maister John MakLuire's doctorate in medicine would have involved, most importantly of all, a period of apprenticeship to an already established physician. But it might also have included further study - perhaps at one of those prestigious centres of medical learning in Europe to which Scottish students, wishing to follow a medical career, were certainly beginning to resort at that time. It would have culminated in the writing of the thesis, on a selected medical topic. The completion of this, in preparation for a graduation not to be expected before July 1630, would presumably have been during that

---

[1] J.S.G. Blair, *History of Medicine in the University of St Andrews*, Edinburgh, 1987, p. 2.

same year. Finally, he would have had to defend his thesis at a disputation at a university, not necessarily his alma mater, before graduating.

His clinical apprenticeship apparently in Edinburgh

It had not been immediately apparent where Maister John MakLuire would have spent his period of preparation for the doctorate in medicine.

The possibility that at least some of it may have been carried out in England (at Oxford or Cambridge) or, less improbably, at one of the European universities, and even that his doctorate in medicine might have been obtained in England or abroad, had had to be considered. Specifically, the records of Oxford, Cambridge, Padua, Paris, Montpellier, Franeker, Groningen, Rheims, Angers, Caen, Orange, Valence, Cahors, Basel and Leyden had been enquired into but it had been recognised that the null findings, throughout, could have been due, merely, to the records of so many of these centres having been incomplete, or even totally destroyed during the Second World War.[2] Nevertheless, no record of Maister John MakLuire having matriculated for further study at any of these centres had been found.

Moreover, it had been becoming apparent that there was no hint in Dr MakLuire's own writings that he had either travelled or studied abroad. On the contrary, there had been positive evidence, in *The Buckler of Bodilie Health*, that his clinical apprenticeship experience (between 1622 and the publication of that book in 1630) had been in Edinburgh and its environs.

These indications had been topographical references to Edinburgh itself - whereof the milk was said to be two thirds water[3]; to Castlehill (part of the High Street), and

---

[2] R.W. Innes Smith, *English Speaking Students of Medicine at the University of Leyden*, Edinburgh, 1932.

[3] J. MakLuire, *The Buckler of Bodilie Health*, Edinburgh, Wreittoun, 1630, p. 47.

Arthur's Seat - runs between which he had recommended as a treatment for obesity[4]; to 'Burdeous' (surely Burdiehouse, south of Edinburgh - a corruption of 'Bordeaux' because of the wine-storage there) - where there had lived a lady who had had a pseudocyesis[5]; and to Jedburgh - where the peculiar blood-letting technique of a surgeon living there, which had involved the under-cutting of the vein, had been a topic for wry comment.[6]

Dr William Scott perhaps his mentor

The identity of the physician in Edinburgh, who would have been already established in 1622, to whom Maister John MakLuire would have been apprenticed from that year, was not elucidated. However, two physicians (and only two) known to have been established in Edinburgh had been identified who were also known to have had, in later years, personal connections with Maister John MakLuire. To either of these, therefore, he may well have been apprenticed. They had been the well-known Dr George Sibbald and a Dr William Scott.

As has already been noted, the first of these two, Dr George Sibbald, had written a *'carmen'* in praise of Dr MakLuire in 1630.[7] This had been in celebration, probably, of the publication of *The Buckler of Bodilie Health*, in which it is printed, but perhaps also of his medical doctorate; and perhaps of his petition to the King - all in the same eventful year, for him, of 1630. It may certainly be presumed that Dr Sibbald, who had been the prime mover in the 1617 attempt to establish a Royal College of Physicians in Edinburgh, but who, despite the implication of Craig's words, is not known to have played any part himself in the 1630 petition, would probably have

---

[4] Ibid., p. 39.

[5] Ibid., p. 133.

[6] Ibid., p. 5.

[7] Ibid., p. x.

encouraged the young Dr MakLuire in it.[8] It had been noted, however, that Dr George Sibbald had not been so close, personally, to Dr MakLuire, as to have been invited to be a witness to the baptism of any of the latter's nine children.

The second of the two, Dr William Scott, had appeared to have been the only fellow-physician who (unlike Dr Sibbald) had been sufficiently close, personally, to Dr MakLuire as to have been invited to be a witness to the baptism of one of the latter's nine children - indeed to that of his second son, William. Now, Dr MakLuire's first son had been named 'John', according to custom, after the paternal grandfather (John MakLuire in Nether Carmonoch) - but perforce, also, after the maternal grandfather (John Greir) and, of course, after the father (Dr John MakLuire) himself. Thus, in respect of Dr MakLuire's second son, William, baptised in 1640, it might have been expected (seeing that both of the grandfathers, and the father, had already been acknowledged in the naming of the first son) that it would have been the next most senior male relative, from either side, who would have been invited to be principal witness, and to have had the boy named after him. However, as no close relative bearing the name 'William' had seemed to have existed, it had appeared that Dr William Scott, who had been the principal witness at the baptism, had also been the person after whom the boy had been named.[9] This had suggested strongly that Dr William Scott had been held in special esteem by Dr MakLuire and that this may well have been precisely because it had been to Dr Scott that Master John MakLuire had been apprenticed from 1622 onwards.

A little is known about Dr William Scott. He was a nephew of George Herriot ('Jingling Geordie') and had

---

[8] W.S. Craig, *History of the Royal College of Physicians of Edinburgh*, Oxford, 1976, p. 46.

[9] SRO OPR 685 1/1, Edinburgh (Greyfriars) Register of Baptisms, 28 June 1640.

been born in 1588/9.[10] He had graduated Master of Arts at the University of Edinburgh on 28 May 1604, at the age of 15, and 'by thesis alone, without examination', that being a plague year.[11] He matriculated at Leyden on 11 November 1621.[12] It seems that he did not already hold his MD degree when matriculating at Leyden, and was not awarded it at Leyden. Presumably, therefore, it was granted after his return to Scotland and, if he was indeed already established as a physician in 1622, presumably in that same year, and possibly at St Andrews, even at the very graduation in July 1622 at which the young John MakLuire graduated as Master of Arts. Dr Scott seems certainly to have been married - possibly a second marriage - to a Helen Hepburn, daughter of Patrick Hepburn of Smeaton, although the marriage is not recorded in Edinburgh. His Will was dated 31 August 1666, so it may be presumed that he outlived Dr MakLuire.[13]

It had seemed possible, if the James Scott, John Mak-Luire's fellow student at St Andrews in 1618/9, who also graduated in 1622, but at Edinburgh, and was also, in later years, a friend invited to witness the baptism of one of his children, was a relative of Dr William Scott, that it might have been through him that Maister John MakLuire may have made Dr William Scott's acquaintance in that year.

Dr William Scott owned a house in the South West Quarter - and was also the owner of a stable nearby.[14] This was a locality, on the south side of the High Street more or less opposite to Galloway's Close, where Dr MakLuire

---

[10] Innes Smith, *English Speaking Students of Medicine at the University of Leyden*, 1932, p. 207.

[11] Manuscript List of Graduates, University of Edinburgh, 28th May, 1604.

[12] Innes Smith, *English Speaking Students of Medicine at the University of Leyden*, p. 10.

[13] SRO CC8/8/72, Testament, Mr William Scott, Doctor in Physick, 31 August 1666.

[14] Extent Roll for the Annuity Tax 1634-1636, Edinburgh City Archives, pp. 581, 506.

was later to have his own house. As Maister, but not yet Doctor, and unmarried, John MakLuire would presumably have lived with the family of his mentor during his period of apprenticeship.

Encouragement from Patrick Sandys of Edinburgh University

The *carmen* in praise of Dr MakLuire with which the present 'search' is prefaced, first appeared in *The Buckler of Bodilie Health* in 1630.[15] It translates - 'You try in vain to disparage, enviously, the name of MakLuire - already it flies, splendid, above the stars'. The *carmen* itself had indicated that Maister John MakLuire would have been well known to Patrick Sandys for some time prior to 1630.

'Pat. Sandaeus', writer of this *carmen*, was the Patrick Sandys who was born about 1567; matriculated at the age of 18 at 'King James his College', Edinburgh, upon its founding in 1585; graduated MA, there, at the age of 20 in 1587; became 'professor', aged 22 in 1589; was the third Principal of the University to be appointed (in 1620); was appointed, in the same year, as minister at Old Greyfriars church in 1620; but demitted both these offices in August, 1622, giving way to the appointment, to both offices, of the fervent opponent of the Five Articles of Perth, Robert Boyd of Trochrig.[16] It would appear that Patrick Sandys continued, meanwhile, in royal favour, and with his university connection - because a royal letter from Hampton Court, dated 3 October 1627, appointed him 'Lecturer of the Laws established in Scotland', and sole 'consentor' to the registering of certain writs.[17] His death was in 1635.[18]

---

[15] MakLuire, *The Buckler of Bodilie Health*, p. x.

[16] H. Scott, *Fasti Ecclesiae Scoticanae*, Edinburgh: Oliver & Boyd, 1915, vol. I, *Synod of Lothian & Tweeddale*, pp. 44-45.

[17] SRO SP1/6, Sir William Alexander, Register of Royal Letters 1626-1631, p. 220.

[18] Scott, *Fasti Ecclesiae Scoticanae*, vol. I, p. 44.

Now, the date of John MakLuire's graduation as Master of Arts at St Andrews in 1622 had probably been in July of that year. This was probably, also, the date of his move to Edinburgh. It may, therefore, have been that Patrick Sandys first made the acquaintance of the young Maister MakLuire just prior to demitting his two offices. As it would probably have been, also, the time when Maister MakLuire began his medical apprenticeship in Edinburgh, it is not improbable that Patrick Sandys gave encouragement to the young Maister John MakLuire by facilitating for him access to the classical medical books at the library of Edinburgh University.

Eight years later, in 1630, the probable year of Dr MakLuire's MD graduation, and of the publication of *The Buckler*, containing Patrick Sandys' *carmen* in his praise, Patrick Sandys would have been aged 63.

Everyday life in Edinburgh in the 1620s

Edinburgh, during the time of Maister John MakLuire's training there, from 1622 to 1630, for his medical doctorate, was the largest of the seventeenth century towns of Scotland. Dundee was the next largest while Glasgow was only one of a number of smaller towns.

Hamilton has recorded how travellers through Edinburgh had described the tightly packed wooden dwellings of the town within the old city wall and how the town totally lacked sanitation and running water. Drinking water had been supplied by water-sellers using water from the many wells of the town, a system which spread disease easily. Washing and bathing were difficult in view of the restrictions on water supply and only the well-off might, with great difficulty, arrange for a bath to be taken, on the rare occasions on which this was considered necessary. The rest of the community simply lived and died in their rotting clothes and the rich used more and more perfume to disguise the smells.[19]

---

[19] D. Hamilton, *The Healers: A History of Medicine in Scotland*, Edinburgh, 1981, p. 44.

McKean, on the more positive side, has described how the departure of James VI of Scotland from Edinburgh to London in 1603 to become James I of Great Britain, had freed the capital from the remorseless aristocratic factionalism that had surrounded the King in Scotland.[20] The Court's departure had released the energies of the lesser men and - above all - of the international traders of Edinburgh. From early in the seventeenth century Edinburgh merchants had operated joint stock ventures, speculation and ship-owning and, through Leith, had traded with all the countries of Europe and the Baltic. There had ceased to be sharp distinction between minor aristocracy, gentry and wealthy merchant, as successful entrepreneurs passed from burgh to countryside and countryside to burgh as may be. McKean has also claimed that although, after the King's departure, sporadic violence continued in the streets, Scotland was enjoying the longest period of stability it had known for centuries. Edinburgh had prospered as never before or possibly since - until the troubles of around 1638. Perhaps Edinburgh merchants overreached themselves in this unfortunately short high-noon of Edinburgh as a mercantile metropolis. Their trading patterns, money-lending, and venture capitalism were founded upon continued growth and confidence: which was shattered by the Civil War.

McKean also describes how a John Taylor, a London waterboatman, had trekked north in 1618 and received the hospitality of a John Maxwell.[21] Taylor had been taken on a guided tour of the town, and in the High Street had seen 'the fairest and goodliest street that ever my eyes beheld'. Taylor had admired the 'buildings on each side of the way being all of squared stone, five six and seven stories high'. He was puzzled that the nobles' and merchants' houses were 'obscurely founded' down the closes, and ruminated why so many people in Edinburgh would wish to cling to

---

[20] C. McKean, *Edinburgh: Portrait of a City*, London, 1991, p. 77.
[21] Ibid., p. 74.

a crag rather than expand on the flat and fertile ground around Leith.

The accession of Charles I in 1625 had been marked by his immediate demands upon the citizens, because of the perceived threat of a Spanish invasion through Scotland, for heavy contributions for the fitting out of ships for his Scottish navy - in particular, in 1626, for the three royal ships *Lyon, Unicorn* and *Thistle*.[22]

The state of medicine in Edinburgh in the 1620s

Little appears to have been written about the state of medicine in Edinburgh at the time of Maister John Mak-Luire's postgraduate training there in the 1620s. It has been in the later 1600s and the 1700s, when developments in medicine were accelerating, that historians of medicine have been mainly interested.

However, one continuing danger for Edinburgh throughout that period was that of plague. There had been several outbreaks during the 1500s, and in the early 1600s, and measures to guard against it, and to deal with it when it broke out, had been progressively formulated. Comrie has discussed the subject extensively.[23] He has described how the practice of using the Burgh Muir for disinfection, and also for burying persons dead of the plague, had gradually grown up. The Muir was in two parts - the clean, or west, Muir (St Roque's Hospital), for the isolation of contacts, and the foul, or east Muir (Sciennes Hospital) for treatment of the sick. The goods and clothing of infected people in the Muir were apparently stored in St Roque's Chapel which stood near the present Grange Loan (see plate II). Also, ships coming from abroad, especially from Danzig, where plague was rife, were forbidden to come to land and watches were set at Newhaven and Leith. Later, in 1645, by which time Dr MakLuire was already well-

---

[22] SRO SP1/6 Sir William Alexander, *Register of Royal Letters 1626-1631*, p. 99.

[23] J.D. Comrie, *History of Scottish Medicine*, 2 vols., London, 1932, Vol I, pp. 202-21.

established as a physician in the city, the plague-stricken were housed in huts in the King's Park below Salisbury Crags.

The 'pest' of 1624 that 'raged not'

Maister John MakLuire's period of postgraduate study and medical apprenticeship, in Edinburgh, starting in 1622, had indeed seen an outbreak of a kind of 'pest' (plague) there in 1624 and this had had its predisposing causes.[24]

Hamilton has described how, three years earlier, in 1621, the very dry summer was followed by torrential rains and flooding which had spoiled the harvest.[25] Prices rose and grain imports from the Baltic increased. It was recorded that never 'in this countrie, in so short a time suche inequalitie of prices of victuall; never greatter feare of famine nor scarstie of seeds to sow the ground ... Everie man was careful to ease himself of suche persones as he might spare, and to live als retiredlie as possible he might. Pitiful was the lamentation not onlie of vaging beggars, but also of honest persons'.[26]

The Privy Council, now politically stronger, issued warnings against the hoarding of food, particularly by those merchants deliberately seeking a price rise - 'unmerciful forestallers and regraitteris'. Export of food was also banned. Imports were encouraged and fasts and prayer were ordered by the Church to help obtain better weather and harvests. There appears to have been little loss of life in 1621 and a good harvest in 1622 would have restored normality. But bad weather destroyed this harvest as well and Scotland entered into a second winter with little food and starvation reappeared. After the starvation came disease, both human and among the ill-fed cattle.

---

[24] J. Ritchie, 'A History of the Plague in Scotland', manuscript, Royal College of Physicians of Edinburgh, 1955.

[25] Hamilton, *The Healers: A History of Medicine in Scotland*, p. 45.

[26] D. Calderwood, *The History of the Kirk of Scotland*, ed. T. Thomson, 7 vols., Wodrow Society, 1842/9, VII, p. 514.

The *Chronicle of Perth* in 1622 recorded that 'about the harvest and efter, their wes suche ane universall seikness in all the countrie as the ellyke has net bene hard of ... Thair wes also grat mortalitie amongs the poore.' The Poor Law broke down entirely: in Midlothian by summer 1623 the Privy Council could report that 'the haill pure are impotent, opprest and overrun...sua miserable and waik that they can hardlie transport thame selffes fra ane parochin to ane other ... the pur is so enfeiblit thair is no constable nor uther persone that can be movit in the parochins to put the said Act in executioun.' There were many accounts of deaths in the streets and highways of those desperately trying to reach food in their last moments. A heroic import of grain from the Baltic and the good harvest of 1623 overcame the crisis.[27]

Calderwood had called the outbreak, which nevertheless followed in 1624, 'pest', but had said that it had been pest which had 'raged not' - i.e. which had not had the usual severity of true plague. Calderwood's confident explanation of this modified severity had been the merciful intention of the Almighty - although undoubtedly angry with the King (James VI and I) for preparing, at the time, to celebrate what, for Calderwood, was the popish festival of Christmas - to do no more than discomfit him. Calderwood's words were:

> This pest raged not; few houses were infected with it; so that it appeared that the cheefe end whereof the Lord had sent it, was to disappoint the king by scattering the people.[28]

It may well have been, therefore, that this 'pest', which 'raged not', was the 'pestilent' (i.e. 'plague-like') fever. It is not known for certain what the 'pestilent fever' was, but Hamilton's convincing suggestion is that, following on from famine and starvation, it was typhus.[29]

---

[27] Hamilton, *The Healers: A History of Medicine in Scotland*, p. 46.

[28] Calderwood, *The History of the Kirk of Scotland*, VII, p. 629.

[29] Hamilton, *The Healers: A History of Medicine in Scotland*, p. 45.

It would seem clear that Maister John MakLuire's clinical experience of the 1624 outbreak provided the basis for his *Treatise on the Pestilent Fever*. That this 'treatise' was, in fact, his thesis for the doctorate in medicine will be argued below.

His MD degree probably from St Andrews University

The failure to find any evidence of Dr John MakLuire having studied abroad, together with the positive evidence of his preparatory clinical apprenticeship having been in Edinburgh, had indicated the high probability at least that his MD would have been obtained in his native land. Now, the university of the city in which he had spent his apprenticeship, Edinburgh, had not itself, at that time, begun to teach medicine or to award MD degrees. Also, there had seemed to be no reason to suspect either the University of Glasgow or that of Aberdeen, rather than that of St Andrews, his Alma Mater, to have been the grantor of his degree.

However, it has to be admitted that there have long been doubts about the early granting of the medical doctorate at St Andrews University. It has been said, and no doubt accurately, that the earliest MD degree to be recorded at St Andrews University had been that of John Arbuthnot in 1696. Nevertheless, as Blair points out, whether this was in fact the first St Andrews degree of this sort is by no means certain, as before 1696 the Senatus records of higher degrees are not generally preserved.[30] Also, one of the points on which John Arbuthnot himself was required to satisfy the University was 'to perform what else in use to be required of candidate to be graduate' - implying there were already requirements 'in use' for medical doctorates. Furthermore, before John Arbuthnot's actual graduation, enquiries had been made 'where the ornaments that are used at doctoral graduations are to be found'. Blair says this suggests a previous such graduation 'but not in the very recent past'.

---

[30] Blair, *History of Medicine in the University of St Andrews*, p. 23.

One could, perhaps, be bolder and say that this clue suggests an indefinite number of previous medical graduations. Indeed, there seem to have been, in the earlier decades of the 1600s, quite a large number of persons in Scotland bearing (in all probability perfectly honourably) the title 'Doctor in Physick', and it seems unjustifiable to assume that all, or even most, of them, at a time when study abroad was still by no means the rule, had obtained their degree abroad. It is more probable that a considerable number of unrecorded medical doctorates would have been granted in Scotland and, in particular, by its oldest university, St Andrews. The indications that both Maister John MakLuire's undergraduate teaching in medicine, and his postgraduate doctoral degree, were from the University of St Andrews simply add to this probability.

Exactly when Maister John MakLuire's doctorate in medicine would have been granted to him is not known, precisely because records of the MD degrees, which it can scarcely be doubted that the University conferred, were either not kept, or have not survived. However, the fact that Dr MakLuire's appellation 'Doctor' is recorded in the letter from Charles I commending his petition for the erecting of a College of Physicians, on the one hand had shown that the degree could not have been granted later than the date of that letter - which had been 2 October 1630.[31] On the other hand, as the pre-requisite period of clinical apprenticeship and preparation could not have been started until after his MA graduation in July 1622, it had seemed, if the required period of apprenticeship was indeed at least eight years, that Maister John MakLuire could not have become eligible for his doctorate before July 1630.

It had therefore appeared that the most likely year in which Maister John MakLuire would have obtained his MD degree (at St Andrews), would have been 1630. The publication of two of his books - *viz.*, *Sanitatis Semita* and

---

[31] SRO SP1/6, Sir William Alexander, Register of Royal Letters 1626-1631, p. 533.

The Buckler of Bodilie Health - in 1630, which, giving him the title of 'Doctor', presumably would have been (immediately) after graduation, had seemed to confirm this. Finally, doctorates were certainly, at a later date, awarded either '*in praesentia*' or '*in absentia*'. But if the grant of the doctorate in the case of Maister John MakLuire was '*in praesentia*', this would have been presumably at the graduation in July of that year.

Chapter Six - *The Tractatus de febre pestilente*

The *Tractatus* a 'pre-fix', not a 'preface'

Dr John MakLuire's *Tractatus de febre pestilente* was published in 1630. It appeared as a 'prefix' (as distinct from a 'preface') to his *Sanitatis Semita* - to which its content is only tenuously related.

The text of the *Tractatus* may not seem, at first glance, to be easily separable from the main text of the *Sanitatis Semita*, to which it is 'prefixed'. However, on careful examination, it would appear that it is the content of the first twelve pages of the book, with the first six lines of page thirteen, which can be recognised as being devoted exclusively to the 'pestilent fever'. In this, the content of these first pages is clearly distinguishable from that of the rest of the book - which is devoted to the quite general measures recommended for the maintenance of health. It seems, in short, that it is these first pages which constitute the text of the *Tractatus*.[1]

Probably his MD thesis

The words '*Tractatus de*' in the title define the work as a 'treatment of' (in the sense of a 'treatise on', or a 'discussion of') its topic - the pestilent fever. That it is his doctoral thesis is suggested by the fact that its appearance (in 1630) was eight years after his graduation as Master of Arts in 1622. These would have been the standard eight years of clinical apprenticeship under an established physician which would have been required for a doctorate. Moreover, while the earlier designation of the future 'Doctor' John MakLuire in the city of Edinburgh records is as 'Maister', it is in 1630 that his designation as 'Doctor' first appears.

---

[1] J. MakLuire, *Sanitatis Semita*, Edinburgh: Wreittoun, 1630, pp. 5-13.

The text of the *Tractatus* would appear to be based upon the clinical experience, by the postgraduate 'Maister John MakLuire', of the 1624 outbreak, in Edinburgh as was discussed in the previous chapter, of what was described by Calderwood, as 'a pest which raged not', suggesting it was not as severe as plague proper, the 'Black Death'.[2]

No other medical theses in Scotland dating from as early as 1630 are, for the purpose of comparison, known. This is not surprising because it would appear that the *Tractatus*, if it is his doctoral thesis, must be the earliest extant Scottish graduation thesis for the doctorate in medicine to have achieved publication. Comrie has claimed this distinction for the Aberdeen graduate, William Broad, the title page of whose 1637 MD thesis he reproduces (see fig. 3).[3] But, clearly, Dr MakLuire's 1630 *Tractatus*, whether or not it is his thesis for the doctorate in medicine, antedated Broad's thesis by seven years.

No influence of a supervisor in the preparation of the text is detectable. This, also, is not surprising, as it is improbable that official supervisors were envisaged in those days. However, no doubt his mentor (Dr William Scott, as here suggested) would have been at hand to advise.

The Latin text and its translation

The Latin text of the *Tractatus* is printed in Appendix C.[4] There are many imperfections in the original. This is mainly because, in the only copy of the book that has been found - that which is in the library of the University of Cambridge - there are printing errors, and disintegration in parts of the very paper of the pages.

A translation into English, kindly carried out by Mr James Robertson of the Faculty of Law at the University of

---

[2] D. Calderwood, *The History of the Kirk in Scotland*, ed. T. Thomson, 7 vols., Wodrow Society: 1842/9, VII, p. 629.

[3] J.D. Comrie, *History of Scottish Medicine*, 2 vols., London: Balliere Tindall & Cox, 1932, p. 369.

[4] MakLuire, *Sanitatis Semita,* pp. 5-13.

Dundee, is added (in Appendix C) to the Latin text. The Latin itself is not of high quality being, in parts, almost telegrammatic - giving rise to the conjecture that it may have been intended primarily for declamatory defence before, rather than reading by, the examiners for the MD degree. Its translation has in many places, therefore, been ambiguous.

There are quotations in the *Tractatus* from the following classical authors - Galen, Hippocrates, Aristotle, Pythagoras, Plato, Avicenna, Theophrastes, Aetius, Aegeneta, Acron, Agrigentius, and Aphir. Of these, only Galen and Aetius are included in the list given by Blair of medical authors available in the St Andrews University library at the time of John MakLuire's student days.[5] Probably, therefore, during the period of his medical apprenticeship in Edinburgh, subsequent to his undergraduate days at St Andrews, he used, with the encouragement of Patrick Sandys, the library of the University of Edinburgh - as is suggested by the *carmen* in his praise written by Patrick Sandys, the former Principal at Edinburgh, who was still active there.[6]

General considerations

The *Tractatus* assumes, as the basis for explanation, the four elements of seventeenth-century science *viz.*, earth, air, fire and water.

It opens with an observation by Hippocrates on the influence upon disease of the time of the year - 'Changes of the seasons bring forth diseases'. Seemingly in confirmation of this aphorism, the text then lists the doleful effects which 'impure' or 'infectious air', may have. It mentions, in particular, various 'dangerous' kinds of fever, attributable to such 'air'. These are the fevers

---

[5] J.S.G. Blair, *History of Medicine in the University of St Andrews*, Edinburgh, 1987, p. 9.

[6] J. MakLuire, *The Buckler of Bodilie Health*, Edinburgh: Wreittoun, 1630, p. x.

which are characterised by skin rashes and sweating - the 'exanthemata' as they are still called nowadays.

The text distinguishes, specifically, as does modern medicine, between epidemic, endemic and sporadic forms of disease.[7] Also, it defines pestilent fevers as those infectious diseases which may have a fatal outcome. It is to the nature, causes and symptoms of such fevers as are 'the most lethal' that Dr MakLuire directs attention.

'Pestilent fever' distinguished from plague proper

The text points out that, according to Galen, pestilential fever is 'sometimes found without plague'. Dr MakLuire was not to have personal experience of plague proper until 1645 when, tragically, he lost to it at least two children and, probably, his former fellow student, Alexander Alexander. However, from his own experience of the plague-like outbreak in Edinburgh in 1624, and from his presumable book-learning at that time about plague proper, Dr MakLuire finds himself in agreement that there is a difference between true plague and pestilent (or plague-like) fever.

Plague (proper), he says, 'afflicts more [individuals]'; is more contagious; always affects [the glands in] the groin or axilla; and sometimes causes carbuncles behind the ears or, indeed, anywhere throughout the body. Although the transmission of plague by the bite of the rat flea was still to be discovered, Dr MakLuire mentions, in particular, pustules which break out on the back and 'are like flea bites'. Pestilential fever, on the other hand, he says, arises without these distinguishing features of plague and 'is diagnosed by other symptoms'. He attributes the drawing of a distinction between plague and pestilent fever to Hippocrates as well as to Galen.

---

[7] MakLuire, *Sanitatis Semita,* p. 6.

The causes of 'pestilent fever'

The 'causes' of pestilent fever, Dr MakLuire says, are both 'internal' and 'external'. The 'internal and immediate' causes lie in the 'humours'. These, if they are to determine what nowadays would be called a healthy 'constitution', resistant to fevers, should ideally be 'at rest' and 'in their own places', rather than 'agitated' and 'beyond their own confines'.

The external causes lie 'for the most part' in the 'air' - basically in the infective impurity of the latter, as is believed, even today, for infectious fevers. But the 'impurity' of the 'air' causing such fevers is described by Dr MakLuire not in terms of microbial 'impurity' but in terms of the admixture of 'moist, earthy, smokey and firey parts' - terms which are nowadays difficult to interpret. More easy to understand (because partly true) is the believed influence of 'humid warm weather' - in producing infectious, impure, 'air'.

Dr MakLuire quotes Galen's assertion that 'hot weather' is 'the worst situation', and 'unhealthy', and that it has created a variety of fevers. The 'heat and moisture' of 'hot weather' do this, according to Galen, 'through rottenness' - presumably through the increased propensity of the various kinds of edible produce to 'go bad', and to provide the nexus, as we now know, for bacterial multiplication.

Galen is also quoted as warning against the noxious effects of 'air' 'from mines', and as mentioning the special susceptibility of birds to such effects. Perhaps there is a recognition here, both of the dangers, to miners, of 'fire damp' and of the use, by them, of caged birds to detect its presence. Also, Galen's reported mention of the special susceptibility of 'four-legged animals' (as distinct from higher-standing human beings) to 'earth vapours' is of interest. It may reflect familiarity, in the volcanic areas of the world better known to the medical writers of antiquity than to a writer in Scotland, with the known phenomenon of the dying of such animals when they wander into pockets of low-lying lethal gases which have seeped upwards from volcanic ground. Galen's reference to birds may also indicate a familiarity he may have had with the phenomenon of birds of prey, attracted by the carrion dying in such circumstances, themselves succumbing as soon as they lower their heads for a meal below the level of the heavy lethal gases.

Whether Dr MakLuire's warnings against 'vapours from ponds, marshes or rivers' (marsh gas, or methane) is realistic, is more questionable. It may be based on a partial realisation of the role, recognised today, of ponds and marshes in the life-cycle of the mosquito, and thus of their role in the life-cycle of the parasite causing malarial fever. Aristotle's claim, that an abundance of frogs (indicating rainy and wet weather), is also an indication of a disease-laden year to come, is also mentioned.

Dr MakLuire seems to recognise, amongst 'originating causes' of pestilential fever, psychological predispositions 'such as sadness, anxiety, especially in time of war'. He also takes into account 'a vile manner and way of living'. This perhaps puzzling phraseology may refer to the 'way of living' (vile indeed) which befell the whole populace of Scotland after the disastrous droughts and floods of 1621, 1622 and 1623. Hamilton's quotation from Calderwood's description of this nightmare of a time, in which 'pitiful was the lamentation not onlie of vaging beggars, but also of honest persons', has already been discussed in Chapter Five. Dr MakLuire mentions, in particular, 'the high cost of provisions' and how men were 'forced to eat root crops ... and other things producing that kind of melancholy'. He uses the Greek words 'μετα λιμον λοιμοσ' - translated here as 'pestilential hunger', and presumably signifying the 'famine' which had worsened over the three years prior to the year 1624.

But, although the 'external causes' of pestilential fever lie, according to Dr MakLuire, 'for the most part' in the 'air', he does recognise, also, another 'external cause', which lies in water pollution. In particular, he points to history as revealing this 'to have happened to armies'. He recognises, explicitly, that such 'defective waters' have their influence not by contaminating the 'air' but by resulting in 'impure sustenance' - i.e. by food-poisoning.

Astrology not entirely discounted

It is interesting that Dr MakLuire, in an age in which astrology was still having its influence, points to the fact that Hippocrates, Galen and Aristotle 'are not seen to concede that the hidden attraction of the stars causes these diseases'. Galen, in particular, he says, denies 'any hidden cause from the stars' and Hippocrates denies any 'divine' (by which is meant celestial, or astral) causation of them.

Dr MakLuire himself emphasises that it is, rather, the standard, down-to-earth, influences recognised in those days - on the one hand 'coldness, heat, dampness and dryness', all affecting the 'air' and, on the other hand, 'defective waters', adversely affecting food intake - which cause diseases.

Nevertheless, cautiously, and perhaps a little reluctantly, he acknowledges that 'since Avicenna and most skilful astrologers have conceded these influences of the stars, they should not be entirely rejected'.

Specific symptoms in 1624

Specific symptoms which Dr MakLuire mentions as accompanying the actual 'pestilential fever' of 1624 included 'black marks breaking out everywhere'. These suggest the subcutaneous extravasations of blood of scurvy (resulting from vitamin C deficiency). He also mentions 'palpitations of the heart' - which could have a variety of explanations. 'Rage with a vehement passion' suggests the complication of what nowadays might be diagnosed as a toxic or infective delirium. 'A headache with accompanying sickness and a falling asleep' suggests cerebral complications causing raised intracranial pressure, and coma. Dr MakLuire's reference to patients who 'seem resting neither being held by a strong lassitude nor by a great vehemence [perhaps in the sense of 'restlessness'], so that although sick they remain without a feeling of pain', raise the possibility that he is referring to what the modern physician would call 'anosognosia' - the pathological unawareness of (serious) disease which is present. This clinical phenomenon he characterises as being deceptive (even) to 'doctors who are most skilled'. Herpes 'of the mouth' (a well-known accompaniment of fevers) is explicitly mentioned. Reference to a bluish colour of the urine raises the intriguing possibility of porphyria. Mention of bile in the urine suggests the complication of liver disease.

The 'happening together' of 'some causes of putridness' suggests a recognition of the possibility of the co-existence of more than one disease. In this connection, Dr MakLuire records that notes on pestilential fevers by Galen, Aetius, Aegeneta and Avicenna point to just such a heterogeneous nature of the symptomatology - 'so that you may hardly see that two [men] polluted with the same contagion will be marked with the same symptoms'.

Therapeutic measures

The laudable general public health measures which Dr MakLuire recommends are

1. 'fires' - apparently with the purpose of encouraging more adequate ventilation
2. 'making stagnant waters flowable'
3. 'burying dead bodies'
4. 'cleansing streets, lanes and alleys'
5. 'choosing good water'
6. 'boiling up everything which is easily boiled'
7. 'windows of the house ... opened
8. 'the bedroom ... fumigated with frankincense'
9. the washing of hands with water 'mixed with a little vinegar'

The specific medication recommended by Dr MakLuire for the individual patient in the prescription given is reassuringly restrained. It is a relief, also, to know that he did not recommend either the bleeding or the purging which, elsewhere, he so extoles.[8]

Finally, because 'external causes' do not produce diseases 'unless concurring with internal causes', the 'immediate cure' that Dr MakLuire recommends (i.e. the primary therapeutic measure) is 'to remove all internal causes'. In order to achieve this end his further advice is that the rules advanced in the subsequent text of the *Sanitatis Semita* should be followed.

The nature of the 'pestilent fever' of 1624

Hamilton's suggestion that the 'pest' of 1624, following on from famine and starvation, as it did, was probably typhus, is convincing, although nothing in Dr MakLuire's description shows (understandably) any suspicion of the aetiological role of body lice as vectors of the disease.[9]

Also, there are, in Dr MakLuire's clinical description (apparently based upon his undoubted experience of the particular Edinburgh outbreak of 1624), symptoms described which are not specific to typhus. These are sufficient in number and quality to suggest that the typhus was complicated by the admixture of other diseases, such as scurvy, and other infections, including some that were water-borne, or milk-borne - such as dysentery, typhoid or paratyphoid fever.

---

[8] MakLuire, *Sanitatis Semita*, pp. 12-13.

[9] D. Hamilton, *The Healers: A History of Medicine in Scotland*, Edinburgh: Canongate, 1981, p. 45.

Figure

Title Page of MD Thesis by William Broad, Aberdeen.

BONVM FACTVM.

DE HYDROPE

THESES,

Quas,

D. T. O. M. F.

Sub Rectoratu Magnifici & Clariſſimi Viri,
D. ARTVRI IONSTONI, Medici Regii.

Ex decreto & authoritate facultatis Medicæ, in
celeberrima Academia Aberdonenſi Regia.

Pro conſequendis in ſacra Medicina doctoralibus Privilegiis.

PRÆSIDE PATRICIO DVNÆO, M. D.
& Facultatis Medicæ Decano.

Publicè diſcutiendas proponit GVLIELMVS
BROAD, Berwicenſis.

Ad primum diem, Iulii, 1637, Loco conſueto.

BONA VERBA DICITE.

ABERDONIÆ,
¶ Imprimebat Edwardus Rabanus,
Anno ut ſupra dictum.

Claimed to be, in 1637, the earliest extant Scottish medical graduation thesis.

(Original in Glasgow University Library)

Chapter Seven - *The Buckler of Bodilie Health* and the *Sanitatis Semita*

Dr MakLuire published, in all, three books, two of them in 1630 and the third in 1634. It would seem that he had applied himself to the task of publishing the first two of these immediately after graduating as 'Doctor in Physick' - which had been, most probably, as has been argued, from St Andrews University, in July 1630. These had been his book in English *The Buckler of Bodilie Health*, and his book in Latin, the *Sanitatis Semita* (to which had been 'pre-fixed' the *Tractatus de febre pestilente* - probably the text of his doctoral thesis).[1] The two books had presumably been prepared beforehand and had only been awaiting, before publication, the stamp of his doctorate.

It would seem that *The Buckler*, in English, was written, primarily, for the general reader, for 'the constant welfare of all his countriemen', and that the *Sanitatis Semita*, in Latin, and including the specific 'pre-fix' concerning the pestilent fever (being a technical medical text), was written for his fellow physicians.

Both books bear essentially the same primary dedication, in English and Latin respectively - to the Lords of the Privy Council of Scotland. Both are on the topic of maintaining health, the former having a more extensive coverage than the latter, and neither being a mere translation of the other. Each book specifies a series of 'canons' - ten in *The Buckler*, and sixteen in the *Sanitatis Semita* - but these do not correlate.

The Buckler of Bodilie Health

Dr MakLuire himself tells us, in 1630, that *The Buckler of Bodilie Health* (fig. 1) was started when it was 'hatched in the Universitie of St Androws [sic] eleven yeares since'[2],

---

[1] J. MakLuire, *The Buckler of Bodilie Health*, and *Sanitatis Semita*, Edinburgh: Wreittoun, 1630.

[2] MakLuire, *The Buckler of Bodilie Health*, p. iv.

that is in 1619, and therefore either in the spring or summer term of his first year as an undergraduate, or in the autumn term of his second year. It had been of interest to note, here, that this would have been prior to the arrival at St Leonard's College of Mr John Wedderburn as Regent, and of the latter's presumably encouraging medical influence. Perhaps, therefore, it had, as claimed, been the encouragement by the young James Montgomery (rather than by Master John Wedderburn) which had provided the impetus for the young John MakLuire to embark upon his ambitious project.

Presumably, the preparation of the book had been continued and maintained up to the time of his graduation, and then continued still further during his postgraduate studies, and clinical experience, in Edinburgh from 1622 to 1630. Some of the influences at work in its preparation would therefore have been from the teaching of his undergraduate days, but most of them would have been from the postgraduate period.

Nothing is known about how the book was received at the time of its publication. Its importance lies mainly in the light it throws on its author's own thinking - both about his work and about the world about him. Nevertheless, it is important to note (as will be discussed more fully below) that the third part - 'A regiment for Women with Child, Bairnes, and Nourses' would appear to have anticipated the work of William Harvey on midwifery (in the chapter *'De Partu'* in the latter's *De Generatione Animalium*) as the first work on that topic by a British author to be published in Britain. Harvey's later work was merely the first such work by an English author. This third part of *The Buckler* would appear, also, to have been, certainly, the first contribution to Scottish paediatrics and, unless Phaer's *Boke of Children* was his own, and not a translation from the French, to British paediatrics also.

Two Dedications and an Address

The book has two dedications. The first, to the Lords of the Privy Council for Scotland, reads as follows:

MY LORDS,

The Philosophers, who haue seriously by contemplation considered the nature of man, haue learned into the schoole of veritie, that he is the chiefe of all creatures under the Sunne, seeing all things in this theatre to be made for his use the Heaven, the elements, and all that doth depend of them appointed for his service: Moreover they found such perfection in his fabricke [anatomy], so great miracles in his works [physiology], that they could not find any thing in all this universe, to whom they should licken him well except the world it selfe, so they haue called him Microcosme, or little world, being (as Plutarch sayeth) the abridgment of the whole globe: For it is certaine that GOD in the creation made all things before man, and when hee was going about to make him, hee made an reflexion of his divinitie, and tooke a view of all his workes, that he might print in this his last worke the quintessence of all other, with the beams of his owne image: as man surpasseth the rest of the creatures in dignitie; so the Magistrates private men; but amongst the Magistrates of this Kingdome, your LL. keepe the first ranke both by place and worth: for in maintaining of peace and banishing of troubles, in advancing and approving of the good, and supp-ressing the evill, your LL. haue given an cleare manifestation of both prudencie and vigilancie.

I knowing how your LL. did affect those who study to the well of the publick haue made bold to publish this smal work with your L. names in the frontispice of it, as most due to you: *nam vestri interest ne quid detrimenti respublica capiat.* Truely if the smyling brightnesse of your LL. sweetly shining countenance had not glansed on my dazzled eyes, I should haue beein forced with Diogenes in the day light with a candle to look for a man fostered with the milke of letters, and now become a father and favourer of all such, whose emolument depends from the advancment of vertuous studies. Your LL. presence at the entrie, will preserue it from the virulent byting of viperous invyers, and so shall incourage me to imploy the small talent the Lord hath imparted to me to your LL. service, and the use of the publick as your LL. Most humble servant I. Macluire D.M.[3]

The second dedication, which is a special, personal, dedication, is to Sir James Montgomery, Dr MakLuire's student friend (Plate III). It is addressed thus:

To the truly nobilitate honorable, and generous gentleman, James Montgomery esqvier, sonne to my Lord Viscount of the Airds, in the Kingdome of Ireland: Health.

In it, Dr MakLuire likens the book's conception and birth to human conception and birth - with himself as the mother and his student friend, Sir James Montgomery, as the father. This dedication reads:

Right Honorable, and worthie Sir:

Having after a long calculation found out tyme of my conception, almost doubting of the father, (as few honest women doe) I knew in end the childe belonged by right to you, which (yet honest woman like) I present to you, willing it should carie your name in the fore-front: Reject it not Sir, either by reason of the unlawfulnesse of the tyme, being now eleven yeeres past since my first conception, where others take but eleven months at the most: the first lineaments being drawne, and carefully: yea fatherly, under the cover of your wings by heate till it tooke lyfe, hatched in the Universitie of S[t]. Androws eleven yeares since or because of the unlikenesse of the birth, which does not resemble you the father, (yet it is

---

[3] Ibid., p. ii.

no wonder Sir) it being (babe like) toothlesse, tonguelesse, sightlesse noselesse: yea, wholly senselesse; and so unable to bite againe the backbytter, or make answere to the Critick babler, to see the Viper in the way, or smell a farre of the sclanderous Censurer, whose throate is become an open sepulcher: You Sir the father, having with the proportion of the members the sharpnesse of the senses, and sweete harmony of these outward decorments, that inward ornament of all, to wit, these eminent faculties of the soule, which kithes in your conception, graue and solide ratiocination, and memerie furnished from former observations, with a copious matter to all sorte of wholesome discourse, so that in-bred naturall wisedome, and painfull acquired learning, hath made you Sir (*absit verbo invidia*) justly to be thought by me (who scarcely seeth any thing clearly) μετρον απαντων, a just dimension of all things, required in a noble generous mynd, and a properly proportioned person. Receaue therefore this silly babe Sir, and let the perfections which are in you, supplie the defects that are in it: maintaine it by your authoritie from the unchristen: yea, uncharitable railing tongues and ryving hands of all Waspe-like searchers of poysoun amongst hony flowers, divel-like by invy hinderers never authors or furtherers of any good enterprise, aiming at the well of the publick, but them I regarde not: receaue you it, let them reject it: to you Sir only being consecrate, I doe offer it as a sure badge of my constant desire out of ardent affection Sir to liue and die, - Your most affectioned servant, IOHN MAKLUIRE, Doctor in Medicine.[4]

There follows, after the two dedications, an address 'To the Reader'. Here, Dr MakLuire speaks of 'an apprehension of supposed weakness' when the science of medicine

---

[4] Ibid., p. iii.

'is inclosed in the person of a young professor' - *viz.*, himself, who had so recently, and still in his twenties, achieved his doctorate. He bemoans the 'doctorate deceavers', presumably the unqualified practitioners 'old ignorant ruffians, practised Man-slayers'. He is particularly scornful of the untrained devotees of uroscopy, to whom 'if once yee send your urine, yee must resolve to be sick howsoever, for they will never leave examining of it, till they have shaked it in a disease'.[5]

A mysterious 'Master Perkins' inveighed against

The address 'To the Reader' includes, in particular, and out of the blue, a demand that a 'Master Perkins', assumed to be a minister but, '*pantodidactos* extravagant spirit (more ignorant than the Oxe or Asse, while he knoweth not his own cribbe)' [a reference to *Isaiah* i, 2-3, the basis, also, for the familiar Nativity tradition], seemingly regarded as trespassing in the field of medicine, should be restrained 'within the borders of his profession'. Who this, presumably English, 'Master Perkins' could have been, and why the appeal to restrain him was addressed 'To the Reader' and not to the Privy Council of Scotland, is not clear.

However, four years later, in 1634, in the very same year in which Dr MakLuire was to publish his third *book The Generall Practise of Medecine*, his printer in Edinburgh, John Wreittoun, had also printed a book called *The Practise of Christianity*, and another one called *A Direction for the Government of the Tongue according to God's Word*, two books by a William Perkins. These have been attributed, by Johnston, to William Perkins, the learned Calvinist Divine of Christ Church College, Cambridge.[6] The latter, however, according to the *Dictionary of National Biography*, had died in 1602, and it had seemed

---

[5] Ibid., p. vii.

[6] G.P. Johnston, 'Three Unrecorded Books Printed by John Wreittoun, Edinburgh 1629-34', *Publications of the Edinburgh Bibliographic Society*, **XII**, 1925, p. 31.

strange if they had been published 32 years posthumously - and in Edinburgh, at that.[7] Moreover, they are theological works with no medical pretentions.

It has also been found, however, that there had been a William Perkins, also from Cambridgeshire, who had matriculated at Emmanuel College, Cambridge, in 1627; had been inscribed at Franeker as a student of theology on October 14, 1629; and had graduated BA at Cambridge in 1631/2.[8] Finally, the fact that this William Perkins obtained the MD degree at Leyden, six years later (1636), suggests that, in 1630, although he had not, by then, graduated even as BA, and certainly could not properly have been entitled to the designation given to him of 'Master', he may indeed, untrained, have been dabbling in medicine.

The entry at Leyden records what would presumably have been the young William Perkins' own assertion that he was the son of the famous Divine of that name. However, the *Dictionary of National Biography* ascribes no children to the latter.[9] Also, this William Perkins, in 1636, gives his age as '30', indicating that he was born about 1606 - four years after the death of the Calvinist Divine. Doubt is therefore cast on his claimed identity and, in view of the vehemence of Dr MakLuire's denunciation, one wonders if the so-called 'Master' Perkins of 1630, five or six years younger than Dr MakLuire himself, was one of Dr MakLuire's 'doctorate deceivers', who was later to publish, not in Cambridge, where the true author would have been remembered, works by the celebrated Divine as if by himself.

The purpose and structure of the book

The essential purpose of *The Buckler* - to defend health and repel disease - is set forth, briefly, on the title page

---

[7] *Dictionary of National Biography*, Oxford, 1917, XV, p. 892.

[8] R.W. Innes Smith, *English-speaking Students of Medicine at the University of Leyden*, London, 1932, p. 180.

[9] *Dictionary of National Biography*, XV, p. 8.

(fig. 1). The book itself is in three parts. The list of 'Contents' does not make this division clear and the liberty is here taken of clarifying this in figs 2, 3, and 4. The word 'Reason' in the second part is clearly a mis-print (repeated) for 'Season'.

The first part

The first part of the book, more briefly titled 'The Buckler of Health' (fig. 2), begins with the comment that the Creator made man with an immortal soul and a body subject to death but that nevertheless man 'may not only prolong his life .... but also preveene sickness .... by the right and moderate use .... of aire, meate, drink, sleeping, waking, motion, and rest, the excretion of the excrements of the body, and the passions of the minde ....'.[10] He puts forward ten canons whereby this may be achieved.

Dr MakLuire's first canon urges the necessity of annual blood-letting and purging - both procedures seen as 'an evacuation of vitious humors'. At this point, he bemoans the fact that there is such a shortage of physicians in Scotland (because, he argues, the reward of them is more verbal than monetary) that 'the Gentlemen commit themselves to bee handled by ignorants':

> And because the reward of Physitians in this countrey being frequently, My Lord, GOD reward you, hath made Physitians to bee scarce, and no wonder, for how shall his L. liue vpon this rent, is it not to content my Lord with the poore folks almes, who get often GOD help you, they differ in forme, but not in matter: this scarcitie constraineth the Gentlemen to commit themselues to bee handled by ignorants, who least they should deale with them as that Chirurgeon of Jedburgh dealt with his patients, who forced all of them of whom hee drew blood, their wound vnder-cotting, to returne to haue it healed, and being asked the reason of this of his

---

[10] MakLuire, *The Buckler of Bodilie Health*, p. 3.

little boy, hee answered, that for making of the wound by opening of the veine, hee got a Weather, but for curing of the same a Kow, that every one may vnderstand for his owne well, I will insist a little on phlebotomie and purging.[11]

If physicians in Scotland were indeed in such short supply, and their pay so meagre, the motive (by limiting their numbers, as suggested by Hamilton) for petitioning for the founding of a College for them, may be called somewhat in question.[12]

The procedure of phlebotomy is described in detail. Amongst other matters, Dr MakLuire argues that blood may be taken in greater measure of men than of women - except, interestingly, in the case of alcoholic women, i.e. those who:

by often sacrificing to Bacchus, their head takes now and then a giddie startling, their tongue a tedious trattling, their taile a vile wauering[13]. These monsters of nature, shame of their sex, crosse of their husband, and disgrace of kin, friend and allyance should be bledde in both the leggs and armes, and in the croppe of the tongue, by a crosse sneck to that end, it may be made slower for talking and stiffer for drinking, least continuing in this wicked mood, they make their husbands Cuckolds, their bairnes bastards and beggars, themselves whoores and theeues [theives?].

---

[11] Ibid., p. 5.

[12] D. Hamilton, *The Healers: A History of Medicine in Scotland*, Edinburgh: Canongate, 1981, p. 68.

[13] The word 'taile' is not given in *The Concise Scots Dictionary* but, as 'tail-toddle' is given there as 'sexual intercourse', presumably 'taile' refers to the genitals.

> Justly many are molested with such beasts, who
> glames [?'snaps'] at the turde for the twelfe
> pence sticken in it.[14]

Here, Dr MakLuire comments, as an example of 'the
corruption of our time', on the eugenic unsuitability, as he
sees it, of marriages outside of one's social class:

> the corruption of our time being such that Tome
> the tinklers sonne metamorphosed in a Gentlman,
> sutes mistresse Marie my Lords daughter, and Sir
> John my Lords second, speares out for Sandie the
> Souters fourtie thousand mark Jennie. This Tom
> aiming at vanitie rather than virtue, comes to
> honours or hornes by his wife, and Sir John
> looking to geare more than to grace, is often per-
> plexed, while the trash is wasted, by a Masie Fae
> or a Maly Dae. I wonder that their vnequall con-
> junctions doe not fill the countrie with monsters
> lyke Mulets which is begotten betuixt a Mare and
> an Asse.[15]

Dr MakLuire also discusses (as the alternative to phlebotomy) the proper handling and use of 'loch-leaches' -
presumably obtained, in his case, from the Nor Loch, only
a few yards from the foot of Galloway's Close, where he
lived.[16] Here, occurs an example of an interesting trend,
seen elsewhere in Dr MakLuire's writings. This is to
move, suddenly, from the concrete to the abstract and
symbolic. He describes how leeches require careful
handling - for example 'with a whyte linnen cloath, for the
bare hand cankers them'. He then goes on, immediately, to
say that 'there bee other Loch-leaches or blood-suckers' -
and he lists the various 'leeches' of human society. Thus,
while medicinal leeches require a sprinkling of aloes to
make them 'fall' human leeches require a sprinkling of
'justice'. 'These grinders of the face of the poore,' he says:

---

[14] MakLuire, *The Buckler of Bodilie Health*, p. 7.

[15] Ibid., p. 8.

[16] Ibid., p. 9.

shall never make an end of sucking. These are vnworthie to bee thought or spoken of by any good Christian, I leave to be handled, yea, justly to bee hanged by the Justice heire and if they amend not, to bee tormented by the great Justice prison-keeper heereafter·[17]

Dr MakLuire, having discussed blood-letting, whether by phlebotomy or the application of leeches, turns to pursuing 'gentle, mediocre and violent' purging. Here, he spends many pages discussing a very large number of purgative remedies. However, he decries purging by 'violent firie remedies, whereby the body is mightily endomaged'. Also, 'bairns' and 'old men after fourtie', he says, do not require yearly purging. Here also, Dr MakLuire moves suddenly to the symbolic:

Their bee other sort of purgatiues, which men call purse purgations, and these are of three sorte as the former, gentle, mediocre, or violent. The gentle comprehend the modest, and moderate charges of an honest house.

The mediocre are the just reward of the physician, the due of the scholemaster, and the fitting of the conscientious merchand compts.

The violent conteane the gorgeous depursements to the Goldsmith for lace, cuppes, and such like, the persuing by law some tedious processe by the firie violence of these two, the poore purse which often taketh an irremediable fluxe, and dyeth of the skitter: His Majestie with his most honourable and wise Counsell, by an act of parliament (evill keeped) hath found out a remedie for the former: would GOD the wisdome and concord of his subjects would admit an other for the latter, for then the Nobilitie and Gentrie should not bee so lukken-handed to other professions.[18]

---

[17] Ibid., p. 10.
[18] Ibid., p. 18.

'Vomitores', as further means to the evacuation of 'vitious humors' are also discussed. Dr MakLuire comments:

> Some of the Ancients thought it to be expedient for the health to vomite everie moneth, and that after a great carrousel but this counsell needeth not to be given to the soukespikkets of our age, who as they drinke like Suiczers, yea rather like swine, they cast [vomit] as Dutches, yea rather like dogs ....[19]

Dr MakLuire's second canon recommends, after the blood-letting and the purging, 'to come to your accustomed dyet by degrees'. His third canon is set against 'lazie lying in winter after six, and summer after seven'. His fourth canon concerns the making, after rising, of 'a cleane house ... from all the excrements which are three-fold'. These are 'the filth of the bellie', the urine, and the 'sweate'. Under this canon, he mentions 'melancholie':

> whose receptacle is the melt [the spleen], if it bee not either expelled in the stomack as daylie it is, whose appetitie it sharpeneth, or by the haemorroides or some other way, it procures melancholie hypochondriake, sometimes the fever quartan [here, a reference to malaria], sometimes other diseases, for this is good, the barke of the roote of Tamarisks and of capres with the foresaid herbs.[20]

Under the same canon, he discusses, at some length, quoting Galen, exercise - the main purpose of which is, to him (although not to us), to get rid of sweat. He emphasises that some exercises employ some particular members of the body:

> as the Tayler his hands and head, the Webster his legges and armes, the Tobacco man his mouth and nose, the Beggar the nailes of his thunbes, and tongue, Coupers, Trumpeters, and Pipers,

---

[19] Ibid., p. 20.

[20] Ibid., p. 25.

their cheekes, hand, and mouth: the most firie and wicked scolds their tongue, and the licentious whoores their taile: these I passe by, not having many particular exercises to treate of used amongst us worthie of consideration, or speciall delineation, and very few vniversal, except the foote-ball, which often doth more good to the Chirurgians, than evill to the Physicians by any helpe the body getteth: the gooffe [golf] and archerie, from the which exercises they come ofter hungrie than sweating, and the tinnice or ketch the best of all, if it bee moderately and orderly vsed.

In all exercises whereby men sweates, (except these that are vnder the sheetes) these things are to bee remarked: first, that in your gaming your mynde be free of all feare, the gadges being little or none, otherwise the mind shall bee in a continuall vexation, and neither body nor mind shall receaue any recreation: Secondly, if in tyme of game you thirst, let your drink bee small aile, taken in a little quantitie, not water, for it by the open passages going streight to the liver, will coole it too much, on the which insueth often hydropsie, nor wyne, for by it the lyver already heate is set on fire, on the which followeth frequently a fever: Thirdly, after your exercise haue a care to cause rubbe away the sweate in a warm chamber with dry warme linnings see that the body rubbed bee straight, least the wrinkels of the skinne doe hinder the issuing of the sweate, see the rubbers bee many and nimble, and that they rubbe not over hard, for this doth stoppe the passages, nor too soft, for it goeth not halfe farre in, but a mediocritie in all things is good.[21]

The adumbrated fifth canon is not specified - but does seem to be represented by the advice about dealing with

---

[21] Ibid., p. 28.

'the excrements of the head'. Here, Dr MakLuire discusses, at some length, the uses of tobacco. He writes:

Tobacco is an hearbe fetched from the West Indies to vs, some calleth it *Nicotiana*, from Master John Nicote, that brought it first to France out of Portugall, hee beeing Ambassadour for the time there. The Portugalles brought it first in Europe, out of the Iland Trinada, and from Peru in the continent of America, some terme it petoun or tobacco.

Tobacco is of a temper hotte and dry, as appeareth first from the effects thereof, as to purge cold and moist humours, as flegme, or pituite: hence it is that it doth harme to fyrie hotte bilious persons, except it bee taken in little quantitie, and that for the cleansing of the head from these cold superflous humours, which a cold stomacke hath sent to it.[22]

Dr MakLuire writes further, of tobacco, as follows:

mee thinks the Tobacco man barking as a dogge at the Moone, at these courious observations and idle restrictions of tobacco, (for so hee tearmes them) and crying that all men at all time when their appetitie inordinate biddeth them, and their purse serveth them may take of it, and it is no wonder that he so doe, for it is meate, drink and cloathes to him: his Shop is the randevouse of spitting, where men dialogue with their noses, and their communications are smoake: in it hee playeth the Ape in counterfaiting the honest Merchant man with his diverse rolles of Tobacco, newcome vp out of the cellar, where they laye well wrapped in dogges skinne and soussed: hee knoweth himself how, and yet sweareth that they are new landed from Verinus, Virginia, or St Christophers ... his wares are both deare and evill; deare while hee taketh a pennie for a pipe,

---

[22] Ibid., p. 30.

and his Welcome Gentlemen: and evill, for he
feedeth his guests neither on rosted, nor sodden
meate; but on white, or blacke-burnt meate,
without drinke, grace, table, plate, truncheiur, or
serviture, yea scarce a stoole to sitte on, and is
not this brave Innes my Masters?[23]

But, under this canon, Dr MakLuire also mentions semen
('man's seed') and *'sanguis menstruus'* ('womans
flowres') - as excrements which may harm by their quantity rather than their quality. And there is also, although
rather incongruous at this point, a very lengthy dissertation
on 'meates' and 'drink'.

After referring to a man who, 'of his owne big belly did
apprehend he was with child', Dr MakLuire goes on to say
that:

I would have such greasie barrells for their
healths sake to take a quarter of an houres course
betweene the Castel-hill and Arthur's seate twise
in the morning, coming thereafter (if they bee
hungrie) to their dinner made vp of an halfe
pennie loafe, two egges, and a cuppe of small
Beere: and after meate, for digestions cause
returning to their walke; going to bed without
supper: if this pyning of the panch doeth not
make him light, I will haue no money for my
medicinall receipt. Let these whose God is their
belly, and guide is their taste (for they inquire
still to John Good-Ales house) and who are no
lesse nose-wise than a browsters Sowe, in
smelling a dish of goode meate a farre off.
Diminish both of the quantitie, and qualitie of
their dishes, and imparte of the superplus to their
needy brother, who is come of Adam according
to the flesh, as well as they, and may bee of
ABRAHAM according to grace, Christian by
profession, and who knoweth but Sanctes by
election. Did the Master preferre thee over his

---

23 Ibid., p. 33.

94

house, and goods for the satisfying of thine
inordinarie appetite, and thy childrens only? or to
giue the bread of the children to dogges or horse,
as our great men doe, rather than to the poore:
and shall not thou expect: yea, when the Master
cometh, get reward of the vnjust steward, amend,
or looke for it.[24]

Dr MakLuire's sixth canon, where he resumes more
organised discussion, concerns 'the passions of the
minde'. Here, his advice is, after meat, to:

abstaine from all vehement motion ....
discoursing of some good purpose, procuring
laughter, joy, and mirth, whereby the spirit may
be revived, and digestion helped.

It is here that Dr MakLuire makes his complaint
(discussed elsewhere) about the 'frowning of our Greats'
on scholarship and adds 'O what a shame it is to see a
great Man without Letters!':

If the great men of the country knew what good
these sort of discourses did for the health of the
body, and the recreating of the spirit, they would
with greater avidity drink in, in their young and
tender yeares letters, for the better fashioning of
their manners and forming of their minde. And
also cary a greater respect to Schollers then they
doe: and not studie only to be well versed in
Arcadia, for the intertaining of Ladies, or in the
rowting of the tolbuith, for commoning with
Lawers. So that they esteeme more of a Page of
the one, or a pok-bearer of the other, then of any
Sholer whatsoever, except my Lord Bishop, or
Mr Parson: this frowning of our Greats hath
moved many poore soules flee first to Dowy, and
then to Rome, and from thence post to hell:
having receaued the marke of the beast that is a
bull of his holynesse to passe Scot-free at

---

[24] Ibid., p. 39.

> Purgatorie, not being able to procure the
> favourable presence, or gratious asistance of any
> noble for his furtherance in studyes and
> advancement in degrees, in the countrie wherein
> hee was borne.

> 'O what a shame it is to see a great Man without
> Letters! Hee is like a faire house without
> plenishing, a goodlie ship without furnishing to
> persue or defend: a Herauldry without honour,
> beeing lesse reall than his title. His vertue is, that
> hee was his fathers sonne, and all the expectation
> of him, is to get an other. No man is kept in
> ignorance more, both of himselfe and men, for
> hee heareth nothing but flatterie, and vnderstand-
> eth nothing but folly; thus hee liveth till his
> Tombe bee made ready, and then is a graue statue
> to posteritie.[25]

The specific 'passions of the minde', which Dr MakLuire
discusses in relation to their effect on the body - all in
terms of the humoral theories dominant in those days - are
joy (excess of which may cause sudden death), 'sadnesse
greiffe or melancholy', cupidity, choler, fear.

Dr MakLuire's adumbrated seventh canon, like the fifth,
seems to have slipped from the author's mind - and cannot
be identified in the text.

His eighth canon consists of brief advice about supper,
where he has some amusing things to say about 'Noble
mens cooks':

> Heere I can not passe by a great vncleannesse of
> Noble mens cooks, who after that they haue
> sweeped the pot with the one end of their apron,
> and the plat with the other, they draw off my
> Lords meate with the whole, dirtie as it is: and for
> to make place to a new speer, placeth the same
> vnder the droppings of the vnrosted meate, inter-
> larding their owne grease amongst these drop-

---

[25] Ibid., p. 57.

pings: and yet the cooke dare not bee reproved, for he in his kitchin is like the devill in hell, curses is the very dialect of his calling, hee is never good Christian vntill a hizzing pot of aile hath slaicked him, like water cast on a fire-brand, and for that time hee is silent: his best facultie is at the dresser, where he seemeth to haue great skill in military discipline, while hee placeth in the fore-front meates more strong and hardy, and the more cold and cowardly in the rear, as quaking tarts, and quivering custards, and such milk-sope dishes, which escape many tymes the fury of encounter, and when the second course is gone vp, downe hee goeth vnto the celler, where hee drinks and sleeps till foure of the clocke in the after-noone, and then returneth againe to his regiment.[26]

Dr MakLuire's ninth canon concerns the expediency of walking 'a little softly' after supper, and the many differing qualities of 'air' that one breathes at such a time. His tenth canon concerns retiring at night, and recommends going to rest and sleep three or four hours after supper. Not unexpectedly, bed-time, with its sexual connotations, also calls for some words on 'Generation'.

This first part of the book ends with a prayer to God, honouring Him 'in the ordinate taking, and moderate using, of all thy creatures, AMEN'.

The second part

The second part of *The Buckler of Bodilie Health* (fig. 3) is entitled 'A Particulare Regiment According to the Complexion, Age, and Season'.

'Complexion'

This is a word used by Dr MakLuire synonymously with the word 'temperature', as he uses it, and its meaning would appear to be closest to that of 'temperament', in

---

[26] Ibid., p. 62.

modern parlance. It represents, he explains, a balance of the 'four elementarie qualities' - *viz.*, 'hot', 'cold', 'dry' and 'moist' ('wak'). Different 'complexions', by a different balance of the elementary qualities, are differently identifiable. Thus, predominance of the hot and humid characterises the 'sanguinean' person (mediated by blood); that of the hot and dry the 'choleric' (mediated by 'bile'); that of the cold and moist the 'flegmatic' (mediated by 'flegm'); and that of the cold and dry the 'melancholic' (mediated by 'black bile'). Each 'complexion' may be, in the balance referred to, 'temperate' or 'intemperate'.

Dr MakLuire says that:

> among all the complexions that are intemperate, there is none to be preferred to the melancholick, provyding it conteine it self within the tearmes of health.

His reasons for saying this are worth quoting as the qualities correspond, in many respects, to those of the cyclothymic temperament of modern psychiatry. He says:

> melancholicks are of all most fit: First, because they do their bussinesse with due deliberation: Secondly: because they are quyet and not babblers or talkatiues, doing their affaires without dinne: 3 because solitarie and retired, so that their spirits not being distracted, they may thinke on their affaires the better, taking greater pleasure in the profound meditation of serious businesse, than in idle toyes. 4. Because they seeme sad in companie, not taking pleasure in gaming, laughing, fooling or in idle spending of the time, and yet they liue verie contented, when they are where they may recreat their spirits, not having any thing, affords them greater contentment, than to moderate their meditations, and to be imployed in serious matters, (it is agreable to all men in authoritie to haue a graue countenance and somewhat severe) 5. Because they are fearefull when they see any danger, not willing rashlie either to

hazard their lyfe, honor, or estate, so they inter-
prise nothing lightly. 6. Because constant in their
opinions, words, and deads, for having past any
thing thorow the alembick of reason they cannot
bee brangled 7. Because slow to wrath as also to
be appeased, except it be those who hath beene
first bilious, and now are melancholicks, they
will haue some shorte fittes, smelling of their
former disposition. 8. Because they are common-
lie good husbands, and doth not spend their
goods idlely. 9. Because they are couragious,
respecting their honour aboue all things.[27]

'Age'

Dr MakLuire says that 'complexion' shows changes with
the process of aging. Man begins life 'hot and humid' and
ends 'cold and dry'. Dr MakLuire specifies five stages of
life - *viz.*, infancy, bairnley, youth, middle age and old age
- but his definitions of these are surprisingly different from
the modern. 'Infancy' extends to the age of fourteen,
'bairnley' corresponds to adolescence and extends from
fourteen to twenty-five which, he says, marks the end of
growth; 'youth' lasts from twenty-five to thirty-five;
'middle age' is from thirty-five to forty-nine; 'old age'
begins at forty-nine. The changing 'complexions' with
ageing require corresponding changes in diet.

'Seasons'

The seasons referred to are Night and Day as well as the
four seasons of Spring, Summer, Harvest, and Winter, and
Dr MakLuire analyses in great detail the effects of these
on the four 'elementary qualities' of hot, dry, cold and
moist. These effects result in 'proper diseases' for the
various seasons. The detail of the analysis, here, extends to
precise consideration of the solstices, the equinoxes, and
the zodiacal signs - e.g. the 'dog days' of the hottest
season of the year during July and August. At first sight,
this detail suggests a basically astrological approach, but

---

[27] Ibid., p. 79.

on closer consideration the approach is really astronomical and meteorological, perhaps a little poetic, and surprisingly free of astrological pre-suppositions.

The third part

The third part of *The Buckler of Bodilie Health* (fig. 4) is entitled 'A Regiment for Women with Child, Bairnes, and Nourses'.

The special interest of this part, as mentioned above, lies, firstly, in the fact that it would appear to be the first British contribution to midwifery (anticipating by some two decades that of William Harvey, for whom the same claim has been made). In it, Dr MakLuire deals with the same two specific midwifery topics with which Harvey, later, in the *'De Partu'* section of his *De Generatione Animalium* also deals - *viz.*, false pregnancy and the believed active part which, it was believed, the foetus played in the process of being born.

In Dr MakLuire's midwifery, there is much good, common-sense, advice about the management of pregnancy, betokening wide obstetric experience. Not surprisingly, purging is dealt with in detail. Dr MakLuire says that the 'properest' time for purging in pregnancy, according to Hippocrates, is from the fourth to the seventh month. Mercifully, bleeding is not recommended. Surprisingly, there is also some frank superstition - for example, for 'failure to carry', he says 'let them weare about their neck the Eagle stone, called by the Greekes *Aetites'*, and he prescribes a special plaster to be applied to the belly and the loins.

It is in this third part of the book that there is a full discussion of true and false conception. Of the latter 'there bee diverse sortes' - either from a 'mola' or from 'a wind or a water'. The case of the lady from Burdiehouse, who was burdened by the latter, and with whom Dr MakLuire ends the book, has already been mentioned.

For a natural birth, Dr MakLuire says that there are three requirements. First, 'alike forwardness both of the mother and the child'. The underlying assumption, here, seems to be that the process of birth is a co-operation between the mother and the child and that their actions should be co-ordinated. Dr MakLuire says that an unborn child, 'requiring more meate than the mother can afford', 'tares with his hands and feete his thinne membranous sheetes'. It would be unfortunate, also, 'if the child gets all the business to do'. Second, 'a due forme' - by which he means a head-presentation. And third, 'that it bee quicke, easie, and without great paine or many symptomes'.

The special interest of this third part of the book lies, secondly, in the fact that it would appear, also, to be, certainly, the first Scottish (and, possibly, the first British) contribution to paediatrics.

In the paediatrics, Dr MakLuire's use of the term 'bairne' is at variance with his own, earlier, and surprising, definition, and comes close to the usual one of today. The term 'nourse' refers, also, not to the 'nurse' of modern terminology but to the 'wet-nurse'.

The time for 'waining' the child is 'when all his teeth are come foorth, for nature doth produce them for the eating of solide meate'. Next, the advice is, 'having attained to the age of five yeares, send him to the Schoole, where hee may with the elements of knowledge, bee informed in the rudiments of pietie, that is, taught to know loue, feare, and serve his GOD'.

The *Sanitatis Semita*

The main interest of the second of Dr MakLuire's two 1630 books, the *Sanitatis Semita* - i.e. 'The Pathway -' or, alternatively, 'The [Roman Soldier's] Protective Vest -', '- of Health' (fig. 5) - probably lies in *the Tractatus de febre pestilente* (discussed above) which Dr MakLuire 'prefixed' to it and which is presumed to be the text of his MD thesis. The text of the *Tractatus* ends with comments about the cure of the sickness with which it has been dealing. The actual words which join it, as a 'pre-fix', to the main text of the book, are *'quod ut fiat, sequentes canones servandi'* which translates as 'that this may be done, the following rules were to be observed' - and there follow, not preventive measures to be adopted specifically against the pestilent fever, but the canons of general health.

The main text of the *Sanitatis Semita* is not just a translation of *The Buckler*, the writing of which had started in 1619, but is, perhaps, a progressive reworking of it in the light of his postgraduate studies and his clinical experience between 1622 and 1630 - in particular his experience of the epidemic in Edinburgh of 1624, 'which raged not'.

The book takes the form of a series of sixteen 'canons' (of health) - which are not the strict equivalents of the ten canons of *The Buckler*, although both begin with three canons on, respectively, phlebotomy, purgation and sleep. The book deals with its subject less extensively, but perhaps more comprehensively, than does *The Buckler of Bodilie Health* and ends with a pious dedication to God.

Figure 1

The title page of 'The Buckler of Bodilie Health'.

THE
BVCKLER OF
BODILIE
HEALTH,

Whereby Health may bee defended,
and fickneffe repelled, confecrate
by the *Author* to the vfe of
his Countrie wifhing from
his heart (though it were
to his hurt) to fee the
fruites of his labour
in the conftanct wel-
fare of all his
Countrie-men.

By Mr. IOHN MAKLUIRE,
Doctor in Medicine.

EDINBVRGH
Printed by Iohn Wreittoun 1630.

Figure 2

The 'Contents' of the first part of 'The Buckler of Bodilie Health'

'The Buckler of Health'

Figure 3

The 'Contents' of the second part of 'The Buckler of Bodilie Health'.

'A particular regiment according to the Complexion,
Age, and Reason*'

* clearly a mis-print for 'Season'.

Figure 4

The 'Contents' of the third part of ' The Buckler of Bodilie Health'

'A regiment for Women with child, Bairns, and Nourses'

Figure 5

The title page of 'Sanitatis Semita'.

SANITATIS SEMITA.

AVTHORE

IOANNE MAKLVIREO. M. D.

CVM TRACTATV DE FEBRE

PESTILENTE PRÆFIXO.

EDINBVRGI

Excudebat Iohannes Wreittoun. 1630.

Plate I

The ruins of the farm house of Nether Carminnow ('Nether Karmunnow', 'Nether Carmonoch'), overgrown with trees and viewed, in 1985, from the point indicated in Fig. 3d, Chapter II.

This is the farm, the hereditary tenency of which fell to Dr John MakLuire's father, John MakLuire, on the death of the future doctor's grandfather, 'John MakLuire in Castelmaddie', in 1617.

1617 was the year before the future doctor first matriculated at the University of St Andrews.

Plate II

The Chapel of St Roque, in the Burgh Muir, Edinburgh.

St Roque, of Montpelier, has been renowned for his dedication to the mediaeval sufferers from the plague.

The Chapel in Edinburgh was used for the storing of the goods and clothing of persons who were infected with the plague.

By courtesy of Edinburgh City Libraries.

Plate III

Sir James Montgomery of Rosemount, second son of Hugh, 1st Viscount Montgomery of the Great Ards.

Sir James was the life-long friend, from childhood, of Dr John MakLuire, and uncle of the young Hugh Montgomery, the future 3rd Viscount, and famous patient of Dr William Harvey.

From a portrait in the possession of untraced descendents in Aukland, New Zealand.

Plate IV

Sir William Alexander 1st Earl of Stirling and Secretary for Scotland. By an unknown artist.

It was through Sir William, as Master of Requests for Scotland, that Dr John MakLuire's 1630 petition to Charles 1, to establish a College of Physicians in Edinburgh, was submitted to the King.

Sir William's relative, and principal amanuensis, Alexander Alexander, was a fellow student with the young John MakLuire. Sir William himself was grandfather of Dr William Harvey's famous patient, the young Hugh Montgomery, known to Dr MakLuire.

In a private Scottish Collection, and on loan to the Scottish National Portrait Gallery. With acknowledgements.

Plate V

Sir Thomas Hope of Craighall, Lord Advocate.

It was to Sir Thomas that Dr John MakLuire dedicated his 1634 book 'The General Practise of Medecine'.

Sir Thomas, as he was required to plead before judges who included his own sons, was given royal permission to do so while wearing his hat.

An engraving from the portrait by George Jamieson, dated 1627, in the Scottish National Portrait Gallery. With acknowledgements.

Plate VI

Dr William Harvey, 1656.

From a painting by William van Bemmel.

With acknowledgements to (c) Hunterian Art Gallery, University of Glasgow.

It seems to have been in November, 1641, and while the Court was still in Edinburgh, that Harvey had examined the cavity in the chest wall of the young Hugh Montgomery, and had obtained his knowledge of the early history of the case, probably, from Dr John MakLuire and the latter's wife, Mareon Greir.

Chapter Eight - His Choice of the Words 'Buckler' and 'Semita'

The two 1630 books of Dr John MakLuire, his book in English, *The Buckler of Bodilie Health*, and his book in Latin, the *Sanitatis Semita*, had raised the question why, as both books were about the protection of health, he had chosen the word 'buckler', for the one, and the word '*semita*' for the other.

The English word 'buckler' bears the dictionary meaning of 'a small protective shield'.[1] The Latin word '*semita*' bears the dictionary meaning of 'pathway'.[2] However, familiarity with the Scots word 'semmit', meaning 'a man's undervest', and reference to *The Concise Scots Dictionary*, which says that *The Dictionary of the Older Scottish Tongue* has 'semat' of (in the Scots of 1456) a Roman tunic, had suggested a further possibility.[3] This was that Dr MakLuire, assuming such a Roman origin for the familiar Scots word, may also have assumed that the Latin word '*semita*' could have the alternative meaning of 'a protective tunic or vest'. If so, it had seemed possible that, with his known penchant for puns and double meanings, Dr MakLuire may have chosen the word '*semita*' to produce a deliberate ambiguity in the title *Sanitatis Semita* - making it mean either 'the pathway', or 'the protective tunic, or vest', 'of health'.

In view of these dictionary meanings, consideration was given to the possible use of the symbolism here, and to the question whether these terms could throw light on Dr MakLuire's general attitude to the practice of medicine. Did he regard medicine as primarily preventive, as represented by a protective shield, or as primarily active

---

[1] *The Concise Oxford Dictionary of Current English*, Oxford, 1952, p. 152.

[2] W. Smith, *A Smaller Latin-English Dictionary*, London, 1902, p. 552.

[3] M. Robertson, ed., *The Concise Scots Dictionary*, Aberdeen, undated, p. 599.

warfare, with the body as a battleground? Here, the *Tractatus de febre pestilente*, concerned with the fight against a specific disease, seemed to suggest that his concern was not wholly with preventive medicine. Also, enquiry into the literature about symbol and imagery seemed to indicate that this is mainly concerned with the medieval period - and nothing significant was found in relation to the 1600s. In particular, the *Dictionary of Symbols and Images*, by de Vries, does not even list the word 'buckler' - although, under 'buckle' it does mention 'buckler' (significantly for the present discussion) as a 'minimal shield'.[4]

Thus, the original question had remained why the word 'buckler' had been preferred for the title of the one book and the words 'pathway', 'protective tunic', or 'protective vest' for that of the other. Here, it had been the personal dedication of *The Buckler of Bodilie Health* to Sir James Montgomery which had raised the further possibility of a particular significance in Dr MakLuire's choice of the word 'buckler'. Specifically, the conjecture had been[5] of a whimsical reference, for the private delectation of his friend, Sir James Montgomery, to whom he was dedicating the book, to the small, presumably metal, plate (*lamella* in William Harvey's Latin) which had been prescribed for the protection of the exposed heart of the latter's nephew, Hugh Montgomery.[6]

Chronological correspondences in support of this possibility were not immediately apparent. Thus, it is not known how old the young Hugh Montgomery would have been in 1630 - because his precise date of birth is not known. Whitteridge concluded that he was born 'c.1623'.[7] A

---

[4] A. de Vries, *Dictionary of Symbols and Images*, Amsterdam, 1974, p. 67.

[5] J.F. McHarg, 'Dr Johnne MakLuire and the 1630 Attempt to Establish the College', *Proceedings of the Royal College of Physicians of Edinburgh*, Publication No 6, 1982, p. 53.

[6] W. Harvey, *Exercitationes De Generatione Animalium*, Amsterdam: Ravestyn, 1662, p. 199.

[7] W. Harvey, *Disputations Touching the Generation of Animals*, trans G. Whitteridge, London, 1981, p. xxiii.

slightly more precise estimate may be gleaned from a foot-
note in *The Montgomery Manuscripts*, which states that an
Inquisition held at Newtown (Inquisitions, Down, no. 109,
Car. I) had found that at the time of the second Viscount
Montgomery's death on 15th November, 1642, his son and
heir (the young Hugh) had been nineteen years of age -
thus indicating that the latter had been born between 16th
November, 1622 and 15th November, 1623.[8] He would,
thus, have been, at the time of the publication of *The Buckler of Bodilie Health*, in 1630, aged about seven.

As for the question whether the young Hugh's injury
would have already occurred by that time, Harvey says,
only, that the injury had occurred during childhood ('*cum
adhuc puer esset*').[9] Also, *The Montgomery Manuscripts*
say, only, that he was 'a boy at school' when Dr Patrick
Maxwell had punctured the abscess.[10] Nevertheless, the
possibility remained that the injury may have taken place
before the boy was about seven years of age. If so, the
prescription of the protective plate may well have been at
the very time of, or only very shortly before, the publication of *The Buckler*.

Such an admittedly conjectural explanation for a whimsical choice, by Dr MakLuire, of the word 'buckler', rather
than 'protective tunic or vest', for that particular book, had
implied, of course, personal knowledge by Dr MakLuire,
at the time of publishing the book in 1630, of the serious
chest injury exposing the heart of the young Hugh Montgomery; of its treatment; and in particular of the small
(presumably metal) plate which is known to have been
prescribed for its protection.[11]

The paper delivered at the 1981 College symposium, had
put forward some suggestions as to precisely how Dr

---

[8] W. Montgomery, *The Montgomery Manuscripts 1603-1706*, ed.
Revd. G. Hill, Belfast: Cleeland, 1869, p. 174.

[9] Harvey, *Exercitationes De Generatione Animalium*, p. 198.

[10] Montgomery, *The Montgomery Manuscripts 1603-1706*, p. 153.

[11] Harvey, *Exercitationes De Generatione Animalium*, p. 199.

MakLuire could have come to have such knowledge. If the return to Kirkcudbrightshire, from a tenancy in the Ards with the Viscount Montgomery, of Dr MakLuire's father, after the death in 1617 of his father is correct, it had seemed that, after completing a nine- or ten-year tenancy of Nether Carmonoch, his father may well have decided to emigrate, for a second time, to Ulster. In particular, it had seemed that he may well have emigrated from Nether Carmonoch in Kirkcudbrightshire (where he certainly was in 1622) to Ulster, prior to 1630, perhaps in company with his immediate neighbour John Greir in Mid Carmonoch (Dr MakLuire's future father-in-law) who, as will be shown below, is known to have so emigrated about 1627.[12]

Now, a scrutiny of the over 13,000 names on the Muster Roll for Ulster of c.1630 had shown that there had been one John MakLuire, and one only, on that list - a John MakLuire who had mustered with the Viscount Claneboye in the parish of Killyleagh, County Down.[13] Thus, if the supposition was correct that Dr MakLuire's father had indeed emigrated to Ulster, for a second time, shortly before 1630, and probably about 1627, he could not have been other than that John MakLuire in Killyleagh parish.

The probability that Dr MakLuire's father, John MakLuire, was the John MakLuire known to be living in Killyleagh parish in 1630 (and probably since about 1627) had seemed to have an important implication. This had been that the latter - as the young Hugh Montgomery would have been aged only about four in 1627 - would have been living so near at hand to Comber at the very time of the young Hugh's original injury, and of its early treatment, there - the boundary of Killyleagh parish being less than five miles from Comber (see fig.) - that he would surely have known about such an extraordinary medical pheno-menon, so widely talked about as a possible miracle.

---

[12] P.J. Hamilton-Grierson, 'Notes on Various Families of the Name of Grierson', typescript transcribed by J.R.H. Greeves, Dumfries County Council Library, 1948, p. 43.

[13] BM Add MS 4770, 'The Muster Roll for Ulster c1630', fol. 249b.

From this circumstance, two alternative possibilities had arisen. One had been that Dr MakLuire's father would have passed word of the remarkable medical phenomenon to his son, Dr John MakLuire, in Edinburgh, recently graduated as 'Doctor in Physick', and a known friend of the Montgomery family. The other had been of an actual visit by Dr MakLuire to his father in Killyleagh in 1630, perhaps just after his doctoral graduation, and prior to marrying his first wife, Mareon Greive (see below). During such a visit he would surely have acquired fuller detailed personal knowledge of the young Hugh's injury and its management and perhaps have even been involved in advising the use of a protective plate.

The possibility will be discussed further below that just such a contemporary clinical knowledge, however obtained, by Dr MakLuire, in Edinburgh, in 1630, of the injury to the seven-year-old Hugh Montgomery, at Comber, and of the prescription for him of the small protective metal plate, may have been a significant factor in facilitating, for Dr MakLuire, a privileged access to Sir William Alexander, Secretary for Scotland. Sir William, newly arrived in Edinburgh, newly created Master of Requests for Scotland, grandfather of the young Hugh, and no doubt concerned about the serious nature of the latter's injury, would surely have been pleased to receive medical news of his grandson, from a qualified physician, such as Dr MakLuire, well-known to the family and, at the same time, to have provided his informant with the opportunity to submit his petition to Charles I for a College of Physicians.

Thus, in view of Dr MakLuire's recently acquired status, in 1630, as a graduate 'Doctor in Physick', his known closeness to the Montgomery family of Co. Down, and his father's probable geographical closeness to them, the conjecture would seem to be very credible that the use of the word 'buckler' in the title of that particular book, in preference for the words 'pathway' or 'protective tunic or vest', was indeed a whimsical reference to the small plate prescribed, probably about that very time, for the protection of the exposed heart of the seven-year-old Hugh Montgomery.

Figure

The proximity to Comber of the boundary of the parish of Killyleagh.

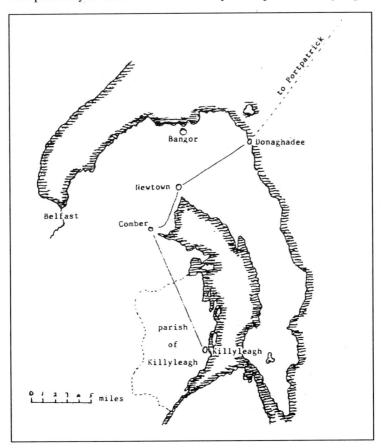

Chapter Nine - His Petition to Charles I

1630 an eventful year for Dr John MakLuire

The year 1630, during which, in the month of September, Dr John MakLuire petitioned Charles I to establish the Royal College of Physicians of Edinburgh, seems to have been an eventful year for him. It had been most probably the year during which he had graduated as 'Doctor in Physick', at St Andrews University, presumably earlier, in July of that year, and certainly before October. It had been the year in which he had published his *Tractatus de febre pestilente* (in Latin) - which would seem to have been his doctoral thesis. It had been the year in which he had published his *Sanitatis Semita* (in Latin), to which the *Tractatus* had been 'prefixed'. It had been the year in which *The Buckler of Bodilie Health* (in English), had been published. And it seems to have been the year in which he had made the decision to marry - either later in that year or, more probably, in 1631.[1]

An influence of William Harvey on the petition?

The general background to the 1630 petition has not hitherto been discussed in detail. However, a speculation that a significant part in determining all three of the abortive attempts to establish a Royal College of Physicians in Edinburgh (including that of 1630) had been played by the contemporaneous findings and teaching of William Harvey, calls for preliminary comment.

Ritchie, after concluding a 'retrospect' of the English, Irish and Scottish medical institutions as they had existed before, during, and subsequent to, Harvey's time, said that he had failed to discover the influence of that great man or his teaching directly affecting more than one of them.[2] That one medical institution, Ritchie had argued, had been

---

[1] J. MakLuire, *The Buckler of Bodlie Health*, Edinburgh: Wreittoun, 1630, p. 133.

[2] R.P. Ritchie, *The Early Days of the Royall Colledge of Phisitians*, Edinburgh: Johnston, 1899, p. 47.

the Royal College of Physicians of Edinburgh. Ritchie had drawn attention to chronological associations with Harvey of the three attempts, of 1617, 1630 and 1657, to establish the College. He had pointed out that only two years before the first attempt, in 1617, Harvey had been chosen to teach and lecture in London; that only two years before the second attempt, in 1630, his great work *Exercitatio anatomica de Motu Cordis et Sanguinis in animalibus* had been published; and that only very shortly before the third attempt, in 1657, Harvey's teaching had drawn to a close.

Ritchie had said that he could not regard these associations with Harvey's time and teaching as mere coincidences - it had appeared to him, rather, that the attempts to establish the College had resulted from them. Ritchie's conclusions, however, certainly in respect of the 1630 attempt, must now be looked upon with scepticism because of the fact (unknown to Ritchie at the time of writing) that Dr John MakLuire, the prime mover in the 1630 attempt, had made, in his three works published in that year, no reference at all to Harvey or, in particular, to the *De Motu Cordis* of only two years before.

The medico-social background to the 1630 petition

There had, in fact, been other, longer-standing, medico-social, factors at work prior to the 1630 attempt to establish the College. In Hamilton's realistic (if perhaps rather cynical) view, although the declared motive in attempts to establish the College, was the need to control unqualified practitioners and quacks and to inspect the drugs sold, it seemed more likely that the motives were to limit the numbers of physicians, curb the practice and wealth of the apothecaries and give themselves a powerful political organisation in Edinburgh.[3]

Hamilton admitted, however, that the physicians argued plausibly from the patients' interests that a college was required in view of 'the frequent murders committed

---

[3] D. Hamilton, *The Healers: A History of Medicine in Scotland.* Edinburgh, 1981, p. 68.

universallie in all parts ... by quacks, women, gardiners
and others grossly ignorant' and 'the unlimited and unacc-
ountable practices of Chirurgeons Apothecaries and
Empiricks pretending to medicines ... all these undertaking
the cure of all diseases without the advice and assistance of
Physitanes'. Doubtless, also, the physicians were apprehensive of the increasing power of the surgeons of Edinburgh.

Hamilton also said that the powers claimed were considerable, but were not unreasonable, and the suggestion that
the physicians should have power over the surgeons and
apothecaries would merely have given the Edinburgh doctors the powers already held by the London physicians.

The earlier, 1617, attempt to establish the College

The first attempt of the Scottish physicians to establish a
College in Edinburgh had been in 1617, under James VI
and I - an attempt fully discussed by Craig.[4] Craig recorded that it had been embarked upon on the occasion of the
visit of the King to Edinburgh in that year. An approach
was made to the King, to whom the views of the physicians of Edinburgh as to the desirability of establishing a
Society or Corporation were presented. As a result of this,
but not until some four years later, on 3 July 1621, the
King had issued orders to the Scottish Parliament that a
College of Physicians be established in Edinburgh. In the
following month (2 August 1621) the Lords remitted the
matter for consideration to the Privy Council of Scotland.
Almost simultaneously, certain Articles 'to be considered
by the Estates' were delivered to the Scottish Parliament.
Apparently, because a 'first draught' of the 'Articles'
(which had come into the hands of Sir Robert Sibbald) had
been amongst papers presumed to have come from Dr
George Sibbald, Craig reasonably concluded that Dr
George Sibbald, uncle of Sir Robert Sibbald, was one of
the prime movers in preparing these 'Articles'.

---

[4] W.S. Craig, *History of the Royal College of Physicians of Edinburgh*, Oxford, 1976, p. 43.

Petition to Charles I

The 1617 proposals came to naught as a result of opposition, in the main, by the Bishops on the Privy Council.
Their opposition would seem to have been partly because
of the believed religious non-conformity (from the royalist,
Episcopalian, point of view) of the proposers and partly
because of apprehension lest their own prescriptive privileges, as Chancellors of the Universities, should be restri-
cted. Opposition also came from the Corporation of Surgeons in Edinburgh who were fearful of curtailment of their
rights.

Dr MakLuire's leading role in the 1630 attempt

The question of a College of Physicians in Edinburgh had
been taken up again in 1630, and it has long been known
that a petition to this end, submitted to Charles I, had
received his favourable commendation. The long-forgotten
fact that Dr John MakLuire had been the petitioner on that
occasion had been re-discovered only shortly before the
tercentenary of the College in 1981.[5] Of crucial importance
in this re-discovery had been the words in the margin
against a contemporary manuscript copy-letter of the letter
from the King commending the petition - 'Doctor Mak-
cleuiris peticeone for erecting a Colidge of Phisiceans'.

The symposium paper of 1981 had suggested that these
marginal words had been 'the crucial and perhaps the only
surviving evidence of the authorship of the 1630 petition'.[6]
It had even been suggested that it had seemed to have been
simply good luck for posterity and history that there had
been one man - James Philp, secretary to the Privy Council
of Scotland, and amanuensis in Edinburgh to Sir William
Alexander, Secretary for Scotland (see plate IV) - who had
shared with Sir William the knowledge of Dr MakLuire's
authorship of the 1630 petition and had recorded it in the

---

[5] J.F. McHarg, 'Dr Johnne MakLuire and the 1630 Attempt to Establish the College', *Proceedings of the Royal College of Physicians of
Edinburgh*, Publication No 6, 1982, pp. 44-98.

[6] Ibid., p. 45.

margin. It has since been discovered that this was only partly true.

Rogers, in *The Earl of Stirling's Register of Royal Letters 1615-1635*, had stated that the Register is comprised of three volumes, 'the most considerable in extent, and most important in character, being that preserved in the General Register House'.[7] This had been the volume, now in the Scottish Record Office, in which the relevant entry first to be discovered had been found (see fig. iii).[8] The other two volumes, Rogers had said, were 'preserved in the Advocates' Library' - which is now the National Library of Scotland.[9] It had been in the first of these two manuscript volumes that a second copy of the relevant letter of commendation by Charles I, in an unknown hand, had been found (see fig. 2).[10]

Now, Rogers seems to have been strangely unaware that there are, in the British Library, three other manuscript volumes of Sir William Alexander's Registers, showing some overlap with the three Edinburgh volumes - but distinct from them.[11] It had been in the second of these that yet a third copy of the letter had been found. This was the copy of the letter made at source, at Hampton Court. It was in the hand of Sir William Alexander's 'relative' and principal amanuensis (discussed above), Alexander Alex-

[7] C. Rogers, ed., *The Earl of Stirling's Register of Royal Letters (1615-1635)*, 2 vols., Edinburgh: Paterson, 1884, II, p. lxi.

[8] SRO SP1/6, Sir William Alexander, Register of Royal Letters 1626-1631, p. 533.

[9] NLS Adv MSS 34.2.12., Sir William Alexander, 'Earl of Stirling's Register (1626-1635)', vol. I and BM Add MSS 23111, Vol II, untitled (1630-1635).

[10] NLS Adv MSS 34.2.12., Sir William Alexander, 'Earl of Stirling's Register (1626-1635)', vol. I, dated 2nd October, 1630 (pages unnumbered).

[11] BM Add MSS 23110., Sir William Alexander, 'Scotch Orders in Council (1626-1635)', vol. I; BM Add MSS 23111, vol. II, untitled 1630-1635; and BM ADD MSS 23112., vol. III, untitled (1635-1640).

ander (see fig. i).[12] There are minor variations in the spelling and content of the three copy-letters, but all include the marginal attribution of the petition to Dr Mak-Luire.

There is, moreover, a fourth copy, embedded in the text of the minutes, of the date 23 November 1630, in the Register of the Privy Council for Scotland, but without any marginal note disclosing the name of the author of the petition to which the letter refers (see fig. iv).[13]

The occasions for Dr MakLuire's 1630 petition

One of the occasions for Dr MakLuire's petition to the King may have been the impatience of comparative youth with the flagging enthusiasm (to which a manuscript of 1657, probably by Dr Purves, refers) of 'the well-meaning petitioners' (i.e. those of the earlier petition of 1617) who 'had themselves become, by that time' (i.e. in 1630) 'many of them aged but all of them wearied out with toil'.[14] It is not known who, or how old, those 1617 'well-meaning petitioners' would have been in 1630. Even Dr Sibbald's age, in 1630, is not known but it would seem that he was probably about twice the age of Dr MakLuire - who would have been aged about twenty-seven.

The more immediate occasion for the 1630 petition would have been, as was suggested in the symposium paper at the time of the tercentenary of the College, the appointment of Sir William Alexander to the post of Master of Requests for Scotland shortly after his arrival in Scotland.[15] Sir William, normally at the Court in London, had been sent to

---

[12] BM Add MSS 23111, Sir William Alexander, vol. II, untitled (1630-1635), p. 24.

[13] SRO PC 1/33, Register of the Privy Council for Scotland, f265v-f266r.

[14] G. Purves, 'Account of the rights of the professors of medicine, 1657', manuscript copy, in an 18th-century hand, presently in the Royal College of Physicians of Edinburgh, pp. 72-73.

[15] Rogers, ed., *The Earl of Stirling's Register of Royal Letters (1615-1635)* I, p. xxxvi.

Scotland by Charles I, as his Royal Commissioner and Plenipotentiary, in July 1630, the importance of the occasion being emphasised by the King's command that the Earl Marischal kill a brace of buck to celebrate Sir William's arrival.[16] Two months later, on 4 September 1630, Sir William had been created Viscount Stirling and his appointment as Master of Requests for Scotland had followed shortly after that.

Thus, the fact that the King's letter commending Dr Mak-Luire's petition was signed less than a month later, at Hampton Court, on 2 October 1630, had indicated that, for the petition to have been sent south and delivered to the King by that date, Dr MakLuire must have submitted it to Sir William, in Edinburgh, more or less immediately upon the latter's appointment as Master of Requests being announced.

The remaining question had been how it had come to be that such a junior physician as Dr John MakLuire had come to seize the opportunity to submit the petition of 1630 for, having graduated in that same year, he may well have been the most junior physician in Edinburgh at the time.

Access to Sir William through his Montgomery connections

Now, Dr MakLuire's closeness to Sir James Montgomery, second son of the 1st Viscount Montgomery of the Ards in Ireland, certainly since student days; probably from childhood; and continuing in 1630, as the dedication of *The Buckler of Bodilie Health* shows, is clear. It is almost certain, also, as will be argued below, that he would have been (already in 1630) familiar with the medical case of Sir James' nephew, the young Hugh Montgomery, aged about seven at the time, and son and heir of the 2nd Viscount, who had sustained, at an unknown age in childhood, a very severe injury to the chest. And the young

---

[16] BM Add MSS 23111, Sir William Alexander, vol. II, untitled (1630-1635), p.18.

Hugh, through his mother, was the grandson of Sir William Alexander, who must have been very concerned about the seriousness of the remarkable injury.

It would seem very probable, therefore, that the young Dr MakLuire would have had personal access to Sir William and that he may have been chosen by the more senior physicians of Edinburgh to act on their behalf in submitting the petition to the King precisely because of that personal access.

The historiography of the 1630 petition

The primary written sources for an enquiry into the historiography of the 1630 petition itself had been

1) the petition itself

2) the King's letter of commendation of the petition to his Privy Council in Edinburgh

3) the aforementioned copy of that letter made at source (Hampton Court)

4) and 5) the two copies made at the point of reception (Edinburgh)

6) the minute, dated 23 November 1630, of the consideration, by the Privy Council in Edinburgh, both of the petition and of the King's commendation of it, and including the instruction by the Council to four named physicians (Drs Jollie, Sibbald, Anderson and McGill) 'to give in some heads and articles' for establishing a College

7) the seventeen Articles submitted by the four physicians to the Privy Council[17]

8) a referral, after subsequent inaction up to the coronation year of 1633, of the matter to the Privy Council for action[18]

---

[17] Sir Robert Sibbald, *Memoirs of the Royal College of Physicians at Edinburgh*, Edinburgh, Stevenson, 1837, pp. 7-13.

9) on 28 October 1634, a cautionary recommendation by the King for the avoidance of pre-judging
the chirurgeans - after which, for a variety of
reasons, nothing further was achieved.[19]

The first account of the history of the successive attempts
to establish the College, as these are enshrined in primary
documents, is that contained in a document, written in
1657, probably by Dr George Purves, and referred to
above. This had come into the possession of Sir Robert
Sibbald but appears to have been lost. A copy of it, in an
eighteenth-century hand, survives, however, at the College.[20] This document, after giving an account of the 1617
attempt under James VI, makes no mention at all of Dr
MakLuire's 1630 petition, or of Charles I's commendation
of it, but jumps to the above-mentioned steps taken in
1633 at the time of Charles I's visit to Edinburgh for his
coronation.

The next account is in an unfinished manuscript by Sir
Robert Sibbald, entitled an 'Account of the Original Institution of the Royal College of Physicians'. This had been
preserved in the Library of the Faculty of Advocates, and
'given to the world' in 1837. It had appeared to have
depended, largely, upon Dr Purves' document and, for that
reason, to have perpetuated the silence about Dr Mak-
Luire.[21] The anonymous 'Historical Sketch' of the College
of 1925, also perpetuating the silence about Dr MakLuire,
had nevertheless dealt with the 1630 attempt - but very
briefly, simply saying that 'In 1630 the attempt [to establ-

---

[18] Purves, 'Account of the rights of the professors of medicine, 1657',
pp. 72-73.

[19] R. Poole, 'Preparatory Notes for a History of the College', Mss
1838, quoted by Craig in his *History of the Royal College of Physicians of Edinburgh*, p. 45.

[20] Purves, 'Account of the rights of the professors of medicine, 1657',
pp. 72-73.

[21] Sir Robert Sibbald, 'Account of the Original Institution of the
Royal College of Physicians' - unfinished manuscript published as *Sir
Robert Sibbald's Memoirs of the Royal College of Physicians at
Edinburgh: A Fragment*, Edinburgh: Stevenson, 1837.

ish the College] was renewed, and King Charles I referred the matter to his Privy Council; but, owing chiefly to the unsettled state of public affairs, nothing more was done in his reign'.[22]

The most recent account had been that of Craig.[23] Craig, although he had been immediately informed about the discovery of Dr MakLuire's authorship of the 1630 petition, had not incorporated the information into his *The History of the Royal College of Physicians of Edinburgh* and had thus not only perpetuated the silence of Dr Purves, and of the brief 'Historical Sketch' of 1925, about Dr MakLuire's leading role, but had introduced some misleading implications. He had said that efforts 'by the physicians [in the plural] of Edinburgh had been renewed in 1630 and, in particular, that Dr George Sibbald had been 'as active in furthering the petition of 1630 as he had been that of 1617'. Craig had referred to a scroll of a petition in Dr George Sibbald's hand which Sir Robert Sibbald says was found among the papers he inherited from the former (his uncle) and had seemed to imply that this petition was submitted in relation to the 1630 attempt, and even that it was the 1630 petition.

However, there had seemed to be no evidence that Dr Sibbald, or indeed any other physician than Dr MakLuire, had been involved in the 1630 petition. It had seemed more probable that this petition of Dr Sibbald, which was addressed not to the King (as was Dr MakLuire's) but to the Lords of the Privy Council, had been submitted in relation to the earlier, 1617, attempt in which Dr George Sibbald had admittedly been a prime mover. Admittedly also, however, Dr George Sibbald, after Dr MakLuire's petition had met with royal approval, had been one of the four physicians ordered to advise further about the matter.

---

[22] *Historical Sketch and Laws of the Royal College of Physicians*, Edinburgh, 1925.

[23] Craig, *History of the Royal College of Physicians of Edinburgh*, p. 46.

How had Dr MakLuire's role continued to be forgotten?

The petition itself, of Dr MakLuire, which, if preserved, would have kept alive the memory of his authorship of it, must have been sent, from Edinburgh, to the King at Hampton Court, because it was read there by the King. Also, the words 'the within peticeone', in the King's letter commending the petition to the Privy Council, surely indicate that it was returned to Edinburgh - presumably into the hand of Sir William Alexander. Its subsequent history is not known. It was not among the manuscripts in Sir Robert Sibbald's collection which was put up for sale in 1722.[24] It is not to be found in the Scottish Record Office. It has not been found in the collection of petitions in the Bankes papers at the Bodleian Library.[25] It may, therefore, have been destroyed, or lost.

The King's letter did not mention by name the author of the petition which it commends. Furthermore, the minute of the Privy Council meeting on 23rd November, 1630, attended by Sir William Alexander, shows that, while the King's commendation of the petition 'was read in their audience', the petition itself was not read, nor the name of its author disclosed to the Council or minuted.[26] Furthermore, the newly graduated doctor's name was, understandably, not put forward to be one of the four experienced physicians ordained by the Council, as a result of the petition, 'to give in some heads and articles' for the erection of a College.

At a later stage, Sir Robert Sibbald's unfinished memo on the pre-history of the College, based on information coming from his uncle, Dr George Sibbald, had included no reference to Dr MakLuire's petition - despite the facts that Dr George Sibbald must have known of Dr

---

[24] *Bibliotheca Sibbaldiana: or, a Catalogue of Curious and Valuable Books ... Being the Library of ... Sir Robert Sibbald*, Edinburgh, 1722.

[25] *Bankes Papers*, Oxford: Bodleian Library.

[26] *Register of the Privy Council of Scotland,* 2nd Series., vol. III (1629-1630), p. 69.

MakLuire's authorship of it and had certainly esteemed Dr MakLuire highly. Possibly, had Sir Robert been able to complete his memo, he would have incorporated an acknowledgement by Dr George Sibbald of Dr MakLuire's authorship of the 1630 petition.

The question had still remained, however, why Dr MakLuire's authorship of the 1630 petition had continued to be hidden for so long since the time of Sir Robert Sibbald. Of probable relevance, here, is the fact that the 'Register of Royal Letters' kept by Sir William Alexander, in which the crucial copy-letter had been found, and which is now held in the Scottish Record Office, had not been lodged, for public inspection, at General Register House in Edinburgh, until 1793.[27] Even then, when Rogers' purportedly comprehensive transcription of the copy-letters in Sir William's Registers was published in 1884, the surviving evidence of the authorship of the 1630 petition - *viz*., the marginal labelling of it, as of each of the copy-letters, was inexplicably omitted by Rogers. It seems to have been because of this that Dr MakLuire's authorship remained hidden (unwittingly) from all except any who consulted not Rogers' printed transcription, but the manuscript itself, of the Register.

It had seemed, in short, that Dr Purves' omission of any mention of Dr MakLuire's petition had remained uncorrected, first, by Sir Robert Sibbald, then by Rogers' transcription of Sir William Alexander's Registers, then by the 1925 'Historical Sketch', and finally by Craig's account, which had added the mistaken implication that the petition by Dr George Sibbald, found in the latter's papers by Sir Robert Sibbald, had itself been the 1630 petition.

---

[27] SRO SP1/6, Sir William Alexander, Register of Royal Letters 1626-1631, fol 1.

Figure

Letter from Charles I, at Hampton Court, to his Privy Council in Scotland, commending the petition of Dr MakLuire to erect a College of Physicians in Edinburgh.

The original letter has not been traced but there are four contemporary copies extant:

(1) A copy, in the hand of Alexander Alexander, principal amanuensis to Sir William Alexander, Secretary for Scotland, who had been left at Hampton Court while Sir William himself was in Scotland.

This copy would have been made at source (Hampton Court) prior to the original itself being forwarded to Sir William in Edinburgh for delivery to the Privy Council there.

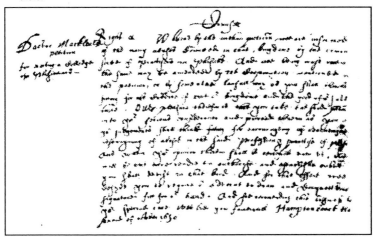

Reproduced by permission of the British Library.

(Ref: Sir William Alexander, Vol II (Untitled) 1630-1635, BM Add MS 23111; 24).

Transcription

Doctor Mackleurs petition

for erecting a Colledge ofor Phisicians

Right etc. Whaeras by the within peticon wee are informed of the many abuses comitted in that, kingdome by the comon sorte of pratisers in phisicke. And wee being most readie the same may be amended by the corporation mentioned in the peticion, or by some other lauful way as you shall think fitting for the credite of that o^r kingdome and the good of o^r sub.s there . OURe pleasure therefore is that you take the said peton into yor serious consideration and proceede therein as you in yor judgements shall think fitting for encourageing of learning and restrayning of abuses in the said profession & practise of phs And when yor opinion therein shall be certefied unto us, we will be the more readie to authorise and establishe what you shall devise in that kind . And for that effect wee desyre you to require o^r advocat to draw and docquett ane signature fit for o^r hand . And soe recomending this bussness to yor speciall care wee bid you farewell Hampton court the second of October 1630

Figure

(II) A copy, in an unknown hand, made in Edinburgh for Sir William prior to delivery of the original to the Privy Council.

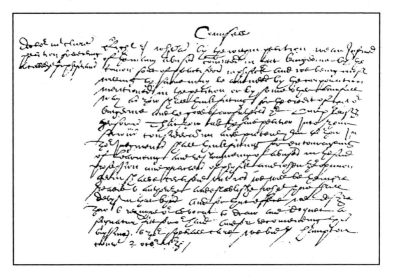

Reproduced by permission of the National Library of Scotland.

(Ref: NLS Adv MSS 34.2.12; under the date 2nd October, 1630).

Figure

(III) A copy, in the hand of James Philp, secretary to the Privy Council of Scotland, made in Edinburgh after the original letter had been read to the Council.

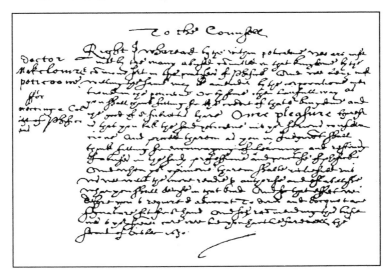

Reproduced by permission of the Keeper of the Records of Scotland with the agreement of the Controller of Her Majesty's Stationery Office.

(Ref: SRO SP1/6; 533).

Figure

(1V) The copy, also in the hand of James Philp, incorporated into the minute of the Register of the Privy Council for Scotland, at Holyrood House, dated 23rd November, 1630, which records the presentation to the Council ("and read in their audience") of "His Maties missive anent ane Colledge of Physicians". Note that there is no mention of Dr MakLuire, the author of the petition.

fol 265v

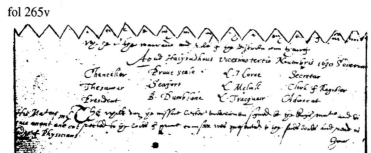

fol 266r

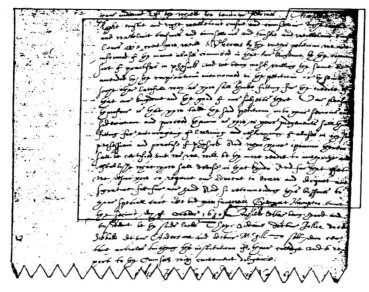

Reproduced by permission of the Keeper of the Records of Scotland with the agreement of the Controller of Her Majesty's Stationery Office.

(Ref: SRO PC 1/33 f265v-f266r).

Chapter Ten - Mareon Greive, His First Wife and Their Home (1631)

A guiding intuition

It had been discovered at a comparatively early stage that Dr MakLuire had undoubtedly been married to a 'Mareon Greir'. The fact had been gleaned from the records, to be seen in the Edinburgh baptismal register, of the baptisms of eight of the nine children to Dr MakLuire. In each of these entries - with a temporary reservation, to be disposed of below, concerning that for his very first child - the name of the mother had been given, unequivocally, as 'Mareon Greir'.

Later, after the historical symposium at the College tercentenary celebrations of 1981, an impelling intuition had arisen that it might be the discovery of the full identity, pre-marriage background, and place of abode, of this Mareon Greir, which might provide the crucial clue to one of the most intriguing possibilities in the search for the identity of Dr MakLuire himself.

The tantalising possibility had been of finding, from this, positive evidence of Dr MakLuire having had just that degree of personal knowledge of the childhood injury sustained by the young Hugh Montgomery at Mount Alexander House, Comber, County Down, and of its treatment and management, which the conjecture of a consultation about the case with the great William Harvey, in Edinburgh, in November 1641, had required for its substantiation.

A marriage, hinted at in 1630, for 1631

There had seemed to be no explicit record of when Dr MakLuire had married Mareon Greir. A clue, however, at least as to when he had intended to marry had seemed to lie on the very last page of his book, *The Buckler of Bodilie Health*, published in 1630. He had ended the book, after a dissertation on the clinical differentiation of true from false pregnancy, with the somewhat cryptic comment

'... for I hope not to be deceaved this twelve moneths by my wife, and so farewell' (fig. 1).[1]

Precisely what Dr MakLuire could have meant by this had called for careful consideration. Why had he not stated, simply, that he hoped not to be deceived (over a question of pregnancy) by his wife? Why had he included the words 'this twelve moneths'? Clearly, first, his hope not to be deceived 'this twelve moneths' (and not 'this nine months', or any shorter interval of time) had signified that he was not referring to a current, believed, nine-month, pregnancy. Nor, second, in those pre-family-planning days, could his reference to 'my wife' have been to an already acquired wife, and to a pregnancy not intended even to start until three months time.

It had appeared that Dr MakLuire's hope not to be deceived 'this twelve moneths' could, on the one hand, have been over an anticipated birth in twelve months time (the result of an intended marriage and pregnancy in three months time). On the other hand, it could have been over an intended marriage, in twelve months time (and the start, then, of a hopefully 'true' pregnancy). The first of these alternative interpretations had thus implied a marriage which, taking place in three months time, would have been intended for later still in 1630 or, much more probably, in 1631. The second interpretation had necessarily implied a marriage intended to take place not until 1631.

His first wife a Mareon Greive

The first seeming clue to the identity of Mareon Greir (whom it had initially been assumed that Dr MakLuire had been planning, in 1630, to marry) had lain in the discovery of the manuscript entry for Dr MakLuire in the Extent Roll for the Annuity Tax which the Town Council of Edinburgh had ordered, on 1 May 1635, to be drawn up

---

[1] J. MakLuire, *The Buckler of Bodilie Health*, Edinburgh: Wreittoun, p.133.

(fig. 2).[2] This had recorded Dr MakLuire, living in the house, to be both the tenant, and the (acting) landlord, 'for umql George Greir's heirs' - of whom, it was initially thought that Mareon Greir might be one.

But it was subsequently established that this entry included a writer's error. The previous owner of the house, on behalf of whose heirs Dr MakLuire had (by 1635) become the accepted [acting] landlord, had been not a 'George Greir' but a 'George Greive, sometime Customer in Edinburgh'. This well-to-do Customs Officer, George Greive, had died in October 1633, and it would seem that it had been at that juncture, and by the provision of the latter's testament, that Dr MakLuire had become the landlord of the house, acting in that capacity on behalf of the lawful heirs and successors of the deceased - *viz.*, George Greive's lawful son and daughter, Alexander and Alison Greive - who were under-age.[3]

Now, George Greive's testament (to which Dr MakLuire had been the principal witness) had also committed his under-age lawful heirs (and a still-younger natural daughter, Margaret, as well as a university student, Alexander Thome, boarded with them) to the continuing care (in the family house, which they were to inherit) of his eldest daughter, Mareon, 'and her spouse' - who was, however, unnamed. Mareon Greive, baptised in Edinburgh on 19 February 1609, had been an illegitimate daughter of George Greive and had, by that time, been aged 24.[4]

It had seemed probable, therefore, because Dr MakLuire clearly had been nominated as both tenant and acting landlord of the house in which George Greive's orphaned children were to continue to live, and to be cared for, that Dr MakLuire had himself been the unnamed spouse (of

---

[2] See Extent Roll for the Annuity Tax (1634-1636), Edinburgh City Archives, p. 99 and Edinburgh Town Council Minutes, 1 May 1635.

[3] SRO CC8/8/56, Testament George Greive, fol. 275 (a), 26 March 1634.

[4] SRO OPR 685 1/1, Edinburgh (Greyfriars) Register of Baptisms, 19 February 1609.

Mareon Greive), who had been exhorted in the testament to share with the latter the continuing care, in that house, of the orphaned children. Presumably, Dr MakLuire had married Mareon Greive, as had been deduced, in 1631, when she would have been aged twenty two, and probably he had been already living, with her, as a tenant, in the same house as his landlord, and father-in-law, George Greive, at the time of the latter's death.

However, the strange fact that, in George Greive's testament, Mareon Greive's 'spouse' was not named, raised the possibility of some irregularity, or even illegality, about Dr MakLuire's marriage to her. Nevertheless, by a further writer's error, this time in the registering of the baptism of the first child to Dr MakLuire by his second marriage - to Mareon Greir (see Chapter 12) - the name 'Mareon Greive' was erroneously inserted (although immediately corrected) as the mother.[5] There is no doubt that the child baptised on that occasion was the son of Mareon Greir - and not of Mareon Greive - because the principle witness at the baptism had been Sir Robert Greir of Lag, the acknowledged Chief of the Greir family. This writer's error nevertheless indicated that a general assumption, until recently, of 'Mareon Greive' as the spouse of Dr MakLuire, had still been current.

His home in Galloway's Close

The precise location of Dr MakLuire's place of abode, which had previously been that of the deceased George Greive, had been deduced from the manuscript of the Extent Roll. In this roll the dwelling-places, in the first third-part of the North West Quarter of the Town, with their landlords and tenants, are listed one by one. Coming down the north side of the High Street, from west to east, the roll reaches the entrance to a close which had no name but which, in the next century, became known as 'Galloway's Close'. Galloway's Close, according to Boog Wat-

---

[5] SRO OPR 685 1/4, Edinburgh (Greyfriars) Register of Baptisms, 30 July 1635.

son still existed, in 1923, 'but shorn of its name'.[6] It was, he said, 'the first close east of Bank Street'. Its site would therefore have corresponded to the west half of the Sheriff Court House (figs. 3a and b) - recently transferred to Chambers Street.

Dr MakLuire's house is defined, in the Extent Roll, as the first on the left as one entered Galloway's Close:

the first turnpike hous on the weast side of & wthin that Close wch lyeath east of & joyneth the former laiche booth.

The house seems to have been quite commodious, with several storeys, extending upwards to a loft, specified by George Greive's testament as the place in which had lain a 'mekle tymber bed' left by a David Balfour.

A drawing, of Galloway's Close, of about 1850, by W. Channing, was found to have survived - in the Edinburgh room of the Central Public Library, Edinburgh.[7] This drawing (fig. 3c) seems to have been made from a point on the east-west arm of St Giles Street close to the site of the Bank of Scotland, and outside the lower (north) entrance to the close. It is a view of the close looking up-hill towards the upper (south) entrance to the close from the High Street.

The door on the right, at the top, in the drawing, would appear to have been, surely, that of Dr MakLuire's house, in 1635. The pattern, in the roof of the close entrance, of the under-side of ascending stairs, presumably joining with those of the 'turnpike' not itself depicted, is clearly to be seen. The wall to be seen, on the right, below, and outside of, the north entrance to the close, is presumably that of the 'yarde at the close foote' extending northwards as far as the steep descent to the Nor Loch - now Waverley Station.

---

[6] C.B. Boog Watson, *Notes on the Names of the Closes and Wynds of Old Edinburgh*, Edinburgh, 1923, p. 19.

[7] W. Channing, *The Edinburgh Scene: Catalogue of Prints and Drawings in the Edinburgh Room*, Edinburgh Central Public Library, p. 75.

Their brief marriage

Nothing is known about the life, together, of Dr MakLuire with his first wife, Mareon Greive. The marriage would seem to have lasted for only about two years, and there seem to have been no children. They would, perhaps, have witnessed together the pomp and ceremony of the entry of Charles I to the town for his Scottish coronation in 1633 as the procession passed the entry to Galloway's Close.

It would have been during these two years that Dr MakLuire would have been preparing his third book, *The Generall Practise of Medecine* - presumably completing its preparation after Mareon Greive's death.

Mareon Greive's death

The date of Mareon Greive's death is not known but it had seemed possible to make certain deductions about it. As she had been still alive at the time of her father's death in October 1633, her death would have been at some date between then and the end of October 1634 (see fig. 4). The latter date is the presumed time of the conception of Dr MakLuire's first child (who was to be baptised on 30 July 1635) by his second wife, Mareon Greir. Mareon Greive's death must have been prior to Dr MakLuire's marriage to Mareon Greir - and thus not later than the end of October 1634.[8] In view of Dr MakLuire's second marriage probably taking place in the summer of 1634, Mareon Greive's death might well have taken place before the end of 1633.

Clearly, as the 1635 Extent Roll shows, Dr MakLuire continued to live in the house in Galloway's Close after the death of Mareon Greive, conscientiously continuing, no doubt, to provide, as exhorted in his father-in-law's testament, 'bed and buird and clothes washing' and general supervision to the latter's orphaned children who

---

[8] SRO OPR 685 1/4, Edinburgh (Greyfriars) Register of Baptisms, 30 July 1635.

had been committed to the care of his late spouse and himself.

Figure 1

The last page of 'The Buckler of Bodilie Health'.

of Health.

The not diftinguifhing of a true concep-
tion from the falfe, hath beene often trouble-
fome and chargable to diverfe: Such was
the cafe of a Lady in Burdeous, who after
nyne moneths carefull carying of her felfe,
leaft fhee fhould hurte her fuppofed child,
and three Weekes troublefome travailing, in
end was delyvered of a fart forfuith:
Let any man who is feared for to be
deceaved either with pillowes vn-
der the kilting, or farts in the
sklrping, fupplie that which
hath beene omitted by me,
for I hope not to be de-
ceaved this twelue mo-
neths by my wife,
and fo farewell.

FINIS.

An intended marriage hinted at for later in 1630 or in 1631.

Figure 2

Extract from the Extent Roll for Edinburgh, ordered on 1st May, 1635, for the years 1634-1636, showing the entry for Dr MakLuire's tenancy in that Close, off the High Street, later to be called 'Galloway's Close'.

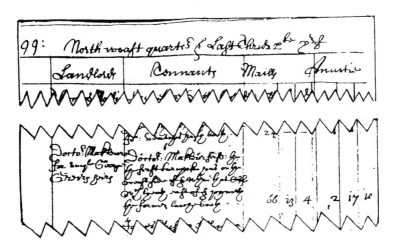

Transcription:

99: North weast quarter & Last Thrid pte yrof		Maills			Anuitie		
Landlords	Tennants	£	s	d	£	s	d
Doctor Makleure for umqle George Greirs heirs	Doctor: Makleur forsd: the the first turnpike hours on the west side of & within that Close wch lyeth east of & joyneth the former laiche booth	66	13	4	2	17	10

Note: Dr MakLuire is shown as both the tenant, and the acting landlord, on behalf of the (under-age) heirs of the deceased 'George Greir'. But this is shown to have been a writer's error for 'George Grieve', who was 'somtime Customer in Edinburgh' and who had died in 1633.

Ref: Extent Roll for the Annuity Tax (1634-1636). Edinburgh City Archives; 99.

Reproduced by courtesy of Edinburgh City Archives.

Figure 2

Galloway's Close, after W. Channing, c1850.

Viewed from a point (near the present site of the Bank of Scotland) outside the lower (North) entrance to the Close, looking up-hill towards the upper (South) entrance from the High Street. The door on the right, at the top, was surely, in 1635, Dr MakLuire's.

Ref: Channing W. Galloway's Close, High Street, c1850, in his Sketches in Edinburgh Vol. 2.

Reproduced by kind permission of Edinburgh City Libraries.

Figure 3

Galloway's Close, High Street, Edinburgh.

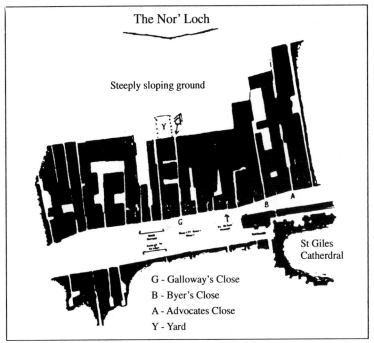

The Nor' Loch

Steeply sloping ground

St Giles
Catherdral

G - Galloway's Close
B - Byer's Close
A - Advocates Close
Y - Yard

(a) Reconstructed map.

(b) Part of Rothiemay's aerial map of Edinburgh (1647).

Figure 4

The death of Mareon Greive about 1633/4.

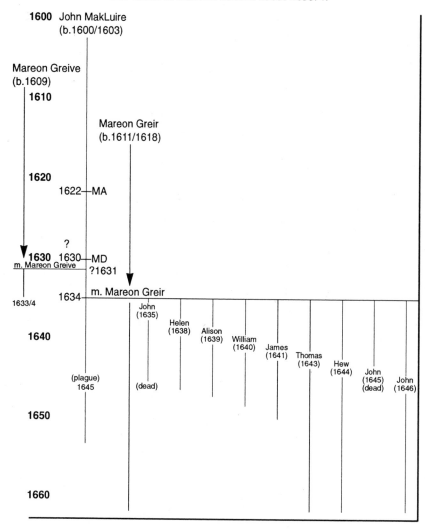

Chapter Eleven - *The Generall Practise of Medecine*

D r MakLuire's third book, The *Generall Practise of Medecine*, was published in 1634. This was subsequent to the death of his first wife, Mareon Greive; the year during which, in a probably brief sojourn in Ulster, he married Mareon Greir, his second wife; and the year in which he received assignation of the lands of Froskan and Croattes (near Cullen, in Banffshire) - probably a transaction in lieu of payment of an out-standing fee. Comment has already been made on the fact that, in the same year, the printer of his book, John Wreittoun, in Edinburgh, had also printed *The Practise of Christianity*, by the William Perkins to whom Dr MakLuire seems, earlier, in 1630, to have taken such exception.

The Generall Practise of Medecine, although it appears under a pseudonym, 'φιλιατρευσ' ('lover of healing' - which, it is interesting to note, was the pseudonym also to be adopted, in the next century, by Sir Robert Sibbald[9]), carries the initials 'I.M.' - surely standing for 'Ioannes MakLuireus'. Also, as the author, in an introductory address, refers to works he has previously had published, a reference, surely, to *The Buckler of Bodilie Health* and the *Sanitatis Semita* of 1630, it is not surprising that this third book has generally been accepted as the work of Dr John MakLuire.

The dedication of the book is 'To the Right Honorable Sir Thomas Hope of Craighall Knight Baronet, Advocat generall to his Majestie of great Britaine, in his Kingdome of Scotland'. It reads as follows:

> It is reported of Caesar (Right Honourable) that oft times he praised his Souldiours good-will, although they wanted skill: And Cicero as well commended stammering Lentulus for his painful industry, as learned Laelius for his passing elo-

---

[9] W. Anderson, *The Scottish Nation*, vol. III, Edinburgh: Fullarton, 1865, p. 451.

quence: Which considered (although wisedome did will mee not to straine further than my sleive would stretch) I thought good to present this small Treatise to your H. protection, hoping your H. will out of your accustomed clemencie, accept it, and take my well meaning for an excuse of my boldnesse, in that my poore will is not in the wane, whatsoever this imperfect worke doth want. The Emperour Trajan was never without suters, because so courteously hee would heare everie complaint. The Lapidaries continually frequented the Court of Adobrandinus, because it was his chiefe study to search out the nature of stones. All that courted Atlanta were hunters, and none sued to Sapho but poets: Wheresoever Mecaenas lodgeth, thither no doubt will Schollers flocke. And your H. beeing a worthie favourer and foster-er of learning, hath forced many through your exquisit vertue, to offer the first fruits of their study at the shrine of your Courtesie. But though they have waded farre and found mynes, and I gadded abroad to get nothing but **ytes: yet this I assure myselfe, that they never presented you their treasure with a more willing mind, then I doe this simple trash, which I hope your H. will so accept. Resting therefore upon your wonted clemencie, I commit you to the Almighty.   I.M.

Sir Thomas Hope (Plate V) had been an influential member of the Privy Council to which Dr MakLuire, in 1630, had dedicated his two earlier books. It is of interest to note, here, also, that both Sir Thomas Hope and Dr MakLuire were to be witnesses at the baptism of a son to Master John Sharp, 'Professor of Divinity in King James his College' (the University of Edinburgh), seven years later, in 1641.[2]

The dedication of the book is followed by an address 'To the Gentlemen Readers, Health'. It reads as follows:

---

[2] SRO OPR 685 1/4, Edinburgh (Greyfriars) Register of Baptisms, 8th August, 1641.

Pan blowing upon an oaten pipe a litle homely musick, and hearing no man dispraise his simple cunning, began both to play so lowd and so long, that they were more wearie in hearing his Musick, then hee in shewing his skill, till at last to claw him and excuse themselves, they said, his Pype was out of tune. So Gentlemen, because I have before tyme rashly reacht above my pitch, and yet your courtesie was such as none accused me, I have once againe adventured upon your patience, but (I doubt) so farre as to be read of my folly, you will at the last say, as Augustus said to his Graecian that gave him oft times many rude verses: Thou hast need (quoth hee) reward mee well, for I take more paines to read thy workes, than thou to write them. But yet willing to abide this quip, because I may countervaile it with your former courtesie, I put my selfe to your patience, and commits you to the Almighty. Farewell. I.M.

The title page of the book (see fig.) states that it comprehends 'the most remarkable maxims' 'collected out of the most famous, both Ancient and Moderne Wryters, for the use of such as be ignorant of the Greeke and Latine tongues' - although, in fact, of the 'Ancient Wryters', only Hippocrates and Aristotle are mentioned, and no 'Moderne Wryters'. It is interesting that the openness thus proclaimed is at variance with the secrecy commonly assumed to have been attached to medical writings, and to have been ensured by resort to the Latin language. The book, although it is well known that the publication of other medical books, dealing with particular topics, had preceded its publication, would seem to be, indeed, the first textbook on general medicine to have been written by a Scotsman and to have been published in Scotland.

The book does not contain any of the asides which characterised *The Buckler*, and which threw light on Dr MakLuire's personal interests and attitudes. It is, by contrast, rather sober, but undoubtedly worthy. Its prime importance is, perhaps, its emphasis upon a clear method of procedure.

The clinical method propounded makes no mention of the careful recording of the patient's precise symptoms, or of the critical importance of careful history taking - perhaps taking these clinical stages for granted - but otherwise it is that which is still, with some elaboration, followed today - *viz.*, (after the history-taking and the physical and mental examination) diagnosis, followed by prognosis, leading to the formulation of appropriate treatment. Dr MakLuire expresses it in the following terms:

> The methodick practising in Physick hath first a knowledge of the disease, next fortelleth the event of it, and last goeth about to cure the same. For that part of Physick which is called Therapeutick, followeth still the diagnostick & prognostick: for whosoever wil use profitable remedies, shuld first remark the things present, next forwarn the future, because it is necessare to understand the present estate of the disease, to that end that remedies proper may be used, then to foresee that which is to come, for the more boldly attempting of the cure, if there bee hope of health: or else to fortell the danger, if one doe feare death ...[3]

The book appears in three clearly distinct parts.

The First Part

The first part of the book is concerned with diagnosis, 'whereby everie disease is knowne'. Twenty canons are formulated, in which one is exhorted to find, successively, the 'place' (meaning the anatomical site), the 'kind' (meaning the type of disease), and the 'cause'.

In finding the 'place', Dr MakLuire says, 'The action offended' - i.e. the function disturbed - 'showes the part'. Dr MakLuire gives, first, here, examples which illustrate the believed correlation between disease of a part of the body and the function of that part which is thereby

---

[3] J. MakLuire, *The Generall Practise of Medecine*, Edinburgh: Wreittoun, 1634, Part 1, Canon I, pages not numbered.

disturbed. He says 'so the hurt of the reason, imagination, and memorie showes the braine to be sicke'. He says 'the losse of sense and motion manifests the nerves or else there origine to be grieved' - thus indicating some knowledge both of the distinction between sensory nerves and motor nerves and probably of the importance of their 'origines' [nerve roots] in the spinal cord. He says 'difficultie of breathing, wills the lights [i.e. lungs] or some of the instruments of respiration to bee interessed'. He says 'the pulse commoved shows the heart to be troubled'. But it is of interest that there is no reference, here (or elsewhere in his writings), to Harvey's work of six years previously announcing his discovery of the circulation of the blood. There follow many other examples of identifying the 'place'.

Having identified the 'part' that is troubled, one must decide whether the trouble is 'by Idiopathie' or 'by Sympathie' - i.e. whether the disturbance is in the relevant organ itself or caused by disturbance elsewhere. One must then go on to identify the 'indisposition' itself. Here, Dr MakLuire distinguishes the 'Symptomes' ('known of the selfe') from the 'signs' ('the actions hurt' - i.e. the functions disturbed). The author's sub-division of sickness into 'similare', 'instrumentall' and 'common', is difficult to follow but it seems to be bound up with the current ideas about the various humors.

Passing on to the 'cause', Dr MakLuire says that this is either 'extern' or 'intern', the latter being either 'antecedent' or 'conjoyned'. The 'cause antecedent' is either '*Plethor* (or plenitud)' or '*Cacochymi*' (its opposite) - all these subdivisions being interpreted in terms of the various humors.

It may be worthwhile quoting what Dr MakLuire has to say about the sickness of melancholia. 'Involutional melancholia' is a term only to be introduced at a later stage in the history of medicine but 'melancholie', he says, abounds in 'the declining age which is between 35 and 45', for it 'receives the bile burnt'. It also abounds, he says, in

'Harvest' (autumn) because autumn, succeeding Summer, 'receives the burnt bile from it'. His clinical description is:

> The life sad occupied in great affaires in contemplation, studying without recreation or exercise of the body, for by it the natural heat diminisheth, and the humors become grosse and thick ... The suppression of melancholie that used to bee by the *aemrodes* [bleeding piles], monthly courses, seages [?ceases], with the scabs or by medecine ... As also by the signes of melancholy, predominant in the body, as are: the colour browne or blackish, of the face and all the body, the skin full of scabs, hardnesse, swelling and paine of the melt [spleen]: The habitud of the body dry and lean, the visage sad and heavy: feare, silence, solitarinesse, urine, imagination, conceits: for the constancie of the spirit comes of an humour melancholick ... The mind slow to wrath, but being incensed, hard to be appeased ... The sleep troubled with horrible dreams as with sightes of evill spirits, tortoures of death, sepulchres, and other things fearful ... The pulse litle, slow, hard ... The appetite depravat sometime disordinat by reason of a sowre mater adhearing to the orifice of the stomacke ... The water clear and whyt, where there is no melancholy mixed, but thick and black where there is some mixed ...[4]

The Second Part

The second part of the book, entitled 'For to foresee the issue of the Disease', is concerned with prognosis, 'whereby the issue is foreshowne'. Thirty canons are formulated, in which one is exhorted to attend, on the one hand, to the 'forces' and 'constitution' of the body; the age of the patient; the season of the year; and the 'forme of life (of the patient)', and on the other hand, to the nature of the disease, the symptoms, and other causal factors.

---

[4] Ibid., Part 1, Canon XVII, pages not numbered.

As for 'constitution', the best, according to Dr MakLuire, is to be 'mediocre' - i.e. neither too fat nor too lean. As for 'age', 'youth' is more favourable than 'old age'. As for the season of the year, 'the Spring is verie wholesome' but 'in Harvest the diseases are very strong and deadly for the most part'. 'The Summer hastens sicknes, but the Winter doth retard them' - and here Dr MakLuire gives plausible, but surely spurious, reasons for his statements, in terms, as usual, of the theory of 'humors'.

The mental attitude of the patient is fully recognised - 'when he beleves the physition and puts in practise his ordinances hee serves him for a second and declares himselfe enemie of the disease ... for it is certaine two is stronger nor one.' Also, 'constancie' or 'satledness (settledness) of the reason' are favourable signs, because it 'bears witnesse of the temperat disposition of the braine', while, on the contrary, 'the alienation and troubling of the reason ... betokens the animal parts to be affected'.

The alternative modes of termination of illness - by 'crise' (crisis) or by 'resolution' - and their significance, are discussed together with a large number of questionable clinical features.

The Third Part

The third part of the book, entitled 'The right methode of curing the disease', is concerned with treatment ('therapia'), 'which poynteth out the methodick, proceeding in the cure'. Forty-nine canons are formulated.

In these canons, one is exhorted, first, to the removal of the cause. Also, it has to be remembered that cure of the malady itself takes precedence over the treatment of symptoms. One precept is to 'cure first the most importunate danger'.

Dr MakLuire draws from the belief 'that all remedies bee contrare in quality to the disease' the doubtful, but not unexpected, conclusion that 'all diseases ingendered of repletion, are cured by evacuation'. He distinguishes three sorts of remedies - 'dyat', 'chirurgie or manuall operation', and 'pharmacie' - all of which are discussed in detail and at some length. In 'chirurgerie', again not unexpectedly, he considers that phlebotomy 'keepes the first rank'. But purgation, also not unexpectedly, is not far behind.

THE
GENERALL
PRACTISE OF
MEDECINE.

Comprehending the moſt remarkable maxims appertaining to the Diagnoſis, whereby everie diſeaſe is knowne, the *Prognoſis,*
Whereby the iſſue is foreſhowne, and
Therapia, which poynteth out the methodick, proceeding in the cure.

Collected out of the moſt famous, both Ancient
and Moderne Wryters, for the uſe of ſuch
as be ignorant of the Greeke and
Latine tongues.

By φιλιατρεύς.

EDINBVRGH,
Printed by *Iohn Wreittoun.* 1634,

Chapter Twelve - Mareon Greir, His Second Wife

The search for the identity of Mareon Greir

The question of the genealogical identity, childhood, and pre-marriage life, of Mareon Greir, Dr John Mak-Luire's second wife, had at first seemed as if it would be impenetrable, even after clarification of the confusing fact that Dr MakLuire had been earlier married to a lady with the very similar name of Mareon Greive. The search for her identity, being long and somewhat complex, is recorded in detail in Appendix D.

The search had had one main hope - to confirm an early intuition. That intuition had been that it would be elucidation of the full identity of Mareon Greir that would be most likely to throw light on the question whether, as previously only conjectured, Dr MakLuire had truly been one of the 'creditable' persons who, according to William Harvey, had furnished him, in 1641, with the early history of the serious injury to the chest wall of the young son of an Irish nobleman, Hugh Montgomery.

It had also been hoped that the search would thus establish, furthermore, as had never, prior to 1981, been even conjectured, that the medically historic visit of the young Hugh to the Court had been while the Court had been in Edinburgh.[1]

Mareon Greir's father a John Greir in Mid Carmonoch

The conclusion of the long search had been that Mareon Greir had been the daughter of a John Greir (younger son of Gilbert Greirson of Castelmaddie) who, in 1627, was to emigrate from his farm of Mid Carmonoch in Kirkcud-brightshire to Ulster for a period of fourteen years, taking

---

[1] J.F. McHarg, 'Dr Johnne MakLuire and the 1630 Attempt to Establish the College', *Proceedings of the Royal College of Physicians of Edinburgh*, Publication No 6, 1982, pp. 44-98.

his little girl, Mareon, with him.[2] That John Greir, later (and after his daughter, in 1634, had married Dr MakLuire and been taken to Edinburgh), had returned, at some date between 1641 and 1643, to Kirkcudbrightshire, to succeed his deceased elder brother as the proprietor of the lands of Castelmaddie and the three Carmonochs - Over, Mid and Nether.

Prior to his temporary emigration to Ulster, this John Greir (because his elder brother, a 'bonnet laird', farming his own land, would appear to have himself farmed Castelmaddie) would appear to have farmed, as his brother's tenant, the other major farm of the estate - Mid Carmonoch. This is a farm, still in existence as 'Carminnows', to which Nether Carmonoch, farmed by Dr MakLuire's father, John MakLuire, had been immediately adjacent (see the map at fig. 3c, Chapter 2).

It seems, from the search, that Mareon Greir would have been born, presumably at Mid Carmonoch, at some date between 1611 and 1618, and that her earliest childhood would have been spent there. When she was taken, by her father, to Ulster, in 1627, she would, according to the search, have been aged between nine and sixteen.

Dr MakLuire's sojourn in Ulster in 1634

How did it happen, in 1634, the year of publishing his third book, *The Generall Practise of Medecine*, that Dr John MakLuire went from Edinburgh over to Ulster, and married Mareon Greir there?

Dr MakLuire's initial intention in withdrawing from Edinburgh in that year would probably have been, while in mourning for his first wife, Mareon Greive, who had died late in the year 1633, to visit his father. But it may also have been to give himself a chance to consider, while

---

[2] Sir P.J. Hamilton-Grierson, 'Notes on Various Families of the Name of Grierson', typescript, transcribed by J.R.H. Greeves, Dumfries County Council Library, 1948, p. 43.

staying with his father in Ulster, the possibility of a second marriage which he may already have had in mind.

Mareon Greir would not have been unknown to Dr MakLuire at that time. Probably, as a lad about to go up to St Andrews University in October 1618, and temporarily staying with his father at the farm of Nether Carmonoch (the 'kindly' tenancy of which had very recently fallen to the latter on the death of Dr MakLuire's grandfather, John MakLuire in Castelmaddie, in 1617), he would have taken notice of the little girl, not older than seven, in the neighbouring farm of Mid Carmonoch. Also, in subsequent years, when visiting his father, as a student, during vacations, and no doubt helping with the farm work, he would have watched her grow, possibly up to the time of her father's emigration to Ulster in 1627, when she would perhaps have reached her teens.

It seems probable that Dr MakLuire's own father, from the farm of Nether Carmonoch, had, for a second time, emigrated to the Ards in Co. Down, in conjunction with his neighbour, John Greir in Mid Carmonoch (Dr MakLuire's future father-in-law), who is known to have emigrated there in 1627, and that the two emigrants, taking up their new tenancies in Co. Down would have thereafter kept in touch.

It would appear to have been some time in 1634, probably with the better weather, after the winter was over, that Dr MakLuire would have taken 'The Old Edinburgh Road' to Portpatrick, crossed to Donaghadee, and then made his way to his father's home. Now, Dr MakLuire's father, John MakLuire, would, with virtual certainty, have been the John MakLuire recorded on the Muster Roll for Ulster as a tenant of the Viscount Claneboye, residing in the parish of Killyleagh.[3] Confidence on this point had been based upon the fact that the John MakLuire recorded there had been the only person of that name on the more than 13,000-strong Muster Roll for Ulster.

---

[3] BM Add MS 4770, Muster Roll for Ulster, c1630.

Sojourning with his father in Killyleagh parish in 1634, only about ten miles from Newtownards, Dr MakLuire would, certainly, from that base, have been in a position to visit with ease the family of John Greir, living at, or somewhere not far from, Newtownards, and to woo the latter's daughter.

His marriage to Mareon Greir, in 1634, in County Down

The precise date of Mareon Greir's marriage to Dr Mak-Luire is not known. However, it must have taken place subsequent to the death of Mareon Greive, the latter's first wife, who was still alive at the time of her father's death in October 1633. And presumably it was not later than October 1634, a date which was nine months prior to the baptism of her first child in July 1635.[4] Most likely, therefore, the marriage would have taken place some time during 1634.

The precise location of the marriage is also unknown. However, the fact that the Edinburgh records show that the marriage had not taken place in Edinburgh, where the baptism of the first child to the marriage was to be registered with the Greyfriars congregation in 1635, had seemed to add confirmation to the assumption, in the absence of evidence to the contrary, that it would have taken place, as would have been in accordance with custom, from the bride's home.

Here, because of the discovery that Mareon Greir's father, John Greir, had emigrated temporarily from Kirkcudbrightshire to Ulster from about 1627 until a date between 1641 and 1643, it had at least seemed clear that, after being taken there by her father, her home, in 1634, would have been in Ulster. More particularly, County Down would have been the most likely destination in Ulster for an emigrant from Kirkcudbrightshire. If so, Mareon Greir's father would have been (according to the Muster Roll for

---

[4] SRO OPR 685 1/4, Edinburgh (Greyfriars) Register of Baptisms, 30 July 1635.

Ulster of c1630 which had been drawn up some three years after her father had emigrated) either the John Greir recorded in that Roll as mustering with the Viscount Claneboye at Bangor or, rather more probably, the John Greir recorded as mustering with the Viscount Montgomery at Newtownards - unless, indeed, as is not inconceivable, his name was listed with both Viscounts.[5]

It would seem, therefore, that Dr MakLuire's marriage to Mareon Greir, in 1634, would have been from her home at, or somewhere not far from, Newtownards.

Their life together in Edinburgh

Dr MakLuire's marriage would have been followed by the couple returning to Edinburgh. Their return would perhaps have been prior to 21 August 1634, because, on that date, Dr MakLuire is recorded as having been assigned (in Edinburgh) the lands of Froskan and Croattes, in Banffshire - probably as a way of settling a debt owed to him by a patient.[6] The appearance of his name on the Extent Roll of 1635 shows that it was to his existing home in Galloway's Close that Dr MakLuire took his bride.

In that year, the couple had seen the baptism of their first child, John.[7] Now, despite the fact that, in the child's baptismal entry, the mother's name was originally inscribed as 'Mareon Grieve', this clearly had been a writer's understandable mistake for 'Mareon Greir'. That it was a mistake is clear chiefly because, as has been noted above, the main witness had been Sir Robert Greir of Lag, but also because an obvious attempt has been made to correct the mistake to 'Grier' (see fig).

The eleven years, from 1635 to 1646, would have seen the baptisms of their further eight children, all in the Greyfriars congregation, in Edinburgh, except for that of their

---

[5] See BM Add MS 4770, Muster Roll for Ulster, c1630.

[6] SRO RS1/41, Assignation, Ogilvie to McCluire.

[7] SRO OPR 685 1/4, Edinburgh (Greyfriars) Register of Baptisms, 30 July 1635.

seventh child, Hugh, in 1644.[8] Hugh was baptised at Mid
Calder (at the time when the plague was anticipated in
Edinburgh), by their young friend (from Comber, in the
Ards), Master Hugh Kennedy, minister there, who named
the child after himself, presumably at the parents' request.
The same Master Hugh Kennedy was also chosen as a
witness to the baptism of their eighth child, in Edinburgh.[9]
In 1636, Dr MakLuire had himself been a witness to the
baptism of a son, 'John', to Andrew Greir, his wife's
brother.[10]

The year 1641 saw, in August, the visit of the King and
Court to Scotland. In particular, November 1641, as will
be argued below, also saw the arrival in Edinburgh,
summoned hastily from abroad, of the young Hugh Montgomery, and the medically historic examination of the
remarkable cavity in his chest wall by the great William
Harvey after consultation with Dr MakLuire (as will also
be argued) about the early history of the case.

Now, John, the first son of Dr MakLuire and his wife
Mareon Greir, although he seems certainly to have survived to the age of nine, must surely have died before the age
of ten because, in 1645, a second son was baptised with the
name 'John'.[11] Presumably, the first John, dying in 1645,
had been a victim of the plague raging in Edinburgh that
year. But, the second son named 'John', born in that fateful
year, would seem also to have died - in infancy - because
yet a third son was baptised with the name 'John' in 1646.
Thus, presumably, the second John had also been a plague
victim. It may well have been the deaths of these two sons,
therefore, and possibly of still others of his children, from
plague, that provided a motive for their father to devote his

[8] SRO OPR 694/1, Mid Calder Register of Baptisms, 12 May 1644.

[9] SRO OPR 685 1/4, Edinburgh (Greyfriars) Register of Baptisms, 30 July 1635.

[10] See BM Add MS 4770, Muster Roll for Ulster, c1630 and SRO OPR 685 1/4, 25 February 1636.

[11] SRO OPR 685 1/5, 9 May 1645.

efforts to becoming the expert on the plague that he was later acknowledged to be.

The duration of their residence in Galloway's Close

Dr MakLuire, who continued as acting landlord of the house left by the deceased George Greive, would have had, living with him, and in his care, the young Alexander Greive, son and lawful heir to the latter. Alexander Greive would have been only seventeen when his father had died in 1633 and only a little older when his older half-sister, Mareon Greive, Dr MakLuire's first wife, died. And, two years after Dr MakLuire's return with his second wife, Alexander Greive himself had died, in 1636, while still under-age - *viz.*, at the age of twenty - leaving his younger sister, Alison as his and his father's next heir and successor.[12] Alison Greive herself would not have achieved her majority until 1643. Not until then, therefore, would she have been free to take on her lawful role as landlord of the house she had inherited. If so, Dr MakLuire would probably have continued in the house, as acting landlord, at least until 1643.

It seems probable, moreover, that, even after Alison Greive's coming-of-age, Dr MakLuire, with his wife, Mareon Greir, would have continued, as Alison Greive's tenant, for the rest of his life. This would have been except for the believed sojourn (at least of his pregnant wife) in Mid Calder in 1644 at the time when the plague, spreading up from England, was threatening to arrive in Edinburgh.

---

[12] SRO C22/15, Retour, Alison Greive, p. 60.

Figure

The baptismal records of the first two of Dr MakLuire's nine children.

30 July 1635

Mr Johnne Mackluir. Doctor in Physick. Marione Grieve, a.s.n.
Johnne. witn. Sir Robert Greir of Lag. Mr Johnne Scharp.
Hew Ros wreater. and William Cochren Marchant

4 July 1638

Mr Johnne Macklure Doctor in Physick. Marione Greir. a.d. named
Helene. witn. James and Wm Cochrens. Mr Johnne Kinneir. Mr
Alexander Kinneir

Note. Only in the first entry is the mother's surname given as 'Grieve'
– and even so with an ink stroke through the letters 've'. In the second
entry (as in all the rest) the mother's surname is given as 'Greir'.

Chapter Thirteen - His Religion, and the Covenant of 1638

Dr MakLuire's religious persuasion

Dr MakLuire's religious persuasion is not clearly apparent from his writings. Moreover, he seems to have had personal contacts with individuals from quite diverse religious and ecclesiastical backgrounds. Like his near contemporary, the physician-philosopher Sir Thomas Browne, Dr MakLuire would at least appear to have been untarnished by what the latter called 'the generall scandall of my profession'.[1] This had been the atheism so understandably arising as 'the new mechanical philosophy', and the mood of sceptical enquiry, were beginning to take hold. It had been manifest, in particular, in medicine, and was epitomised by the saying '*ubi tres medici, [ibi] duo athei*' - 'wherever [there are] three doctors, [therever there are] two atheists'.

Dr MakLuire's writings show the insertion, here and there, of brief prayers, and other indications of a personal piety. One aspect of his more philosophico-theological position is expressed in his dedication of *The Buckler* - which is to the Lords of the Privy Council. There, after commenting how the philosophers had called man 'Microcosme, or little world, being (as Plutarch sayeth) the abridgement of the whole globe', he continues:

> For it is certain that GOD in the creation made all things before man, and when hee was going about to make him, hee made an reflexion of his divinitie, and tooke a view of all his workes, that he might print in this his last worke the quintessence of all other, with the beams of his own image:[2]

---

[1] Sir T. Browne, *Religio Medici and Other Works*, ed. L.C. Martin, Oxford, p. 3.

[2] J. MakLuire, *The Buckler of Bodilie Health*, Edinburgh: Wreittoun, 1630, p. i.

Dr MakLuire's antagonism to contemporary Roman Catholicism is clear from his remarks, already quoted, about 'poore' scholars having to flee to Douai (the Counter-Reformation centre for the training of missionary priests to convert Britain) if they wished to obtain the level of education they sought. But his antagonism to Puritanism (or was it Calvinism?) seems no less clear.

That antagonism is seen from his complaint, in 1630, about a 'Mr Perkins', apparently a minister, whom he accuses of engaging, unqualified, in medical practice.[3] As noted above, it would appear that this 'Mr Perkins' may have been the William Perkins, presumably a Puritan, who was said to have been the son of the distinguished Cambridge, Calvinist, Divine of that name. That young William Perkins had not yet, in 1630, graduated BA (at Cambridge), and had not, therefore, been entitled even to the appellation 'Mr'. It is ironic, perhaps, that at a later date he did actually graduate MD at Leyden![4]

Finally, it had seemed, in view of the regard in which Dr MakLuire had been held by Patrick Sandys (who had had to give up his charge of Greyfriars church because of his adherence to the 'Five Articles of Perth'; and of his close association with the Montgomery family - in particular with Sir James Montgomery, courtier to both Charles I and Charles II - that he probably shared their royalist loyalty, their Episcopalian persuasion, and their coolness towards the Covenant.

Dr MakLuire's attitude to the Covenant of 1638

The Covenant of 1638 was of such importance in the history of Scotland that it is inevitable that the question, in particular, of Dr MakLuire's attitude to it, should have arisen.

It had seemed probable, if he was indeed of royalist and Episcopalian persuasion, that Dr MakLuire would have

---

[3] Ibid., p. viii.

[4] R.W. Innes Smith, *English Speaking Students of Medicine at the University of Leyden*, Edinburgh, 1932, p. 180.

hesitated about signing the Covenant. But it had also seemed, from the fact that the baptism of his first child, on 3 July 1635, and of his second child, on 4 July 1638, had been in the Greyfriars congregation, that he would have been a member of that congregation at the very time of the historic signing, there, between those two dates, of the original Covenant. This had taken place on the three successive Sundays of 13, 20 and 27 March, 1638. The manuscript copy of the Covenant which is preserved in the City of Edinburgh Museum is believed to be that which was signed on that occasion. It had consequently been of interest to find that Dr MakLuire's signature is not amongst the myriad of names inscribed on that historic document.

Several other, extant, copies of the 1638 Covenant were searched for the signature of Dr MakLuire - *viz.*, the one at the High Kirk of St Giles;[5] the four at the National Library of Scotland;[6] the one at the British Museum, 'apparently subscribed at Edinburgh';[7] the one at Blair Castle (which bears the signature of Dr G. Sibbald); the two at the Edinburgh University Main Library;[8] and the four at its Library at New College.[9]

The Hewison (29)[1] copy seen at New College, signed 'in the North Kirk of Leith', on 7th and 15th April, 1638, was of some interest because, on it, the signature of a 'Johne MakLuire' (see fig) was found. This was, indeed, the only 'John MakLuire' signature which was found. It had been concluded, however, that this signature is not that of Dr John MakLuire because, first, Dr MakLuire was known to be living in Edinburgh at that time, as a member of the

---

[5] 1638 Covenant, at the High Kirk of St Giles.

[6] NLS, Adv. MSS 20.6.14, 20.6.15, 20.6.19, 1638 Covenants and the Minnigaff parish Covenant on permanent loan.

[7] BM, Add. MS 4851, 1638 Covenant.

[8] Hewison 20, 1638 Covenant, and one other of uncertain origin, University of Edinburgh, Main Library.

[9] Hewison 28, 29, 30, 31, 1638 Covenants, University of Edinburgh, New College Library.

Greyfriars congregation, and because, second, he would have been expected to have included in his signature, with his name, either the title 'Mr' or the title 'Dr'. However, there is an unknown number of extant copies of the Covenant, on one of which his signature may yet be found.[10] Even so, it had been felt that absence from the Greyfriars signing may have been based upon royalist and Episcopalian sympathies and, in particular, upon his personal loyalty to his courtier friend, Sir James Montgomery.

---

[10] J. K. Hewison, *The Covenanters*, vol. I, Glasgow, p. 487.

Figure

Covenant signature of a 'John MakLuire' – not Dr MakLuire.

Ref: Single signature from (Manuscript) 1638 Covenant, Hewison 29.

Reproduced by kind permission of New College Library, University of Edinburgh.

Chapter Fourteen - His Prior Acquaintance with the Case of Hugh Montgomery

The findings of the fore-going search (Chapter 12) for the precise identity of Dr MakLuire's second wife, Mareon Greir, had thrown light on highly relevant connections that both Dr MakLuire and his spouse had had with County Down - in particular on the former's fairly brief sojourn there, in 1634, during the course of which his marriage took place.

His probable re-encounter with Hugh Montgomery in 1634

The possibility has already been touched upon that Dr MakLuire may have had a prior familiarity with the astounding injury sustained by the young Hugh Montgomery, in or before 1630, and have had, perhaps, even clinical involvement in the prescription of the small protective metal plate. It has been suggested that he may have given a cryptic indication of this in his use of the word 'buckler', when dedicating *The Buckler of Bodilie Health* to his student friend, Sir James Montgomery, second son of the 1st Viscount Montgomery, and uncle to the young Hugh.

It had seemed probable, also, chiefly because of the personal friendship which he continued to enjoy with Sir James Montgomery that Dr MakLuire, during his sojourn in Ulster in 1634 (and probably staying with his father in the parish of Killyleagh, prior to his marriage to Mareon Greir), would have availed himself of the proximity of Killyleagh to the home of the young Hugh at Mount Alexander House, Comber, and have visited (or re-visited) the family. Comber is less than five miles from the boundary of Killyleagh parish (see Chapter 8).

Now, the young Hugh Montgomery would have been aged eleven or twelve at the time. Also, it is just possible, although rather improbable (if the injury had not occurred as early as 1630), that Dr MakLuire's sojourn would have coincided with the injury itself, which is recorded as having occurred 'while he was a child' (*'cum adhuc puer esset'*). If so, he would have heard the widespread local talk about it, as a possible miracle.

It is more probable, however, that the sojourn would have coincided with a later phase in the management of the medically unique condition affecting the boy. Also, Dr MakLuire's probable encounter, or re-encounter, with the case, in that year, because of his medical status, would presumably have taken a professional form, perhaps as a consultation with Dr Patrick Maxwell, the family physician.

Mareon Greir's longer-term acquaintance with the case

Mareon Greir would appear to have had a longer-term acquaintance with the case. Her arrival in childhood, in 1627, with her father, John Greir, to the latter's new tenancy (probably with the Viscount Montgomery), would have been at a time when the young Hugh Montgomery would have been aged only three or four. Thus, unless the original injury had been before the age of three or four, or later than the age of eleven or twelve (his age in 1634 when Mareon Greir returned to Scotland with her husband) - both of which had seemed unlikely - it had appeared that Mareon Greir would certainly have been living in Ulster, and probably not far from Comber, at the very time of the boy's original injury.

Now, while it is not known precisely when, in childhood, the young Hugh had sustained the original serious chest injury, it is known, from *The Montgomery Manuscripts*, that he was already 'a boy at school' when the resultant abscess was 'pierced' by Dr Patrick Maxwell.[1] Mareon Greir would therefore have also been living near at hand at that time and at the time of all subsequent treatment and management procedures - in particular at the time of the prescription of the small protective metal plate.

Such believed geographical closeness of Mareon Greir to the boy may have been of less importance than closeness

---

[1] W. Montgomery, *The Montgomery Manuscripts 1603-1706*, ed. Revd. G. Hill. Belfast: Cleeland, 1869, p. 153.

of social contact with the Montgomery family of which her father was a tenant. Also, here, there had been a conjectural possibility that Mareon Greir had even been related to Dr Patrick Maxwell, through her paternal grandmother, Agnes Maxwell, daughter of John Maxwell of Butill Maynes, Kirkcudbrightshire.[2]

The information about the young Hugh's condition which Mareon Greir herself would have acquired, and have been able to share with Dr MakLuire, would have supplemented his own - if it was not already familiar to him,

Master Hugh Kennedy's undoubted familiarity with the case

A further factor was of great relevance. This was the known friendship, in Edinburgh, in the 1640s, of Dr Mak-Luire and his spouse Mareon Greir, with Master Hugh Kennedy, the young minister at Mid Calder. This friendship, certainly of Mareon Greir, would seem to have dated from an acquaintance with him, in County Down, when he had been a boy, living at Comber.

Now, coming, like the young Hugh Montgomery, from Comber (a fact not mentioned in the *Fasti* of the Church of Scotland, but discovered from the manuscript of a Deed), the young Hugh Kennedy, whose father, a Thomas Kennedy, had been servitor to the 1st Viscount Montgomery, had been a co-eval of the young Hugh Montgomery.[3] Moreover, he had been a fellow-student with him at Glas-

---

[2] Sir P.J. Hamilton-Grierson, 'Notes on Various Families of the Name of Grierson', typescript transcribed by J.R.H. Greeves, Dumfries County Council Library, 1948, p. 41.

[3] See H. Scott, *Fasti Ecclesiae Scoticanae*, Edinburgh, 1915, vol. I, *Synod of Lothian & Tweeddale*, p. 177; SRO RD3/12; 25, Discharge, Kenidie to Greir, Dundas & Uthers; Hamilton-Grierson, 'Notes on Various Families of the Name of Grierson', p. 131; and T. 3688/C , Will of Hugh Montgomery, 1st Viscount of the Ards, 10th May, 1636 in 'De Lacherois Papers: Family History, Etc', in the possession of Mrs G. Stone, The Manor House, Donaghadee, p. 154.

gow University.[4] Furthermore, the two had graduated together there in 1641.[5] It had seemed, in short, that Hugh Kennedy, as has been supposed of Dr MakLuire before him, had been a 'lad o' pairts' chosen by the Montgomerys to be a student-companion - in this instance to the young Hugh Montgomery, son of the 2nd Viscount-to-be.

Undoubtedly, therefore, Master Hugh Kennedy would have been thoroughly knowledgeable about the young Hugh's injury and, in particular, about the protective plate which he wore. It could also be concluded, from these facts, that Mareon Greir herself would have been little less closely acquainted with the young Hugh Montgomery since his childhood in Comber, than she would have been with the young Hugh Kennedy. She would herself certainly have shared Hugh Kennedy's knowledge about the young Hugh Montgomery's injury, about its early treatment, and about its later management.

This would have been knowledge which, in the unlikely event that Dr MakLuire was not himself thoroughly acquainted with it already, Mareon Greir would also have shared with him in 1634 at the time of their marriage.

Positive evidence thus established

In this way, it had appeared, from the full enquiry into the identity of Mareon Greir, that positive evidence had indeed been established in support of what had previously been conjectural. This was that Dr MakLuire would have had prior knowledge about the early history of the case of the young Hugh Montgomery and thus have been equipped to be one of the 'creditable' persons (in the plural) who were available in Edinburgh, in November, 1641, and with whom Harvey says that he consulted about the injury. The others could have been his wife, Mareon Greir, and Dr Patrick Maxwell - who is certainly recorded as having

---

[4] C. Innes, ed., *Munimenta alme Universitatis Glasguensis 1450-1727*, 4 vols., Glasgow: Maitland Club, 1854, III, p. 24.

[5] Ibid.

been in attendance upon the King when the Court, later, had moved to Oxford.[6]

---

[6] Hamilton-Grierson, 'Notes on Various Families of the Name of Grierson', p. 140.

Chapter Fifteen - Meeting William Harvey in Edinburgh

It had been conjectured, in 1981, that Dr MakLuire, as a prominent Edinburgh physician, would at least have formally met with the great William Harvey (plate 6) during one or both of the latter's two visits to Edinburgh with the King - in 1633 and 1641 respectively.[1]

The first royal visit to Edinburgh, in 1633

In 1633, Dr MakLuire and his first wife, Mareon Greive, would probably have witnessed the impressive procession as Charles I entered Edinburgh, in great state, on 15th June of that year, for his Scottish coronation. They may well have viewed the procession, either from the entrance to the Galloway's Close where they were living, or from the vantage point of the attic which is known to have been theirs. They would have watched the splendour as it passed, against the background of the triumphal arch (adorned with representations of all the Scottish monarchs, from Fergus to Charles himself), which had been erected at the west end of the Tolbooth, mid-way between St Giles Church (not yet a Cathedral) and Galloway's Close.[2]

Now, William Harvey was in attendance upon the King, on that visit to Edinburgh, and it had therefore seemed justifiable to conjecture that Dr MakLuire, as one of the established physicians of Edinburgh, would have been formally introduced to Harvey while he was in Edinburgh - although, understandably, there is no documentation to support that probability.

---

[1] J.F. McHarg, 'Dr Johnne MakLuire and the 1630 Attempt to Establish the College', *Proceedings of the Royal College of Physicians of Edinburgh Tercentenary Congress 1981*, ed. R. Passmore, Royal College of Physicians Publications, No 6, 1982.

[2] Anonymous, *The History of Scotland from the Earliest Period*, 11 vols., Glasgow, Blackie & Son, undated, VI, p. 403.

The second royal visit, in 1641

There had, however, in 1981, been a series of bolder conjectures. The first of these had been that it had been the sojourn of the King and Court in Edinburgh in 1641 that had seen the medically celebrated occasion of the visit paid to it by the young Hugh Montgomery, eldest son and heir of Hugh, 2nd Viscount Montgomery of the Ards. This was the visit during which the cavity in the chest wall of the young man, dating from a childhood injury, and exposing his beating heart both to view and to touch, had been examined by Harvey and demonstrated to the King in person. The second conjecture had been that Dr MakLuire, resident in Edinburgh at the time, already had prior familiarity with the young Hugh's case. The third conjecture, which depended upon the establishment of the second, had been that Dr MakLuire had been one of the 'creditable persons' with whom Harvey says that he consulted about the early history of the case.

Prior to 1981, there seems not to have been any idea, even provisional, that the young Hugh's visit to the Court might have been when the Court had been in Edinburgh. It had been pointed out, indeed, in 1981, that it had been other venues which had usually been assumed. It had been felt, therefore, that the very possibility of the examination of the young Hugh by the great William Harvey having been in Edinburgh (in November, 1641), and in consultation with Dr MakLuire, would have been of particular interest for the history of medicine in Scotland, and have called for further investigation.

William Harvey's revolutionary discoveries

William Harvey was Britain's great Renaissance man. He played a leading part in the biological advances in Europe during the first half of the 1600s. He was a great, perhaps the greatest, of Britain's early experimental scientists. His most important work, the *Exercitatio Anatomica De Motu Cordis et Sanguinis in Animalibus*, had already been published, in 1628, five years before his 1633 visit to Edinburgh. His next most important work, the *De Gener-*

atione Animalium, at the time of his 1641 visit, was yet to be written.

Harvey had been born in Folkstone in 1578. He had attended the King's School in Canterbury and Caius College Cambridge and had spent four years at Padua, where he obtained his doctorate in medicine in 1602. He had been taught, there, by the anatomist Fabricius, famous for his studies of the veins and of their valves - the full significance of which, for the circulation of the blood, was left to Harvey, later, to prove.

After returning to London, Harvey engaged in medical practice and became a Fellow of the Royal College of Physicians, and physician to St. Bartholomew's Hospital. He was appointed Lumleian Lecturer in Anatomy and Surgery. He became Physician Extraordinary to James VI and I and, when Charles I succeeded the latter, he was made Physician in Ordinary.

Harvey had gradually become convinced that the blood circulates, rather than that it ebbs and flows - as previously believed. It had not been until 1628, however, that he had published the experimental proof of his discovery in the *De Motu Cordis*. This discovery was regarded by many as fanciful and raised doubts about his reliability as a sober clinician, with the result that his practice declined.

It had been five years after the publication of this radical discovery that Harvey, in 1633, had accompanied Charles to Edinburgh for the latter's Scottish coronation. During that first visit to Edinburgh Harvey had been granted permission to absent himself from the Court in order to visit the Bass Rock, off the coast near to North Berwick, in order to study the vast numbers of gannets nesting there.

Harvey, at the time of his second visit to Edinburgh, in 1641, had already been collecting the material for his second book the *De Generatione Animalium*. This would eventually incorporate an account of his historic examination of the exposed heart of the young Hugh Montgomery on the occasion on which the latter had visited the Court (wherever the Court may have been located at the time). What was done, on that historic occasion, was described explicitly, by Harvey, as an experiment, as 'this wonderful experiment'. The result of the 'experiment' was not a development from, and had no bearing upon, the earlier discovery that the blood, as a result of the action of the heart, circulates. Its counter-intuitive result was totally otherwise - that the substance of the heart was insensitive.

That occasion, on which the young Hugh Montgomery had paid a visit to the Court of Charles I, and had had his living heart studied by William Harvey, and demonstrated to King Charles I, has become famous in the history of medicine. It has even formed the basis for an acclaimed historical novel - but displaced into the reign of Charles II - Rose Tremain's *Restoration*.[3]

'This wonderful experiment'

There are two accounts extant of the 'wonderful experiment'. The earlier of the two is that by Harvey himself in his *De Generatione Animalium*, published in 1651. The account is given in that chapter in the book which deals with the question of the insensitivity of the blood, a question more real to those of Harvey's day than to us. Harvey (in Whitteridge's translation) writes as follows:

A most noble youth, eldest son of his excellency the Viscount Montgomery of Ireland, when he was still a child had a great mishap from an unexpected fall, causing a fracture of the ribs on his left side. The abscess having been brought to a suppuration, a great quantity of putrid matter flowed out and sanies oozed for a long time from the very wide cavity, as he himself told me and other creditable persons who were eye-witnesses. When this young man was about eighteen or nineteen, he travelled through France and Italy and then came to London. All this while he had a very large gap open in his chest, so that his lungs (as it was believed) could be seen and touched through it. When this was told to his serene

---

[3] R. Tremain, *Restoration*, London, 1989.

highness King Charles as a marvel, he immediately sent me to the young man to find out the truth of the matter. What happened? When I first came near him and saw a lively youth with a pleasing countenance and estimable bearing, I thought that I had been told something far from the truth. But having saluted him duly, as the custom is, and explained the cause of my coming to him on the King's command, he immediately showed me everything and laid bare part of his left side, taking off the small plate which he wore to protect it from any blow or injury from without. I immediately saw a vast hole in his chest into which I could easily put my first three fingers and my thumb. At the same time I saw just inside the opening, some fleshy, projecting part which was driven backwards and forwards with an alternating movement, and I touched it very cautiously with my hand. I was astounded at the extraordinariness of the thing and I scrutinized everything again and again, and when I had investigated everything carefully enough, it was evident that the old, vast ulcer, beyond the help of any skilled physician, had healed as by a miracle, and was covered over on the inside with a membrane and guarded all round the edges with hard skin. But the fleshy part, which at first sight I believed to be proud flesh and everyone else thought was a part of the lung, I clearly saw from its pulsation and separate or rhythmical movements (for I put both my hands at the same time one on his wrist and the other on his heart), and by comparing this with his breathing, that it was not any lobe of the lung but the cone of the heart, which was covered on the outside by some excrescent spongy flesh as with a protective screen (a thing which frequently happens in foul ulcers). This fleshy accretion the young man's servant cleaned daily from the muck that collected around it, by injections of warm water, and covered it up with the plate. When this was done, his master was fit and ready for any exercise or journey, and enjoyed his life happily and safely.[4]

The later of the two accounts (which is to be found *in The Montgomery Manuscripts*) claims to have the authority of the young Hugh Montgomery himself.[5] This account represents what William Montgomery of Rosemount, Hugh Montgomery's much younger cousin, understood himself to have been told, in 1651, by Hugh Montgomery, no longer so young, and in exile in Leyden. William Montgomery, a student at Leyden at the time, had felt honoured and delighted to have been visited there by his older cousin, Hugh, by then the 3rd Viscount, whom he idolised.[6] These recollections of his cousin's reminiscences on that occasion had not been set down by William Montgomery until between 1696 and 1706 - some sixty years after the event itself. Strangely, Sir Geoffrey Keynes, in his definitive *Life of Harvey*, does not even mention this account.[7] Neither does Whitteridge, despite the fact that, in the introduction to her translation of the *De Generatione Animalium*, she quotes a reported credible, rueful, remark of the King to the young Hugh on the occasion, a remark which in fact is only to be found in this later account 'Sir I wish I could perceive the thoughts of some of my nobilities' hearts as I have seen your heart'.[8]

The location of the Court at the time

What has never been clear from the two accounts of this famous clinical study of the living heart has been where the Court had been located at the time. The two accounts put forward two mutually incompatible venues.

---

[4] W. Harvey, *Disputations Touching the Generation of Animals,* trans. and ed. by G. Whitteridge, London, 1981, p. 249.

[5] W. Montgomery, *The Montgomery Manuscripts 1603-1706*, ed. Revd. G. Hill, Belfast: Cleeland, 1869, p. 151.

[6] Ibid., p. 251.

[7] G. Keynes, *The Life of William Harvey*, Oxford, 1966.

[8] Montgomery, *The Montgomery Manuscripts 1603-1706*, p. 152.

The first of the accounts, by Harvey himself, certainly seems to imply that the Court had been in London - although it does not explicitly say so. Harvey's introductory words to his account are as follows 'When this young man was about eighteen or nineteen, he travelled through France and Italy and then came to London'.[9] This is, no doubt, as a statement, true but, it may be noted, while Harvey does certainly seem to imply London as the location of the Court at the time, he does not explicitly say so.

Moreover, while Harvey is known to have been in the habit of making copious and precise notes of all his scientific observations, it is not certain that his 1641 notes about this unique study were not amongst the notes which, to his intense chagrin, were destroyed when his lodgings in Whitehall were vandalised by the parliamentarians at the start of the Civil War in the following year, 1642. Consequently, it is possible that his contemporaneous record of the 'wonderful experiment' had to be reconstituted from memory. Certainly, the record was not published until March 1651, almost ten years after the event itself. Whether or not his original notes were vandalised, what would have been, for Harvey, the unimportant detail of the location of the Court at the time, may well have been only hazily remembered, and as ambiguously recorded as seems, for whatever reason, to have been the case.

The second of the accounts asserts, flatly, that the Court had been at Oxford at the time. This is the account, recorded between 1696 and 1706, by William Montgomery, the young Hugh's still younger, hero-worshipping, cousin, but in his old age.[10] It is based upon his recollection of what Hugh Montgomery, no longer so young, himself had recounted to him while in exile in Holland in 1651.

It would seem understandable, from the two accounts, why it has been widely assumed, tacitly, that the Court had

---

[9] Harvey, *Disputations Touching the Generation of Animals,* p. 250.

[10] Montgomery, *The Montgomery Manuscripts 1603-1706,* p. 251.

been either in London (Whitehall), or at Oxford, at the time. In 1981, however, Gwenneth Whitteridge (ignoring altogether the claim of Oxford) argued cogently for Hampton Court being more probable than London while McHarg, in the same year, tentatively raised, for the first time, the possibility of Edinburgh.[11]

The young Hugh Montgomery's return home from abroad

Both accounts, although contradictory as to the location of the Court at the time, are in agreement that the medically historic visit of Hugh Montgomery to the Court had been in the course of the latter's journey, from a curtailed Grand Tour of France and Italy, to his father's home. That, since the latter had succeeded to the viscountcy, had been no longer at Mount Alexander House, Comber, but at Newtown House, Newtownards. It is from the 'Oxford' account that we learn, also, that it had been because of the 'horrid' Irish Rebellion, which broke out on 23 October 1641, that he had been urgently summoned home, by his father.[12]

Now, for the medically historic encounter with Harvey to have taken place when the Court was at Oxford (as the second account avers) it would have had to have taken place later than 29 October 1642, the date on which Charles and the Court first arrived at Oxford.[13] This would have been more than a year after the Irish Rebellion, which had been the occasion for him being recalled with such urgency. Thus, firstly, it is simply not credible that the recall to the young Hugh, and his hasty return, would have taken more than a year and, secondly, the young Hugh is clearly recorded, in the very same 'Oxford' account, as having been already in Ireland, fighting with distinction against the rebels, for months before his

---

[11] Harvey, *Disputations Touching the Generation of Animals,* pp. xxiii and 55.

[12] Montgomery, *The Montgomery Manuscripts 1603-1706*, p. 151.

[13] P. Gregg, *King Charles I*, London, 1981, p. 369.

father's death - which was on 15 November 1642.[14] It cannot be, therefore, that the Court was in Oxford at the time of the young Hugh's medically famous visit. Even so, there are reasons to suppose that a second visit to the Court, a year later, when it was in Oxford is quite probable - with William Montgomery causing the confusion by condensing into one, in his own mind, accounts which he had heard, at Leyden, of two visits of his cousin to the Court.

Admittedly, the chronology of the young Hugh Montgomery's recall and hasty journey home in October/November 1641 is not known with precision. However, the Glasgow University records show that he had graduated Master of Arts there in 1641, and that Glasgow graduations, in those days, had been between March and July.[15] The record of his graduation is not 'in absentia' and presumably, therefore, it would have been after being personally present at his graduation that he would have set out on the Grand Tour, in the Spring or Summer of 1641.

Also, the summons home would surely have been sent out immediately upon the sudden outbreak of the Irish Rebellion on 23 October of that year. How long it would have taken to reach him is not known. It may be relevant to note, however, that news of the Irish Rebellion had reached Edinburgh in four or five days, and also that a three-day postal service, by horseback, between London and Edinburgh had been established in 1635.[16] In which case, the summons from Newtownards may have been deliberately sent first to Edinburgh so that it might catch this quick service south and arrive there in little more than a week. Its onward transmission in Europe is more uncertain. It is unknown whether the young Hugh was still in Italy at the time or, perhaps, in France, already on his

---

[14] Montgomery, *The Montgomery Manuscripts 1603-1706*, p. 153.

[15] C. Innes, ed., *Munimenta Universitatis Glasguensis 1450-1727*, Glasgow: Maitland Club, 1854, III, p. 24.

[16] See D. Stevenson, *Scottish Covenanters and Irish Confederates*, Belfast, 1981, p. 43 and Montgomery, *The Montgomery Manuscripts 1603-1706*, p. 16.

way home. Consequently, it is not known how long it would have taken the summons to reach him. At least it may be presumed that his response would have been immediate and his return in haste.

The intended continuation of the young Hugh's journey home to Newtownards, after coming, indeed, to London (as Harvey's account specifies), would surely not have been westward, to the long crossing of the Irish Sea, and to a subsequent lengthy journey northward, to County Down, through an Ireland already in rebellion. It would, surely, as would have been usual, have been northward, 'through England' (to use, again, the possibly significant words used by Harvey), breaking off at Scotch Corner, making for the Solway route to Scotland, and for Portpatrick. Portpatrick was in fact known, at that time, as 'Port Montgomery', after the young Hugh's grandfather, the 1st Viscount, who had built a great church there for travellers to and from Ireland.[17] The Portpatrick to Donaghadee crossing was not only the shortest sea-crossing to Ireland but, for the young Hugh, would have been both the safest, at that time of rebellion, and the most convenient, route by bringing him to within only eight miles of his father's home at Newtownards.

The successive locations of the Court at the time

The question, where the Court would most probably have been located (from the outbreak of the Irish Rebellion on 23 October 1641, onwards) that the journey home of the young Hugh Montgomery would have come near enough to it to make his visit to it possible, has hitherto not been systematically examined. Nevertheless, the chronology of the movements of the Court, unlike that of the movements of the young Hugh, is precisely documented.

Thus, it is known in particular that at the time of the Irish Rebellion on 23 October 1641, the Court (which had been

---

[17] Montgomery, *The Montgomery Manuscripts 1603-1706*, p. 124.

in Scotland since 14 August) was in Edinburgh.[18] It is known also, that it was to continue there until its departure for London on the 18 November.[19] The departure date, thus, is not, as erroneously (and, in the present context, misleadingly) stated, by Keynes, as early as the 8 November.[20] After a leisurely journey through England it had arrived at Theobalds on 24 November for the King's reception at the Guildhall on 25 November, after which the King had stayed over night at Whitehall.[21] On the following day, 26 November, he had moved immediately to Hampton Court.[22] The King had remained at Hampton Court, except for two day-visits to London, until responding to an invitation by London, on 9 December, to return to the city for Christmas. Back in London, there had followed the hectic weeks of confrontation with Parliament, after which the King had fled from the City, on 10 January 1642, to Hampton Court - but for only a single night, before going to the greater safety of Windsor Castle.[23]

Now, Harvey's biographer, Sir Geoffrey Keynes, is certainly mistaken in saying that the visit to the Court by the young Hugh Montgomery took place 'probably about 1640' - if only because the visit was, clearly, subsequent to the outbreak of the Irish Rebellion in October 1641.[24] Whitteridge, on the other hand, is, with equal certainty, correct in concluding that the visit would most likely have been during November 1641.[25] Also, the several success-

---

[18] C. Carlton, *Charles I. The Personal Monarch*, London, 1983, p. 228.

[19] M. Napier, *Montrose and the Covenanters*, London, 1838, II, p. 167.

[20] Keynes, *The Life of William Harvey*, p. 285.

[21] Gregg, *King Charles I*, p. 339.

[22] *Calendar of State Papers Domestic 1641-1643*, London: Public Records Office, 1866, p. 188.

[23] Ibid., p. 252.

[24] Keynes, *The Life of William Harvey*, p. 155.

[25] Harvey, *Disputations Touching the Generation of Animals*, p. xxiii.

ive possible locations of the Court, at the time when the journey home of the young Hugh Montgomery would have brought him nearest to it, can be listed.

If the visit was, as Whitteridge concluded, during November 1641, these successive locations are, in chronological order: 1) in Edinburgh, prior to 19 November 1641; 2) somewhere in England, between 19 November and 25 November, during the Court's journey south - perhaps, for example, at York, during the rest-day there on Sunday, 21 November; 3) in London on the single day of 25 November (the day of the King's reception there) and for part, only, of the next day; 4) at Hampton Court, for a few weeks - indeed until beyond the end of November and into mid-December.

Thus, in consideration of the fact that during November 1641, there was only one night that the King spent in London (*viz.*, that of the 25 November), Whitteridge's conclusion that Hampton Court is more probable than the London implied by Harvey, is scarcely to be doubted.

However, the possible venue during November which must be given priority, at least of consideration, over both London and Hampton Court, is Edinburgh, at some date prior to 19 November 1641. Indeed, as there would have been twenty-six days between the outbreak of the Irish Rebellion on 23 October and the departure of the Court from Edinburgh on 18 November, this would clearly have been long enough for the young Hugh to have received his summons home - especially if he was already in France, on his way home - and to have arrived at the Court, in Edinburgh, before 19 November.

Thus, Edinburgh would appear to be at least as possible as the Hampton Court suggested by Whitteridge.

Reasons for taking a detour to Edinburgh

Whether Edinburgh would be, also, more probable than Hampton Court is a separate question. Here, it is curious that neither of the two accounts gives, or suggests, a reason for the young Hugh Montgomery having paid the

visit to the Court on the occasion which turned out to be
medically so historic - *viz.*, a reason why he would
(presumably) have taken the detour via Edinburgh (on his
way home via Portpatrick) to do so.

Here, also, it is not improbable, on the one hand, that his
father, at the time of recalling him, told him that the Court
was currently in Edinburgh, and instructed him to visit it,
there, in the course of his journey home. Alternatively, the
young Hugh, when passing through London in early November, and confirming that the Court was still in Edinburgh, may have made his own decision not to turn west at
Scotch Corner, as he would normally have done (for the
shorter, Solway, route) but to take the rather more circuit-
ous route via Edinburgh, in order to visit the Court (see
fig.). The disadvantages of such a slightly longer detour
would have been counter-balanced by the twin advantages
of a shorter journey than one going all the way home, and
of the opportunity, in Edinburgh, of a rest.

The young Hugh's intention in thus making for the Court,
at that time of rebellion in his native Ireland, would surely
have been to deliver those assurances of loyalty which the
'Oxford' account records that he did deliver on the medically famous visit, and to seek any possible instructions
from the King, both for his father and for himself. And if
he should prove to be too late to catch the Court before it
left Edinburgh for London, he would have had reason to
hope, still, to meet it as it made its way south.

Other clues to the venue

The two accounts, although incompatible as to the venue,
usefully supplement and complement each other in respect
of some details. Indeed, it is possible to interpret some of
these details as further clues to the venue.

Thus Whitteridge claims, of the detail of the King's
comment about the hearts of his nobilities (recorded only
in the 'Oxford' account), that it 'accords well enough' with
the venue which she suggests of Hampton Court.[26] But the

---

[26] Ibid.

But the comment accords equally well, if not better, with Edinburgh. One of the main purposes of the King in visiting Scotland at that time had been to find out about the thoughts of the hearts of his Scottish 'nobilities'

Another significant detail from the two accounts is the reference (recorded only in the account by Harvey) to 'other creditable persons who were present'. Harvey's actual words are *'uti ipse mihi, aliique (qui aderant) fide digni narrarunt'*.[27]

Whitteridge, in a free translation of these words, following two earlier, and similarly free, translations, by an anonymous author in 1653, and by Willis in 1847[28], gives 'as he himself told me and other creditable persons who were eye-witnesses'.[29]

But, in translating *'qui aderant'* so freely as 'who were eye-witnesses', all three translators would seem to have imported into the original text a meaning - *viz.*, 'eye-witnesses of the original injury' - not justified by the actual words. Indeed, there would seem to be no reason to depart from the literal meaning of the words *'qui aderant'* as 'who were present' - meaning 'present (with Harvey) at the time of his medical history-taking, and of his examination of the young Hugh, at the Court', and able to give Harvey information about the early history of the case. That meaning does not, of course, imply that they were not, also, eye-witnesses of the original injury or of its early treatment.

---

[27] W. Harvey, *Exercitationes De Generatione Animalium*, Amsterdam: Ravestyn, 1662, p. 198.

[28] W. Harvey, *De Generatione Animalium*, anonymous English translation, London: James Young, 1653, p. 285 and *The Works of William Harvey MD*, trans. by Robert Willis, London: Sydenham Society, 1847, p.382.

[29] Harvey, *Disputations Touching the Generation of Animals,* p. 250.

The 'other creditable persons'

A persuasive answer to the question, who these 'other creditable persons who were present (*'qui aderant'*)' could have been and, in particular, where such persons lived, might also suggest a clue to where, also, the Court would have been at the time.

It had not been found possible to identify any such 'creditable' persons, knowledgeable about the early history of the young Hugh's injury, who would have been residing in London, or Hampton Court, at the time of a visit to the Court when it was there. One 'creditable' person, who would have known about the childhood history of the young Hugh's heart condition, and who would normally have been present at Court, would have been the young Hugh's maternal grandfather, Sir William Alexander, 1st Earl of Stirling, and Secretary for Scotland. He, however, had died the year before - in 1640.[30] Another 'creditable' person, also knowledgeable about the case, who was normally at Court, was the young Hugh's uncle, Sir James Montgomery, but it is known that, from the outbreak of the Irish Rebellion on 23 October 1641, he had been, not at Court, but in Ulster helping his older brother, the 2nd Viscount, against the Irish rebels.[31] A third 'creditable' person, who had 'pierced' the young Hugh's abscess in childhood, and who is recorded as having been at the Court in Oxford, just prior to the death of the 2nd Viscount, in mid-November 1642, had been Dr Patrick Maxwell, previously family physician to the Montgomery family.[32] Dr Maxwell's presence at the Court, but a year later, in 1642, after it had moved to Oxford, would seem to be well attested. There is, however, no evidence that Dr Maxwell had been with the Court, in Edinburgh, a year earlier, in November 1641.

Two 'other creditable persons' (i.e. other than the young Hugh himself) who it has been possible to identify as

---

[30] *Dictionary of National Biography*, Oxford, Rpt. 1973, I, p. 280.

[31] Montgomery, *The Montgomery Manuscripts 1603-1706*, p. 310.

[32] Ibid. p.153.

having been present (*'qui aderant'*) - at least in Edinburgh
- at the time of the medically historic encounter of Harvey
with the young Hugh Montgomery (if this encounter was
indeed in Edinburgh) have been Dr John MakLuire and his
wife, Mareon Greir. The virtual certainty of their presence
in Edinburgh in November 1641, is established by the
facts that their fifth child, James, had been baptised in
Edinburgh on 9 September, that very year, and that their
sixth child, Thomas, was to be baptised, there, on 15
March, only two years later.[33]

Dr MakLuire's prior familiarity with the young Hugh's case

The prior familiarity with the case of Hugh Montgomery
by both Dr John MakLuire and his spouse, Mareon Greir,
independently, has been argued in Chapter 12. It had
seemed that their personal acquaintance with the young
Hugh, and with the early history of his injury and its treatment, in County Down, perhaps from about 1630, when he
would have been aged seven or eight, and certainly from
1634, when he would have been aged eleven or twelve,
would have ensured a welcome to him on his appearance
in Edinburgh. Dr John MakLuire and his spouse, Mareon
Greir, would also have been available, in Edinburgh, to be
consulted, at the Court, by William Harvey.

In conclusion, therefore, it would appear that while Oxford
can be confidently excluded as the venue for the medically
historic encounter of William Harvey with the young
Hugh Montgomery; and Hampton Court assessed as
admittedly more probable than London; Edinburgh is no
less possible than Hampton Court. Also, the known
residence in Edinburgh, in November 1641, of the
physician, Dr John MakLuire, and his wife Mareon Greir,
who both would appear to have been familiar with the
young Hugh from the time of his childhood at Mount

---

[33] SRO OPR 685 1/4, Edinburgh (Greyfriars) Register of Baptisms,
9th September, 1641 and SRO OPR 685 1/5, Edinburgh (Greyfriars)
Register of Baptisms, 15th March, 1643.

Alexander House, Comber, County Down, strongly suggests that they were, or were amongst, the 'other creditable persons who were present' and who had been able to supply Harvey with the early history of the case. This would make Edinburgh not only no less possible for the location of the Court at the time, but more probable, than Hampton Court.

Figure

Alternative routes to Portpatrick.

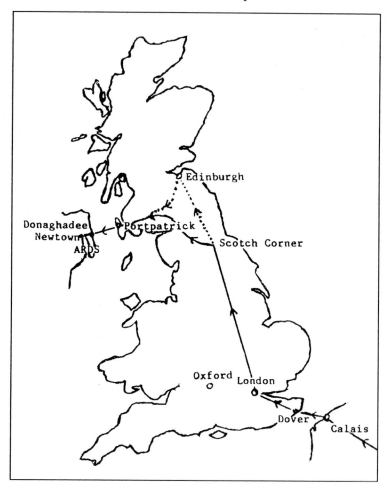

Chapter Sixteen - His Professional Standing

The development of his reputation

The acquisition of a reputation, by Dr MakLuire, even at an early age, had seemed to have been indicated by the two '*carmina*' in his praise, written by Patrick Sandys, formerly Principal of Edinburgh University, and Dr George Sibbald, respectively.[1] These had appeared in 1630, when Dr MakLuire had been still in his twenties. The year 1630 had been the probable year of his graduation as 'Doctor in Physick', crowning what had appeared to have been an eight-year medical apprenticeship in Edinburgh, during which such a reputation would have been given its foundation. It had also been the year in which he had published his first two books - *The Buckler*, and the *Sanitatis Semita*, with the *Tractatus* 'pre-fixed' to it. His third, important, book, enhancing his reputation, *The Generall Practise of Medecine* was published in 1634.

It had certainly seemed that Dr MakLuire's reputation, in subsequent years, had grown. He was to become recognised by the authorities as an expert to be consulted about a variety of medical matters. In particular, he was to become a nationally recognised expert on the plague.

It may even be that he was specially recognised for the purposes of what could be called the forensic psychiatry of the time (see below). Such special recognition would have been for the recommending of the compulsory 'warding' of mentally disturbed individuals - although it had seemed more likely that any fully qualified 'Doctor in Physick' would have been recognised for this purpose.

---

[1] J. MakLuire, *The Buckler of Bodilie Health*, Edinburgh: Wreittoun, 1630, pp. ix-x.

Recognition of his professional standing

The recognition by the authorities of Dr MakLuire for the purposes of medico-legal work is shown by the case of Sir John Hay, knight, sometime Clerk Register.

Charles I had arrived again in Scotland on 14 August 1641. Soon afterwards, on Thursday, 19 August 1641, his second Scottish parliament had received a petition by Sir John Hay, one of five convicted 'incendiaries' (*viz.*, himself; the Earl of Traquaire; Sir Robert Spotswood; Mr John Maxwell, once bishop of Ross; and Dr Balquaquell) 'to dispense with his going to prison for two or three days, till he should recover his health'.

The House had ordained Sir John to 'obey the proclamation' but had suspended the execution of it until the next day (when):

> he shall produce under the hands of Doctors Arnot, Kinkead, and Macklure, or aney tuo of them, upone ther othe and conscience, that in respect of his sicknes he cannot go to the Castle.[2]

The Dr Arnot included in this instruction was probably the 'John Arnot', fellow student at St Andrews with the future Dr MakLuire, who had graduated MA with him in 1622.

It seems that Sir John had either recovered from his sickness by the following day, or Dr MakLuire and his colleagues had not, 'on oath and conscience', been able to support his petition because, on Friday, 20 August, Sir John Hay 'on his humble petition, receives from the House a warrant to the Constable of the Castle to receive him as prisoner'.[3]

His expertise on the pestilent fever and the plague

It may be supposed that Dr MakLuire's interest in, and clinical experience of, 'the pest' began with the outbreak

---

[2] J. Balfour, *The Historical Works of Sir James Balfour*, 4 vols., Edinburgh: Aitchison, 1824, III, p. 47.

[3] Ibid., p. 48.

in Edinburgh in November, 1624 - two years after his graduation as Master of Arts.[4] This was, however, as has already been mentioned, a 'pest which raged not' - i.e. was not as severe as plague proper, and was a mere pestilent (or plague-like) fever - probably typhus.[5]

It has already been suggested that Dr MakLuire's clinical experience in Edinburgh in 1624 probably provided the material for the *Tractatus de febre pestilente* which, it has also been suggested, may have been the thesis for his doctorate. He had had this printed in 1630 as a 'pre-fix' to his *Sanitatis Semita*, although the latter book is on the unrelated topic of general health.

Six years later, on 11 May 1636, Dr John MakLuire is recorded as having been elected, gratis, burgess of Glasgow. The reason for this election, or for it having been gratis, is not recorded. However, 1636 had been a year of nation-wide alarm about the near approach of plague to Scotland. Plague had been diagnosed in Newcastle in the very same month as Dr MakLuire had been elected to the Glasgow burgessship, and Newcastle may, indeed, have been the signal for Glasgow (although it was to escape the infection at that time) to seek Dr MakLuire's advice.[6] It would appear that Dr MakLuire was probably not paid any money for his advice and that his only reward from Glasgow in 1636 had been the burgessship, given 'free' of payment by himself.

Dr MakLuire's first encounter with the plague proper would appear to have been with its spread northwards to the Scottish border in 1644.[7] It seems probable that it was a perception, by him, of a threat to Edinburgh, in that year, that persuaded him to transfer his wife, pregnant at the

---

[4] J. Ritchie, 'A History of the Plague in Scotland', unpublished MS, Royal College of Physicians of Edinburgh, 1955.

[5] D. Calderwood, *The History of the Kirk of Scotland*, ed. T. Thomson, 7 vols., Wodrow Society, 1842/9, VII, p. 629.

[6] Ritchie, 'A History of the Plague in Scotland'.

[7] Ibid.

time, to the comparative safety of Mid Calder - where she could give birth to their child, Hugh, who was baptised there on 12 May 1644.

The actual outbreak of plague in Edinburgh early in 1645, seems to have had personally tragic consequences for Dr MakLuire. It seems certain that two of his sons fell victim to the disease that year, along with his old friend Alexander Alexander.

It may be noted, also, in relation to that fateful year of 1645, that a Gilbert Kennedy, who later brought a complaint against Dr MakLuire (see below), is mentioned in the Kirk Session Minutes of Mid Calder. These had recorded an order - 'the pestilence being in Edinburgh that none resort thereto', and that Gilbert Kennedy be removed, 'being come from Edinburgh on 15th June, 1645'.[8]

It would seem that Dr MakLuire's next encounter with the plague had been with the memorable outbreak in Glasgow in the autumn of 1646.[9] According to Duncan, a systematic visitation of the plague colony there had been decided upon and, on 17 July 1647, a Dr Rae, 'possibly a physician reputed to have skill in the treatment of the plague', had been written for.[10] Apparently Dr Rae had not turned up, and Dr MakLuire had been engaged. On 26 July 1647, the burgh council records that it:

> Geives power and commissioune to the deacone conveanor and John Grahame to meit Doctor McCluir and aggree with him to attend the visitatioune of the toun for ane monethe to come[11]

It had been on this occasion that the burgh council, no doubt desperate for help, but embarrassed by their past

[8] SRO CH 2/266/1, Mid Calder Kirk Session Minutes, fol. 78a.

[9] J.D. Marwick, ed., *Extracts from the Records of the Burgh of Glasgow (1630-1662)*, 2 vols., Glasgow: Scottish Burgh Records Society, II, pp. 702 and 119.

[10] A. Duncan, *Memorials of the Faculty of Physicians and Surgeons Glasgow 1599-1850*, Glasgow, 1896, p. 12.

[11] Marwick, ed., *Extracts from the Records of the Burgh of Glasgow (1630-1662)*, pp. 702 and 119.

niggardliness towards Dr MakLuire, had also agreed 'to geive him ten dollouris for bygaine service to incuridge him'.[12]

The circumstances would suggest that this unspecified 'bygaine service' had been advice, given to the council in 1636, about the nation-wide alarm, at the time, about the threat of plague. It appears that, in recognition of his 1646-1649 work in Glasgow Dr MakLuire had been elected, on 10th April, 1649, to the Guild Brethren.[13] By October, 1649, it had been certified that there had been no more plague in Glasgow.[14]

A charge against him of 'wrongous' detention not sustained

A charge against Dr MakLuire (of interest for the history of forensic psychiatry in Scotland) had been brought before the Privy Council for Scotland, on 4 November 1647, by the aforementioned Gilbert Kennedy of Airyoll-and for wrongous detention in the Tolbooth, Edinburgh.[15] Airyolland is a farm in the parish of Inch, westward from Glenluce, and not far from Stranraer (see fig.) but it would appear that this Gilbert Kennedy also had a dwelling in Edinburgh.[16]

It would seem that Gilbert Kennedy had been originally warded, presumably earlier in 1647, in the tolbooth of Stranraer. The warding had been at the instance not only of Dr John MakLuire, but also of the Provost and baillies of Stranraer, and of a Hew Kennedy of Airyhemming - Airyhemming being a farm immediately adjacent to that of Airyolland (see fig.). Probably, this Hew Kennedy had

---

[12] Ibid.

[13] J.R. Anderson, ed., *The Burgesses and Guild Brethren of Glasgow (1573-1750)*, Edinburgh, 1925, p. 93.

[14] Ritchie, 'A History of the Plague in Scotland'.

[15] *Register of the Privy Council of Scotland*, 2nd Series, VIII (1643-1660), p.174.

[16] Ibid.

been a relative of Gilbert Kennedy who perhaps had been required to give his consent to the 'warding'. It had not been clear for what reason (whether or not 'for riot') he had been warded on that earlier occasion.

Gilbert Kennedy had claimed that he had 'obtained letters of suspension of these captions'. But it is recorded that he had subsequently 'come out of the tolbooth' at Stranraer 'inorderly'. He had then been again warded (explicitly 'for riot'), this time in the Tolbooth in Edinburgh, by the same group of persons.

Gilbert Kennedy's own somewhat convoluted statement of his complaint against Dr MakLuire had been that the latter, having:

> accepted from him an assignation to a larger sum due to Sir Robert Adair of Kinhilt, knight, than was required to pay his debt, had thereupon granted a backbond promising to continue the caption and allow the assignation in payment of the debt whenever Sir Robert paid, and that he had then transacted with Sir Robert to qualifie his satisfaction and transferrid the complenars said assignatioun in his favoures[17].

Shortly after the charge against Dr MakLuire and the others, on 4 November 1647, there had been registered, on 17 December 1647, a very lengthy legal document, difficult to understand, and the relevance of which to the case is doubtful, of a 'discharge' by Dr MakLuire, to Sir David Home of Wedderburne - the latter having at some time borrowed 1700 merks from Gilbert Kennedy of Airyolland.[18] Two weeks after the registering of that document, the summons to Dr MakLuire and his associates to compear had been executed, on 30 December 1647, and delivered to his house in Edinburgh.[19]

---

[17] Ibid.

[18] SRO RS1/57, Discharge McLure to Home.

[19] *Register of the Privy Council of Scotland,* 2nd Series, VIII (1643-1660), p. 180.

On 21 January 1648, Dr MakLuire and the others charged had not appeared at the hearing, and Gilbert Kennedy had been put at liberty but ordered to compear on 27 January 1648.[20] However, on that date, there had been a claim from Gilbert Kennedy that he could not compear because of threats against him.[21]

The complexities of the case had seemed to be too great, and the surviving documentation too patchy, for full elucidation of what reasonable grounds Gilbert Kennedy may have had for complaint against Dr MakLuire. It had been noted, however, that the behaviour of Gilbert Kennedy two years earlier, in coming out of plague-stricken Edinburgh and illicitly moving to Mid Calder may have been due to impaired judgement attributable to mental disturbance.

The facts are rather suggestive of Gilbert Kennedy of Airyolland, if originally warded in Stranraer 'for riot' rather than for any civil offence, having been suffering from temporary mental disturbance. Paranoid and litigious behaviour, showing impairment of 'judgement', is often attributable to hypomania, and such an illness may reasonably have called, indeed, for 'warding', for his own protection and for the protection of others. The necessity for warding him may also have required the support of a medical opinion (i.e. Dr MakLuire's, despite his apparent personal involvement), as well as consent by a responsible relative (presumably Hew Kennedy of Airyhemming). It would appear that, from January, 1648, the affair had faded from the records in mystery.

---

[20] Ibid., p. 175.

[21] Ibid., p. 182.

Figure

Airyolland and Airyhemming in Galloway.

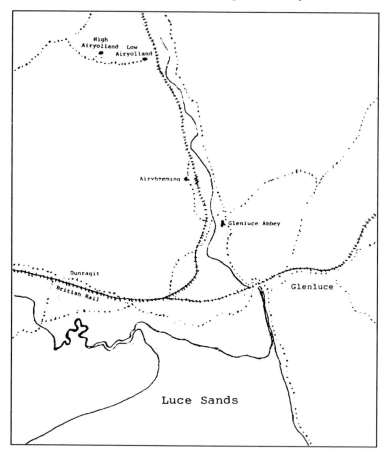

Chapter Seventeen - His Death

The precise date of his death unknown

No record either of the precise date, or of the cause, of Dr MakLuire's death has been found. The death and burial of his widow, Mareon Greir, in the Greyfriars burial ground, in Edinburgh, recorded as having taken place on 21 February 1671, suggests that, as she was not buried at the village of Spott, in East Lothian, where her second husband had acquired an estate, she may have been widowed for a second time, and have chosen to be buried next to her first husband.[1] Unfortunately, the legible burial records for Greyfriars do not start, however, until 1658, and are not able to show, therefore, whether, or when, Dr Luire himself may have been buried there.[2]

Clearly, Dr MakLuire had been alive at the time of his election to the Guild Brethren of the burgh of Glasgow on 10 April 1649.[3] Clearly, also, he had been deceased prior to the re-marriage of his widow on 9 June 1653.[4]

One possibility had therefore been that, as Glasgow was not declared to be free of plague until October 1649, he himself had succumbed to the Glasgow epidemic he had been called in to advise about.[5] It had seemed unlikely, however, that he would have been elected to the Guild Brethren (as a token of thanks) before significant risk of infection had passed.

---

[1] H. Paton, ed., *Register of Internements in the Greyfriars Burying-ground, Edinburgh, 1658-1700*, Edinburgh,1902, Old Series, 26, 21 February 1671.

[2] Ibid.

[3] J.R. Anderson, ed., *The Burgesses and Guild Brethren of Glasgow 1573-1750,* Edinburgh, 1925, Old Series, 56, p. 93.

[4] H. Paton, ed., *The Register of Marriages for the Parish of Edinburgh 1595-1700*, Edinburgh, 1905, Old Series, 27, p. 287.

[5] J.A. Ritchie, 'History of the Plague in Scotland', unpublished MS, Royal College of Physicians of Edinburgh, 1955.

His death

A more intriguing possibility had been that he had been still alive, early in the year 1652, and had been the unnamed 'firm Friend in Edinburgh' of Sir James Montgomery who, according to the 18th century 'Lodge's Irish Peerage', had helped Sir James, in February or March, 1652, after Charles II's escape to the Continent, to himself escape from Edinburgh - in disguise.[6] Dr MakLuire had certainly been a 'firm Friend in Edinburgh' of Sir James, and no other person in Edinburgh at the time who could have been so described has been identified.

The escape from Edinburgh of Sir James Montgomery in 1652

Sir James Montgomery had been at his home in Ulster, after the execution, on 1 January 1649, of the King to whom he had been a faithful courtier. He had continued there until Cromwell had over-run that country in October 1649. He had then had to flee to his native land of Scotland but, on being detected there, he had been ordered, by the Committee of Estates, because of his known absence of commitment to the Covenant, to leave Scotland before the end of the year. He had therefore retired to Holland, residing chiefly at the Hague, and joining himself, there, to his new King, Charles II, whose restoration was being planned.

Sir James, despite the injunction against him, had accompanied the King when the latter, after being invited back to Scotland, had landed safely at Garmouth on Spey on 23 June 1650.[7] With the King's return, however, there had been intense pressure to purge the royal household of 'malignants', a pressure countered by pressure from the King to be allowed to keep at least a few of his faithful courtiers, of which few Sir James had been one. On 4 December 1650, according to Balfour, and arising from this situation, there had been a 'Report concerning Sir

---

[6] *Lodge's Irish Peerage*, London, 1754, p. 366.

[7] J. Balfour, *The Historical Works of Sir James Balfour*, 4 vols., Edinburgh: Aitchison, 1824, IV, p. 61.

180

James Montgomery redd and remitted to the severall bodies'.[8]

Next, on 18 December, Balfour had noted:

> Sir James Montgomeries bill to be liberat of his band from entering the kingdome, read; and after some debait, he was liberat from the penalty of the same, and he acknowledged ane lawfull subiect.[9]

Presumably, Sir James Montgomery was present at the coronation of Charles II at Scone on 1st January, 1651, but his movements during the rest of that year are not clear. It is simply said, by *Lodge's Irish Peerage*, that (understandably, in view of the ambiguous official attitude towards him) he 'was obliged to abscond'.[10] What is not clear is at what stage he had found it necessary to abscond. Possibly, he remained with the King during the latter's march into England; possibly he was present at the battle of Worcester, and 'absconded' after that, making his own way back to Scotland. However, it seems rather more likely that he was 'obliged to abscond' while still in Scotland - because his next known appearance had been in Scotland.

What is recorded, in *Lodge's Irish Peerage*, is that:

> finding the King's Affairs entirely ruined by the Loss of Worcester Fight, he went disguised as a Merchant to a firm Friend in Edinburgh, by whose means he procured a Pass to travel to London.

This had been in an attempt to follow his King into exile, an attempt which was tragically thwarted. Having reached Newcastle 'finding the Roads pestered with Soldiers on their March, he sold his Horses, and took the Sea in a Coal-barque'.

---

[8] Ibid., p. 205.
[9] Ibid., p. 206.
[10] *Lodge's Irish Peerage*, p. 368.

His death

Shortly afterwards, the barque had been pursued by pirates and Sir James had been shot off Flamborough Head. He had died from his wounds and had been 'buried' at sea on 12 March 1652.[11]

Dr MakLuire's survival thereafter not long

If Dr MakLuire had indeed been still alive to be that 'firm Friend in Edinburgh' who, in February/March, 1652, had been able to help Sir James Montgomery in his escape, he could not for long have survived Sir James - because his widow's remarriage, to William Ross, writer, had been in the following year, on 9 June 1653.[12] Allowing for a twelve-month period of mourning, this had suggested that Dr MakLuire had died before 9 June 1652.

Indeed, the touching possibility had arisen that Dr Mak-Luire may have forfeited his own life precisely because of loyalty to his friend, Sir James Montgomery and, as a result of his part in the latter's escape having been discovered, may have been adjudged traitorous by the Cromwellian authorities, and have suffered accordingly at their hands.

---

[11] *Lodge's Irish Peerage*, p. 366.

[12] Paton, ed., *The Register of Marriages for the Parish of Edinburgh 1595-1700*, p. 287.

Chapter Eighteen - His Place in the History of Medicine

Dr John MakLuire's life spanned the first half of the seventeenth century - by which time the Renaissance, which had begun about the end of the fourteenth century in Italy, had already spread to other countries of Europe, including Scotland. Three questions therefore arise - first, to what extent Dr MakLuire may have been influenced by Renaissance pioneers in science and medicine earlier than himself; second, to what extent he may have been influenced by those who were his contemporaries; and third, to what extent he may himself have been a pioneer in exerting an influence on medical thought and practice.

Influence by earlier medical pioneers

Some of the earlier pioneers of medicine who may have influenced Dr John MakLuire may be amongst those cited by Comrie in his *History of Scottish Medicine*. William Schevez (1428-1497), for example, had practised medicine in St Andrews and had founded a valuable library there.[1] It would have been through this library that Schevez may have had an influence upon the young John MakLuire during the latter's student days at St Andrews from 1618 to 1622. The earliest medical studies of the young John MakLuire, forming part of his course for the Master of Arts degree, would have included both the works of the medical writers of antiquity and, presumably, those also of some more recent writers - some, perhaps, from Schevez' library.

Thomas Phaer (1510-1560) is reported by Aikin to have published, in 1544, a translation into English from French of *The Pestilence*.[2] Also, Gilbert Skene, of Aberdeen, in 1568, had had printed, in Scotland, his treatise, in the

---

[1] J.D. Comrie, *History of Scottish Medicine*, 2 vols., London, 1932, I, p. 83.

[2] J. Aikin, *Biographic Memoirs of Medicine in Great Britain*, London, 1780, p. 78.

vernacular, *Ane Breve Descriptioun of the Pest*, based on his own experience of the plague. Both of these may, therefore, have been works known to Dr MakLuire, in the 1620s, and influencing him while preparing his own *Tractatus de Febre Pestilente*, based on his experience of the outbreak of an epidemic of such a 'pestilent' (i.e. 'plague-like') fever in Edinburgh in 1624. These authoritative works would probably also have been ready to hand for reference when, by then a recognised expert, Dr MakLuire was invited by Glasgow to advise about the plague there in 1647.

Peter Lowe of Glasgow who, in 1596, had published (also in the vernacular) *A Discussion on the Whole Art of Chirurgie* - said to be the first textbook of surgery to be written in English - had obtained, three years later, in 1599, a charter from James VI for the Faculty (eventually to become the Royal College) of Physicians and Surgeons of Glasgow. In this, his purpose had been to unite all who practised medicine or surgery there. Possibly, therefore, his book, presumably known to Dr MakLuire, may have encouraged the latter to complement that pioneer contribution to surgery with a comparably pioneer contribution to medicine by publishing, in 1634, his *The Generall Practise of Medecine*. That work, also in the vernacular, would appear to have indeed been the first textbook of general medicine by a Scotsman to be printed in Scotland. Possibly, also, Lowe's 1599 petition to the King to found the Glasgow Faculty was a factor in encouraging Dr Mak-Luire, in 1630, to petition for a College of Physicians in Edinburgh - partly with the intention of complementing the Incorporation of Barbers and Surgeons which was already established in Edinburgh.

Vesalius, the foremost anatomist of all time, in 1543 (the very year that Copernicus had revolutionised astronomy by the publication of his *De Revolutionibus Orbium Coelestium*), had rendered a service to medicine wholly comparable to that of Copernicus to astronomy by the publication of his *De Humani Corporis Fabrica*. In the following year (1544), according to Aikin, Phaer had published a *Description of the Veins in the Human Body.*[3] Eleven years later (in 1555) Vesalius had made an early move which was to pave the way for Harvey's discovery that the blood circulates, rather than ebbs and flows, as had hitherto been believed. This, Vesalius had achieved by retracting an earlier anatomical pronouncement he had made of the existence of 'pores' in the interventricular septum which, had they existed, would have allowed the passage of blood from one ventricle to the other and have been against the idea of the blood circulating. In fact, Servetus, in 1551, had already published, in his *Restitutio Christianismi*, an account of the pulmonary circulation - but this had attracted little attention as it had appeared in a theological work. It had only been with Vesalius' successor Columbus who, in his *De Re Anatomica*, had also published a description of the pulmonary circulation, that attention had been drawn to the discovery. Although Dr MakLuire, in his published work, makes no mention of these pioneers of anatomy, it is difficult to imagine that he was not conversant with, and influenced by, their findings.

Roesslin (or Rhodion), a medical man practising first in Worms and then in Frankfurt-on-Main, had published, in 1513, a work called *Der Swangern Frawen und Hebammen Rosegarten*. A Latinised version of this, entitled *De Partu Hominis*, had appeared in 1540, in an English translation by a Richard Jonas, as the *Byrth of Mankynde*. This, although clearly not itself an English work, was the first separate work on midwifery in the English language. In its subsequent editions it had maintained its place as a textbook of midwifery in Britain until the eighteenth century. The editions nearest to the times of Dr MakLuire would have been those of 1604, 1613 and 1626. It would thus seem very probable that Dr MakLuire would have been familiar with, and influenced by, one of these three editions at the time when, in the late 1620s, he would have been preparing the midwifery notes ('For women brought to bed') for inclusion in the chapter entitled 'A Regiment for Women with Child, Bairnes, and Nourses' with which

---

[3] Ibid.

his *The Buckler of Bodilie Health* of 1630 ends (see fig. 1).

Influence by contemporaneous pioneers

Francis Bacon (1561-1626), one of the Renaissance pioneers who were contemporaries of Dr MakLuire, in his *Novum Organum* of 1620, urging the inductive method, may not have escaped the notice of Dr MakLuire prior to the latter's three publications of 1630 - although there is nothing in those publications to indicate this.

The great Galileo (1564-1642), some 36 years older than Dr MakLuire, who had studied medicine (at Padua), and who is considered to be a founder of the experimental method in science, had certainly been active at the time (in the 1620s) when Dr MakLuire would have been preparing his three works of 1630. However, Galileo's major work, his *Dialogue concerning the Two Chief World Systems - Ptolomaic and Copernican*, had not been published until 1632, two years later than Dr MakLuire's works of 1630. And his *Dialogue concerning two new sciences* had not been published until 1638 - four years later than Dr MakLuire's final work, *The Generall Practise of Medecine* of 1634. It would seem improbable, therefore, that Dr MakLuire, who nowhere mentions Galileo, was influenced by him.

Descartes (1596-1650) was certainly a contemporary of Dr MakLuire. But he also cannot have influenced Dr MakLuire because his *Discours de la Méthode* was not published until 1637, well after all Dr MakLuire's publications, while his textbook of physiology was not published until some years after Descartes' own death.

Fabricius (1533-1619), the distinguished anatomist and embryologist, and successor of Vesalius at Padua, had published, in 1600 (about the time of Dr MakLuire's birth), his *De Formato Foeto*. Clearly, therefore, this work also may have been read by the student, John MakLuire, in 1618-1622 - and rather more probably during the years 1622-1630 when it would appear, from the latter's midwifery comments in *The Buckler of Bodilie Health*, that he was building up his clinical experience in both midwifery and child care.

Sir Thomas Browne (1605-1682) was almost the same age as Dr MakLuire. However, his publications were all of a later date than those of Dr MakLuire and he cannot, therefore, have influenced him at all.

Finally, the great William Harvey, also contemporaneous with Dr MakLuire, although about 22 years his senior, is perhaps the most significant of the medical pioneers of the Renaissance. Harvey had been taught, at Padua, by Fabricius and, as Guthrie remarks, it was Harvey who really brought the Renaissance to Britain.[4] Now, Harvey's great work, his *De Motu Cordis et Sanguinis* of 1628, certainly appeared two years prior to Dr MakLuire's three works of 1630. These works, however, had probably been in preparation for years prior to 1628 - *The Buckler*, certainly, since 1619 - and there is no indication that the *De Motu*, even if it had come to the notice of Dr MakLuire before 1630, influenced him in the preparation of any of them. In any case the movement of the heart and of the blood was of little relevance to the fields of study covered by MakLuire's first three works. Harvey's other great work, on the other hand, the *De Generatione Animalium*, which included his writings on midwifery, had not been published, in Latin, until 1651 and, in English, until 1653 and could not, therefore, have had any influence upon the works of Dr MakLuire - whose last publication, *The Generall Practise of Medecine*, had appeared in 1634.

MakLuire a pioneer author on general medical topics

Dr John MakLuire was certainly a pioneer medical author on general medical topics. His own *Tractatus De Febre Pestilente* of 1630, if it is, as it would seem to be, his MD thesis, must be the earliest extant MD thesis to have been printed in Scotland. It was published seven years earlier than the MD thesis of William Broad, of Aberdeen (see fig. 2) - hitherto believed (see Comrie) to have had that

---

[4] D. Guthrie, *A History of Medicine*, London, 1945, p. 175.

distinction.[5] The pioneering nature of his *The Generall Practise of Medecine*, as a text-book on general medicine, has already been discussed.

MakLuire an early British contributor to midwifery

Dr MakLuire was also a pioneer British writer, specifically, in the field of midwifery. Spencer, in 1927, but referring back to his Harveian Oration of 1921, claimed that the author of the first original work on midwifery to be published by an English author had been William Harvey.[6] Spencer's claim for Harvey's priority was repeated by Curtis in 1933; by Guthrie in 1945; by Johnstone in 1948; and by Lees in 1994.[7] The work by Harvey referred to by Spencer was the chapter on parturition (*'De partu'*) in his *De Generatione Animalium* of 1651. In that chapter, Harvey discussed two specific midwifery topics. These were the clinical phenomenon of false pregnancy (mentioned very briefly) and the 'cause' of parturition (discussed at greater length).

However, while Spencer's narrowly English claim cannot be denied, he is mistaken in adding that it 'justifies Aveling's description of Harvey as the Father of British Midwifery'.[8] This is because Dr John MakLuire, when writing, in 1630, about both of the two specific midwifery topics which Harvey's work was later to deal with, antedated Harvey by two decades, and Dr David Kinloch, the author of *De Hominis Procreatione*, by even more.

It had been on both of the two specific topics dealt with by Harvey in the part of his *De Generatione* devoted to midwifery that Dr MakLuire had anticipated him. This is shown by the fact that Dr MakLuire, in 1630, in *The*

---

[5] Comrie, *History of Scottish Medicine*, I, p. 369.

[6] H R. Spencer, *History of British Midwifery*, London: 1927, p. 3.

[7] See A.H. Curtis, ed., *Obstetrics and Gynaecology*, Philadelphia, 1933, p. 9; Guthrie, *A History of Medicine*, p. 183; R.W. Johnstone, 'Edinburgh Harveian Oration', unpublished, 1944; and M.M Lees, 'Edinburgh Harveian Oration', unpublished, 1994.

[8] Spencer, *History of British Midwifery*, p. 3.

Buckler, under the heading 'A false conception from wind or water', had written:

> Such sorte of false conceptions befalleth when the monethly courses are stopped to a woman using the company of man, and her belly riseth, the rest of the marks of a true conception concurring, she not having for all this conceaved any lively thing, but something correspondent in substance to some of the elements, as wind or water ... The not distinguishing of a true conception from the false, hath beene often troublesome and chargable to diverse: Such was the case of a Lady in Burdeous [i.e. Burdiehouse, south of Edinburgh] who after nyne moneths carefull carying of her selfe, least shee should hurte her supposed child, and three weekes troublesome travailing, in end was delyvered of a fart forsuith.[9]

These were words which Harvey, two decades later, in 1651, seems almost to have echoed for, in discussing the clinical phenomenon of false pregnancy, Harvey was to write:

> I ... knew of a noblewoman who had born more than ten children and whose courses were never interrupted except when she was pregnant. Being later married to a second husband, she judged from the wonted signs that she was with child, and from the movement also which she herself perceived many times in the night, and her sister also who then lay with her in the same bed, and all the arguments which I could suggest could not dissuade her from that opinion, till at the last all her hopes vanished in flatulence and fatness.[10]

---

[9] J. MakLuire, *The Buckler of Bodilie Health*, Edinburgh: Wreittoun, 1630, p. 131.

[10] W. Harvey, *Disputations Touching the Generation of Animals*, trans. G. Whitteridge, Oxford, 1981, p. 399.

Also, Dr MakLuire, in 1630, in the section of *The Buckler* entitled 'A Regiment for Women with Child, Bairnes, and Nourses' (see fig.), and the portion headed 'Of their governement, the tyme of their birth, and after the same', had anticipated Harvey by expressing the same belief that Harvey was to affirm - *viz.*, that the foetus plays an active part, in co-operation with the efforts of the mother, in 'causing' parturition. Dr MakLuire had written:

> so the child requiring more meate than the mother can afford, and greater libertie to take the aire, he tares with his hands and feete his thinne membranous sheetes.[11]

These, again, are words which Harvey, it seems, was later, in 1651, to echo. In discussing the 'cause' of parturition Harvey was to dissent from the view of his teacher, Fabricius, that in viviparous creatures it is the weight of the foetus that is the 'cause' of its being born. After referring to the hatching of oviparous creatures (such as birds, fish, butterflies and other insects) through the breaking of the egg shell, or the cocoon, by the foetus itself, and not by the mother, Harvey was to go on to write:

> And so it is also probable that in the birth of viviparous creatures the chief cause of being born must be attributed to the foetus itself, I mean to its own endeavours, and not, as Fabricius would have it, to its weight. For indeed what does its weight contribute to the production of the foetus in four-footed animals which stand upright or sit, or to a woman who is lying down? Nor does the endeavour of the foetus proceed only from its bulk or from the abundance of the waters, as Fabricius thinks ... But the foetus itself with its head turned downwards, approaches the gates of the womb and opens them by its own strength and struggles out into the light.[12]

---

[11] Ibid., p. 108.
[12] Ibid., p. 405.

MakLuire the first contributor to British Paediatrics?

There can be no doubt, however, that Dr John MakLuire, in 1630, in *The Buckler of Bodilie Health* - specifically in the sections headed 'Of the nurse'; 'Of waining the child'; and 'Of the diseases befals children' - made the first contribution, at least to *Scottish* paediatrics.

Now, G. F. Still, in *The History of Paediatrics*, and the chapter headed 'The First English Writer on Diseases of Children' wrote that in 1545 appeared the first work on diseases of children ever written by an Englishman. This, he claimed, was the *Boke of Children*, first published in London, and written by Thomas Phaer. It formed part of a little volume in which were included some other works by the same writer. Still wrote that, as the title page of that publication stated that the whole volume was 'newly corrected and enlarged', it had been assumed that there must have been an earlier edition of the *Boke of Children*. Still questioned this. He referred to a copy of *The Regiment of Lyfe* in the library of the Royal College of Physicians of London which is believed to be of an edition which Herbert had said appeared in 1544. This copy is described as:

> A new booke entytled *The Regiment of lyfe* by John Bourot, lately translated out of Frenche by T. Phayer; with a singuler treatise of the pestilence by T. Phayer'. mo. Lond. Ed. Whytchurch.[13]

In that earlier publication, the *Boke of Children* was not present at all, and Still argued that, if this 1544 edition is the first edition which was 'newly corrected and enlarged' in the 1545 edition, these words almost certainly referred to the addition of the *Boke of Children* to it.[14] Still quoted Fuller as having said, in the latter's *Worthies of England*, that Phaer '(though he made none) he out of French did translate many usefull Bookes'.

---

[13] J. Bourot, *The Regiment of Lyfe*, trans. T. Phaer, London, 1544.

[14] G.F. Still, *The History of Paediatrics*, Oxford, 1931, p. 108.

But Still claimed that it was hardly fair of Fuller to say that Phaer made no book himself and was merely a translator. Aikin, in 1780, had stated that, in 1544, Phaer 'From the same language [French] also translated a book on the *Diseases of Children*' but that in 1560 Phaer 'only acknowledged the *Regiment of Life* to be a translation from the French'.[15]

Still felt justified in concluding, from this statement of Aikin, that the only work Phaer translated from the French was the *Regiment of Life* and not, as Fuller had seemed to imply, the rest of his medical writings. However, while it cannot be denied that Phaer translated from the French the *Regiment of Life*, it seems by no means certain that the *Boke of Children* was not also a translation from the French by Phaer.

If the *Boke of Children* was indeed a translation, and not an original English work, it would be Dr John MakLuire, in *The Buckler of Bodilie Health* of 1630, who made the first contribution to British, as well as, undoubtedly, to Scottish, paediatrics.

Was Harvey influenced by MakLuire's midwifery?

In view of the fact that it was MakLuire, and not Harvey, who made the first contribution to British midwifery, the question which arises becomes not whether Dr MakLuire was influenced by Harvey on the two specific midwifery topics mentioned above, but whether Harvey was influenced by MakLuire. Furthermore, if, as has been argued above, Harvey met and consulted with Dr MakLuire in Edinburgh in November 1641 (over the young Hugh Montgomery), the question arises whether Harvey, at that time, may have discussed with Dr MakLuire the latter's midwifery experience, as already published in *The Buckler* of 1630, and whether, in subsequently turning to the writing of his own midwifery chapter, '*De partu*', for the

---

[15] J. Aikin, *Biographic Memoirs of Medicine in Great Britain*, London, 1780, p. 78.

De Generatione of 1651, Harvey was influenced by the publication of Dr MakLuire which had ante-dated his own.

More probable than plagiarism on the part of Harvey, however, is that both would have been influenced by the *Byrth of Mankinde* (not itself a British contribution to midwifery), which ante-dated them both, and which would presumably have been well known to both of them. Even so, in that work, there is no mention of the phenomenon of false pregnancy (which MakLuire wrote about before Harvey) although it does emphasise the active part which both of them believed that the foetus played in parturition - in such statements as 'if it [the child] bee so faint, weake and tender, that it cannot turne it selfe or dooth it very slowly'[16] and:

> Also if the childe be dead in the mothers belly, it is a very perillous thing, forsomuch as it cannot bee easily turned, neither can it weld or help it selfe to come forth, or if the child be sicke or weakened so that it cannot for feeblenesse helpe it selfe[17]

Dr John MakLuire's own influence on the history of medicine

In conclusion, Dr John MakLuire appears not to have made any innovative medical discoveries. He had, however, written, in Latin, and from his own experience, about the nature and management of the pestilent (or 'plague-like') fever, mainly for the benefit of his fellow physicians. Clearly, also, he had been generally recognised, at a later date - after losing (probably) two of his own sons to it - as an expert on the plague itself.

Furthermore, he had perceived the social need to take action to protect the sick from dangerous charlatans by the establishment of a Royal College of Physicians.

---

[16] T. Raynalde, *The byrth of mankynde, set forth in English*, London, 1613, p. 92.

[17] Ibid., p. 93.

More generally, he had been recognised by the civil authorities both of Edinburgh and Glasgow as a leading expert in the medicine of his day - including its forensic aspects.

Finally, Dr John MakLuire had pioneered the encouragement of positive health and had been a pioneer in deliberately presenting current medical thought and practice in the vernacular - notably, as has been seen, in the fields of midwifery and paediatrics.

A
REGIMENT
FOR VVOMEN
WITH CHILD,
BAIRNES, AND
NOVRSES.

THE good Gardner hath not only a care of the impe and tree; but alſo of the ſeede which kyths by his carefull chooſing, and labouring of the ground for this end. At whoſe example,(that this my worke ſhould not be manck in any thing) I haue made digreſſion conteining the ſafe keeping, and right gouerning of the ground, wherein man his ſeede is ſowne.

Women with child are likned to one bearing a weightie burden, by a ſmall threed tyed to their hands, who going, ſoftlie, and warily may happily bring their burden to the purpoſed place: but if they bee agitate by any inordinate or violent motion, eaſily their burthen partly by the weight, and partly by reaſon of the ſmall

ſtring

Appendix A

A crucial palaeographic study

It had been a crucial palaeographic study, at the Scottish Record Office, of the original manuscript of the 'Register of Hornings and Inhibitions for Kirkcudbright-shire', that had led on to the firm conclusion that a John McCleure, tenant ('in Castelmaddie') of Gilbert Greirson 'of Castelmaddie', and dying in 1617, had been Dr MakLuire's paternal grandfather. Also, because John McCleure, Dr MakLuire's father, already tenant in Nether Carmonoch by 1622, had been a tenant of the same Gilbert Greirson, it had seemed clear that their tenancy had been of the heritable, 'kindly', type. Furthermore, the conclusion that Mareon Greir, Dr MakLuire's wife-to-be, had been a daughter of Gilbert Greirson's younger brother - who had modified his name from 'John Greirson' to 'John Greir' - had been followed by the equally crucial discovery that the latter had emigrated to Ulster in 1627. Finally, he would seem to have become, there, a tenant of the Montgomerys. Thus, there can be no doubt, because John Greir would have taken his daughter Mareon with him to Ulster, that it would have been there, close to the Montgomerys, that Dr MakLuire married her in 1634.

But how had the palaeographical study come about in the first place? While searching in the Ewart Library, Dumfries, the author had felt a suspicion, on coming across the words 'John McCleune in Castelmaddie', in a passage in Reid's typescript transcription of the 'Register of Hornings and Inhibitions for Kirkcudbrightshire', that these might be either a mis-transcription or an original mis-writing of 'John McCleure in Castelmaddie'.[1] It had been this that had prompted the study of the original manuscript of the Register - which had almost immediately shown that the name of the deceased testator referred

---

[1] 'Register of Hornings and Inhibitions for Kirkcudbrightshire', vol. 1, 1614-1621, transcribed R.C. Reid, Dumfries and Galloway Collection, Ewart Library, Dumfries, p. 24.

to in the original horning, had been given as 'Jonet McClane in Castelmaddie', just as Reid had transcribed it.[2] Similarly, it had also confirmed that, in the relaxing from that horning, the seemingly unchallenged 'correction' of the name had been to 'John McCleune in Castelmaddie', just as Reid had transcribed it.[3] In short, it had seemed that the suspicion, on the one hand, of a mistranscription had not been borne out.

However, next, it had been, on a closer study of one particular feature of the hand-writing of the relevant entry in the manuscript Register, that the suspicion of an original miswriting had, on the other hand, been fully borne out.[4] It had appeared that the writer of the entry had habitually written what was the unquestionable letter-pair 're' in two quite different ways, depending upon whether the letter-pair occurred at the end of a word, or otherwise. In the latter case, it had appeared that the writing of that letter-pair had taken the usual calligraphic form for that era. In the former case, however, (i.e. when the letter-pair 're' had occurred at the end of a word), the manner of writing these two letters had been indistinguishable from that in which the writer, elsewhere, had always written the letter-pair 'ne'.

To test out the consistency of this apparent quirk in the handwriting of this writer, the first page of the text of the relevant relaxing from horning (reproduced in fig. 1) was studied in a particular way. A series of consecutive examples, amounting to twenty-nine, of what was the unquestionable letter-pair 're' from this text (fig. 2) was identified, carefully traced, and transferred for display in two columns according to whether the letter-pair had occurred at the end of a word or otherwise (fig. 3). It had then become clear, from the table, that the apparent quirk in the handwriting of this writer had been consistent.

---

[2] SRO DI 70/1, Register of Hornings and Inhibitions for Kirkcudbrightshire, p. 114 (b).

[3] Ibid., p. 152 (a).

[4] Ibid.

Whenever writing the letter-pair 're' at the end of a word, the writer had indeed regularly written it in a manner indistinguishable from the manner in which he normally wrote the letter-pair 'ne'.

Now, the name in the Register under scrutiny, and accurately transcribed by Reid as 'John McCleune in Castelmaddie', appears five times in the portion of the original text which was being studied palaeographically. These examples of the name in the writer's handwriting had therefore been similarly traced carefully as shown in fig. 4. In two of these examples (in line 16 and line 21 respectively) the terminal two letters could, indeed, be interpreted as 're' rather than as 'ne'. Also, in the other three (in line 14, line 28 and line 30) the terminal two letters of the surname are written in a manner indistinguishable from the manner in which the writer normally wrote the letters 'ne' - and therefore in a manner in which, as had been shown, he would also have been in the habit of writing the letter-pair 're', whenever it occurred at the end of a word.

It had been in this way that the palaeographic study had established that the name intended by the writer of the relevant passage in the 'Register of Hornings and Inhibitions for Kirkcudbrightshire' had been 'John McCleure in Castelmaddie'.

Figure 1

Portion of text studied.

Line

From the first page of a Horning against Gilbert Greirson of Castelmaddie.

Ref: (Manuscript) Register of Hornings and Inhibitions for Kirkudbrightshire. SRO DI 70/1; 152(a).

Reproduced by kind permission of the Keeper of the Records of Scotland with the agreement of the Controller of Her Majesty's Stationery Office.

Figure 2

Transcription with all 're' letter-pairs identified.

Line

1   APUD Kirkrict vigesimo septn die mensie Novem
2   bris Anno Dm' millesimo sexcentesimo decimo octa•••
3   THE Quhilk day ye lres of relaxa'nn w^t ye execu'nis yrof •••
4   undrewritt' war prd'cit be Thomas Carrok messgr and regrat in ye stewart•••
5   court buik of Kirkrict be Jon Newall not' clerk deput yrof conforme to ye act
6   of plia't off ye qlk ye tennor followis JAMES be ye grace of God
7   King of Great Bratane France & Ireland Defendar of ye Faith to o^r lovitte
8   Thomas Carrok messgr mesagris or shreffis in yt pairt •••• & •••••••
9   speciallie ••••••• greiting Forsamiekle as it is humblie meanit & shawin
10 to us be ore lovit Gilbert Greirsone of Castelmaddie that qr he is
11 alle^t denuncit o^r rebell & put to o^r horne be vertew of o^r uyeris
12 lres of horneing direct & execut at ye instance of Edward Forrester Comissr
13 of o^r Comissariat of Kirkrict agains ye said complen' as alle^t intromettore
14 w^t ye guids & gere of umqle Jon McCleune in Castelmaddie for not pductionn
15 & exhibitionn befoir ye sd Commisr of ye testament & inventore of ye guidis
16 and gere of ye said umqll Johne McCleune not conferaeing of ye samen and
17 peying tort yearfore maist wrongoualie Considdering it is of veritie
18 yt ye said compleinar was nevir laulie nayer plie nor at his duelling
19 place at ye insta'ce of ye sd Edward Forrester Commissagr of Kirkrict fon^d for exhi
20 bitionn & pductionn before him of ye sd testament & inventar of ye said guidis
21 & gere of ye sd umqle Jon McCleune Lykeas ye prddit denuncia'nn following
22 was lefft be ye messgr executor of o^r saidis uyeris lres by ye knowledge &
23 directionn of ye sd Edward Forrester agains ye sd compleinar sva yt ye sd
24 prdd'it charge & denuncia'nn cam nevir to his knowledge in dew tyme
25 Secundlie o^r saidis uy'is prddit lres ••• •••• execut at ye instance
26 of ye said Edward Forrester agains ye said complein' for not pdductionn &
27 exhibitionn of ye testament and inventar of ye guidis & gere of ye
28 sd umqll Jon McCleune nayer aucht he to have beine chargit yrfore nor can he
29 be subject to gif inventar yrof conforme ye samen or pey tort yrfore ——
30 because it is of veritie yt he is nayer exe'r no'at to ye sd umqll Jon McCleune
31 nor intromettar w^t his gudis & geir bot be ye contrair ——

Figure 3

Analysis.

The letter-sequence 're' tabulated according to its occurrence at the end of a word - or not so.

No.	Line.	Word.	end	not so	No.	Line.	Word.	end	not so
1	3	l<u>re</u>s		ɹ	16	15	invento<u>re</u>	ŋ	
2	3	<u>re</u>laxa'nn		ɹ	17	16	ge<u>re</u>	ℼ	
3	4	und<u>re</u>writt'		ʝ	18	17	yearfo<u>re</u>	ℳ	
4	4	<u>re</u>grat		ɹ	19	18	Fo<u>rre</u>ster		ɹ
5	7	G<u>re</u>at		ʝ	20	20	befo<u>re</u>	ɾ	
6	7	I<u>re</u>land		ɹ	21	21	ge<u>re</u>	ɲ	
7	8	sh<u>re</u>ffis		ɹ	22	22	l<u>re</u>s		ɹ
8	9	g<u>re</u>iting		ɹ	23	23	di<u>re</u>ctionn		ɹ
9	10	o<u>re</u>	ℼ		24	23	Fo<u>rre</u>ster		ɹ
10	11	<u>re</u>bell		ɹ	25	25	l<u>re</u>s		ɹ
11	12	l<u>re</u>s		ɹ	26	26	Fo<u>rre</u>ster		ɹ
12	12	di<u>re</u>ct		ɹ	27	27	ge<u>re</u>	ɾ	
13	12	Fo<u>rre</u>ster		ɹ	28	27	yrfo<u>re</u>	ɲ	
14	13	intrimetto<u>re</u>	ℼ		29	29	yrefo<u>re</u>	ℳ	
15	14	ge<u>re</u>							

Conclusion:

there was a quirk in the writer's writing, whereby he regularly wrote a **terminal** 're' as 'ne'.

Figure 4

The writer's manner of writing 'John McCleure'.

Comment

Line 14    Clearly, some uncertainty about spelling. The terminal'ne' exemplifies the quirk. (blotting in the original)

Line 16    The terminal'ne' exemplifies the quirk, although'v' was a way of writing 'r'.

Line 21 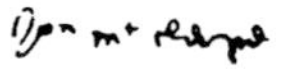   The'ŋ' could be an 'r', but otherwise the terminal'ne' exemplifies the quirk.

Line 28 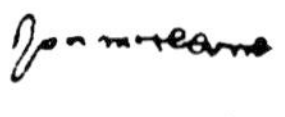   The terminal ne exemplifies the quirk.

Line 30    The terminal ne seems to exemplify the quirk.

Appendix B

Dr John MakLuire's maternal (Denholme) connections

An enquiry into Dr MakLuire's maternal (Denholme) connections was pursued in the hope of finding some indication of where his mother may have been residing; at the time of her alleged pre-marriage adultery; at the time of her presumed marriage to John MakLuire (Dr MakLuire's father); and thus at the time of her giving birth to the future Dr MakLuire.

The enquiry had begun with a possible clue from the record of the 1622 trial. This had been the clearly erroneous substitution, in one place, of the Christian name 'Katharene' for 'Alison' (Denholme).[1] 'Katharene' had seemed to be unlikely as a simple mistake to have been made for 'Alison'. The possibility, rather, of there having been an historically identifiable 'Katharene', connected with Alison Denholme's family, whose name, during the preparations for the trial could have become accidentally incorporated into the documentation, had arisen.

It had then appeared, from wider searches, mainly in testaments of contemporaneous Denholmes, that apart from Denholmes living in Edinburgh, perhaps the most prominent Denholmes of the time, to whom Alison Denholme might have been related, had been the Denholmes of West Scheill, near Carnwath, Lanarkshire (see fig.).

It had seemed that, ever since a Simon Dennum, in 1506, had inherited West Scheill, Denholmes had, for more than two centuries, been either proprietors of or tenants in West Scheill - a mansion which was pulled down in recent years, and of which a drawing, based upon an aerial photograph taken at the time, is shown in the fig.[2] It had appeared that, at the time of the 1622 trial, the tenant in

---

[1] SRO JC 2/6, Justiciary Court, p. 98.

[2] Retour Symon Dennum, Inc. Spec., Lanark, 462, 16 February 1506 (Omissa - Symon Dennum heires John Liddaill, avi - West Scheill in baronia de Carnwath lxxxiv, 374).

West Scheill had been a John Denholme - who was to die seven years later - and it had been noted, from his testament, that his wife's Christian name had indeed been 'Katherine'.[3] She had been a 'Katherine Pantonn (or Pautonn)' and it had been noted that if, as seemed probable, she was the 'Katherine Pawtonn' who was baptised in Edinburgh on 18th January, 1600, she would have been aged twenty-two at the time of the 1622 trial.[4] It had seemed, therefore, that this Katherine could not be excluded from having been, in some way, involved in the preparation of the documentation of the trial - although no actual evidence for this was found.

In looking, therefore, for other clues, attention had turned again to the record of the royal remission for adultery in the Register of the Great Seal (see Chapter 2, fig. 2), and had taken note that Alison Denholme's father had been specified, there, mainly by blanks, as 'umql ***** D*n-nane in ***** '. While it was unfortunate, therefore, that neither his Christian name nor the location of his place of abode were specified, at least it was clear first that he was already deceased in 1622 and second that the little word 'in' indicated that he had, indeed, been a tenant farmer.

In searching, next, for a tenant farmer named 'Denholme' in Kirkcudbrightshire, it had been found that, among the quite large number (559) of signatures on the 1637 Kirkcudbright petition against the Service Book, there had been one, and only one, Denholme signature. This had been the signature of an 'Adam Denholme in Blauqu/*[5] (surely Blauquhairn)' - who, incidentally, it had been thought might have been a descendant of an Adam

---

[3] SRO CC14/5/3, Testament John Denholme in West Scheill, 1630, fol. 86b.

[4] SRO OPR 685 1/1, Edinburgh (Greyfriars) Register of Baptisms, 18 January 1600.

[5] Document torn at this point.

Denholme, goldsmith, elected a burgess of Edinburgh in 1562.[6]

Clearly, this Adam Denholme in Blawquhairn in 1637 (who must have succeeded the David McClure who had been tenant there in 1623) could not, himself, have been the father of Alison Denholme, as her father had been already deceased in 1622.[7] It had seemed possible, however, as the only farmer in Kirkcudbrightshire in 1637 to have been identified as bearing the name 'Denholme', that he may well have been related to him.

It had been the discovery that there had been only one identifiable 'Denholme' tenant farmer in Kirkcudbrightshire in 1637, and that his tenancy had been in Blawquhairn (previously tenanted by a McClure), that had suggested that Alison Denholme, Dr MakLuire's mother, at the time of her alleged adultery with Dr MakLuire's father; at the time of her subsequent marriage to him; and later, perhaps, at the time of Dr MakLuire's birth, may have been dwelling at Blawquhairn.

[6] Roll of Edinburgh Burgesses (1406-1700) - Adam Denholme, goldsmith, 1562.
[7] *Register of the Privy Council of Scotland*, Series 1, XIII (1622-1625), p. 217.

Figure

The Denholme manor house at West Scheill.

(a) Drawing, from an aerial photograph taken shortly before demolition.

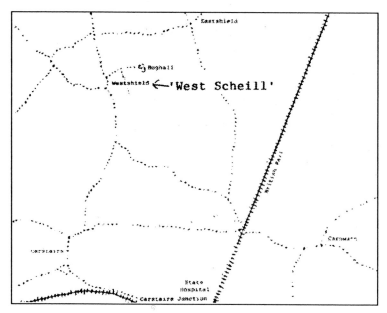

(b) The site of West Scheill.

Appendix C

The *Tractatus de febre pestilente* by Maister John MakLuire, Edinburgh: Wreittoun, 1630

Mutationes temporum morbos gignunt, ut ait Hipp. Nam qualis aer, talis spiritus: quales spiritus, tales humores, & humores quales, tales partes solidae: Aer autem est purus vel impurus, & contagiosus: & quemadmodum purus aer saluti confert ita impurus morbos perniciosos generat, ut lippitudines, tusses, raucoines, anginas, gravedines, variaque ac perniciosa febrium genera, praesertim vero illa, in quibus maculosa cutis apparet, cum totius corporis sudore, a quo febrium genere plurimi mortales perditi sunt.

Cum vero morborum omnium febres hae sint maxime laethales, de earum natura, causis ac signis nonnulla subtexemus.

Ex morbis, qui humano generi contingunt, aliqui sunt communes, seu populares, aliter a Graecis επιδημιοσ dicti: alii singulorum hominum proprii, quos Graeci σπυραδικοσ, sparsos vel seminatos vocant: popularium morborum quidam sunt civitati alicui peculiariares, hoc genus morbi ενδημιοζ Graeci vocant: alii sine discrimine cunctas regiones peragrant, qui nomine generis επιδημιοσ appellantur: rursum isti Epidemii, si mortales jugulant pestiferi dicuntur, atque haec pestilentia, & pestilens febris vocatur.

Nonnunquam pestilens febris sine pestilentia reperitur, ut docet Gal. in 3. de praesag. ex pulsibus, & 3. de morb. popularibus sect. 3. Hoc autem interest judicio nostro, inter pestilentiam & pestilentem febrim, quod illa plures, enecat, magisque contagiosa est, & in inguinibus, aut sub axillis sit semper, nonnunquam post aures carbunculi exoriunter: in hac vero, in toto corpore, sed maxime in dorso pustulae quaedam erumpunt, quae in genere exanthemata vocantur, sive etiam maculae pulicum punctionibus similes: interdum vero, & sine his pestifera febris exoritur, quae per alia Symptomata paulo post referenda dignoscitur: haec morborum distinctio desumitur ex Hipp. & Gal. in primo de ratione victus sententia nona, in 2. de locis, aere & aqua, in 3. de Epid.sect.3. senten. 20, & 28.

Febrium pestilentialium causa, alia externa, alia interna: interna & proxima causa est humoris agitatio quae eos excitat, & de potentia in actum reducit. Nam natura humores suis locis quiescentes facilius regit, quam agitatos & extra suos limites digressos; externa causa pestilentis fabris, ut plurimum est aer: aerem non hic purum & elementarem intelligere oportet: Nam vix putredinem admittit, sed mixtum ex vero aere & partibus aqueis vaporosis, & terreis fumosis, & igneis.

Aer autem mixtus vel proprio & innato, vel alieno & adventitio vititio est contagiosus, proprio vitio, praesertim cum intemperie callida humida tenetur.

Hoc Gal. admonuit cap. 4. d temperamentis, dum ait calidam Coeli constitutionem pessimam esse, & pestilent-em: Item 1. differentiis febrium hoc nobis insinuavit, dum docet methodum, qua corpora a pestilente febre tuta (?) redderemus.

Idem docet in morbis vulgaribus constitutionem scilicet calidam, humidam, morbos ex putredine creare, & in 1. Epid. sect. 1. *** Adventitio autem contaminari docet, 11. Meth. cap. 5. inquiens, perspicuum vero est, & aeris subst-antiae, quae per anhelitum ducitur curam esse habendam, ut nimirum sit optime temperata, & a quolibet ipsam inquinate, quam mandissima; neque ex metallis, nec forna-cibus, aut profundis canitatibus aliquam mixtionem suspi-ciens, neque ex leguminum aut olerum animalium ve, aut alius cujuslibet rei putredine, neque halitus ex stagnis aut paludibus aut fluviis admittens: Hoc idem Avicenna sen. 3. 1. canon innuit. Aetius autem lib. 5. cap. 94 docet signa, si aeris vitio vel aliunde contingat: si inquit aeris vitio hi morbi proveniunt, primum aves hoc malo afficiuntur; sin vero ob terrarum exhalitionem, quadru pedum erit prima calamitas: Arist. 1. probl. ait gravem morbosumque annum fore, cum copia renarum processerit, nam pluviam humidamque tempestatem denotar.

Possunt etiam vitiosae aquae pestilentiam causare, id in exercitibus frequenter accidisse historiae prodidere: tum etiam cibus, & alimentum impurum malos humores in corpore procreant, ac ita putredini obnoxia faciunt.

Siderum autem occultos influxus hos morbos causare, non videntur Hipp. Galen. ac Arist. concedere, sed tantummodo aerem hunc a Coelo per lumen & motum, ad frigidum, calidum, humidum, & siccum immutari: Atque hisce primis qualitatibus intervenientibus reliquos deinde omnes effectus produci: Ab Hipp. multis quidem in locis hoc haberi potest, sed praecipue in lib. de aere, locis, & aquis: ab Arist. lib. 2. de Coelo, & 1. sect. probl. 11. Galen. vero omnibus in locis, ubi de aeris immutatione aut corruptione, non ratione exhalationum loquitur, sed semper primarum qualitatum vitio evenire contendit, nullam qualitatem occultam in ipso merito stellarum agnoscens, ut omnibus patere potest, ejus explanationes legentibus, in Aphir. in lib. de natura humana, & in lib. de morbis popul. Ostenditque Hipp. nihil aliud significare per divinum, quam ambientis nos aeris constitutionem. Verum tamen cum Avicenna, & peritissimi Astrologi hos astrorum influxus concesserint, non omnino videntur rejiciendi.

Febris pestilentis materia est vel spiritus, vel humores, spiritus ob siccitatum vix corrumpunctur, cum referant naturam ignis, qui humiditatem omnem putredinis materiam absumit aliquam tamen contagionem in principio assumunti sed statim eam humoribus communicant, si solis spiritibus infectis tantum esset, citius necaret, ac in excrementa tanta non solveretor, sed cum sudore tautum, ut aliae ephemerae.

Humores sunt vel bilis, vel melancholia adusta bilem designant sitis inexhausta, bilis vomitus, lingua arida, incendium maximum circa regionem cordis, & ventriculi, tum delirium, cum excrementis biliosis.

Melancholiam demonstrant tum causae generantes, ut maeror, pavor, praesertim tempore belli, tum ratio victus impura, in annonae caritate, quo tempore coguntur homines vesci radicibus, fabis, leguminibus, aliisque id genus Melancholiam procreantibus: Hinc vulgare illud μετα λιμον λοιμοσ, hisce adde signa concomitantia, ut Maniam cum studio, stigmata nigra undique erumpentia, cordis palpitationem, tum carbunculum, qui cum pruritu, rubore, ardore vehementi oritur, quo sensim increscente, pars uritur crustosumque ulcus, quasi candente ferro inducitur, crassum, retoridumque sanguinem ostendens.

Notae pestilentis febris inveniunter apud Galenum, in tertio de praesag. ex pulsibus, & sexto de morbis popul. sect. 1 sentent. 3. & apud Aetium, lib. 5, cap. 92, & Aegenetam, lib. 2. cap. 35. & apud Avicen. sen. 41. tract. 4. cap. 1, quae variantur pro varia corporis humorumque constitutione, ita ut vix videas duos *idem contagione inquinatos, similibus premi, symoptomatis. Quosdam cruciat capitis dolor cum conjuncta gravitate, & in somnum protensione: alios vero vigiliae molestae, bilis vomitus, frequens jactatio, delirium; alii, nec siti vehemente, nec inappetentia, nec magno incendio teneri videntur, ita aegri sine sensu doloris inopinatim discedunt, adeo ut a principio ob sui levitatem clarissimis medicis febres hae imposuerint: hosce sitis inexhausta premit cum inappetentia, tum algore externo, & ardore interno; cum febre ardente: Hisce pustulae erumpunt, & exanthemata, aliis carbunculi, & bubones, pulsus quibusdam frequens ac vehemens, nonnullis imbecillis, ac languidus, lingua ut plurimum arefacta, anhelitus tetri odoris, & intra os intuentibus, modo color erysipelatis modo herpetis apparet, urinae aliae turbulentae, & lividae redduntur, atque hae saepius, aliae vero plusquam natura postulat, aquosiores, dilutioresque sunt, aliorum, sed rarius exquisire naturalibus similes sunt; colore & crassitudine; interdum valde biliosae, modo nigricantes cum subsidentiis depravatissimis: Sudores interdum valde faetent, alvi excrementa biliosa graviterolent, in universim quorundam excrementa omnia, lotia scilicet alvi dejectiones, sudores sputa anhelitus, propter insignem putredinem faedisunt odoris. Nam ut odor bonus condictionem denotat, ita faetidus putredinem quae coction** adversatur, teste Theophr. 6. de causis planntarum, cap. 15. & 17. Est autem putredo secundum

Arist. 4, Meteor. corruptio in unoquoque humido propriae & naturalis caliditatis ab adventitio calore: nam ingenitus cujusque rei calor, rem ipsam conservat, alienus corrumpit. Visis ita in universum putredinis causis, quae morbos procreare solent, quotiescunque; harum aliqua, vel omnes concurrerint, iis obviandum, mature erit; Nam fero medicina paratur. Cum mala per longas invalucre moras. Aeris itaque; intemperies propria ignibus frequentioribus est emendanda, prout olim Acron Agrigentius, ac Hipp. per urbem Atheniensem fecisse feruntur; tum adventitia est amovenda quantum fieri potest, aquas stagnantes fluxiles reddendo, cadavera mortua sepeliendo, vias, vicos, ac angiportus, omni faeda colluvie purgando, vitiosa & impura alimenta vitando, tum aquam bonam eligendo; id est, quae omni advena qualitate caret, sapore *viz.* odore, colore, quae bibentibus jucunda, cujus facilis ex ventriculo, praecordiisque discensus, cito incalescens, ac infrigescens; omnia quae per illam elixantur facile excoquens:nullo veneno, limosoque corpusculo commixta, sed quae **nitidissima & pellucida cernitur, aestate gelida **hieme admodum tepida, pestilentia vero gras**ngite, fenestrae domus ad Orientem & Septentrionem pandantur, ad austrum vero, & occasum pandantur, cubiculum suffiatur ex thure, foliis **uri, aliisq; quorum suffitus aerem corrigit; cum manus aqua, tantillo aceto permixta laventur, spongiola aceto imbuta, quae frequenter moderetur, capsulae(a) includator, ac mane prodituri **Odimant ex hoc elect. ad juglandis magnitudinem.

Bol. armen. aqua scabios. lotae unc. 1. flor. nymph. & bugloss. condit. utriusque unc. 11. corte. citri. & flor. ros. condit utriusque unc. 1. cinam. drach. semin. citri a cortic. purgati. margarit. corall. rubri. singulorum drag. 1. ambr. scrup. 11. Camph. scrup. 1. misceantur cum succo mali citrei aut punici.

Sed quia causae externae nisi concurrentibus internis morbos non gignunt: Aeris enim intemperies quantumvis valida, nisi corpus humoribus vitiosis repletum, putredini obnoxium reddatur, non inficit: proxima itaque; cura sit, causas omnes internas removere; quod ut fiat, sequentes canones erunt servandi.

(These final words serve to link the 'tractatus' with the main text of the 'Sanitatis Semita' - which follows).

Translation by Mr James J. Robertson

(The words in curved brackets are alternative translations. Those in square brackets are implied).

'Changes of the times (seasons) bring forth diseases,' as Hippocrates says. Such as air and breath(ing): breath and moistures (fluids) and fluids and solids: Air is pure or impure and infectious, and just as pure air is advantageous for health, so impure [air] generates pernicious (dangerous) diseases such as inflammations of the eyes, coughs, hoarsenesses, quinsies, heavinesses of the limbs and heads and various dangerous kinds of fevers, especially those in which the skin appears spotted, with sweating of the whole body by which kind of fevers most deaths occur.

Since these fevers of all diseases may be the most lethal, we shall consider (bring together) some things about their nature, causes and symptoms.

Amongst the diseases which affect humankind, some are universal or generally found among peoples, otherwise called 'epidemic' by the Greeks: others are particular to individual people, which the Greeks call 'sporadic' or scattered or sown around. There are certain common diseases peculiar to a certain state, this kind of disease the Greeks called 'endemic': others indiscriminately pass through whole districts, these are called generically, 'epidemics'. Again, these epidemics, if they kill, are called pestilential, and this infectious disease (plague) is indeed called pestilential fever.

Sometimes pestilential fever is found without the plague as Galen teaches in [Book] 3, *On Symptoms*, from tapping (?) (stroking) and in [Book] 3, *On Common Diseases*, section 3. But there is a difference in our judgement between plague and pestilential fever, because it (plague) may afflict more (individuals) and is more contagious and it may always be in the groins or under the armpits (?);

sometimes carbuncles arise behind the ears, in fact over the whole body but more so pustules break out on the back which are called 'exanthemata' and are like fleabites: and indeed without these things pestilential fever arises which is diagnosed by other symptoms to be dealt with a little later: this distinction of the diseases is taken from Hippocrates and Galen, in the first place, the 9th opinion concerning the rule and ways of living, in the second place on the role of air and water, in the third place *On Epidemics*, section 3, opinions 20 and 21.

The cause of pestilential fevers is either external or internal: the internal and immediate cause is the motion of the moisture which arouses them and diminishes the power of movement. For nature more easily controls humours (moistures) which are at rest in their own places, than those which are agitated and beyond their own confines; the external cause of pestilential fever is, for the most part, air; one must understand that air here is not pure and original: For it is not wholly pure (?) since the air is indeed mixed with moist, earthy, smokey and firey parts.

Air is mixed (composed) either with its own innate quality or is contaminated by chance with an external fault, or with its own defect, especially where it is subject to humid warm weather.

Galen suggested this at chapter 4 on the right proportions of things where he says that hot weather is the worst situation and is unhealthy: Likewise at [chapter] 1 this has created for us a variety of fevers, and where he teaches a method whereby we may safely restore the body from unhealthy fever.

Likewise he demonstrates the nature of common diseases, namely, that heat and moisture create diseases through rottenness(?). and in [Book] 1 of the *Epidemics* (?), section 1. ... But by chance it proves to be polluted [N.B. this is a literal translation and the meaning is not clear], [Book] 2 *Methodology* (?), chapter 5 saying, it is truly clear, and of the substance of the atmosphere, which is induced by deep breathing (gasping) that a cure may be had, that without a doubt it may be best tempered, [no matter how foul and consuming it may be. (?)];[1] neither trust any mixture from metals (mines, minerals?), furnaces or deep caverns (?), nor from the rottenness of pulses or vegetables or animals or of anything whatsoever, nor allow vapours from ponds, marshes or rivers: Avicenna indicates this at opinion 3, rule 1. However, Aetius at book 5, chapter 94 indicates symptoms where it may happen from a defect of the air or from another source, where he says these diseases arise from the defect of the air, birds are especially affected by this evil. On the other hand, the first to suffer from earth vapours will be the four-legged animals: Aristotle [Book] 1 on problems says that the year will be noxious and disease-laden when an abundance of frogs appear, since this indicates rainy and wet weather.

Also, defective waters can cause pestilence, history has revealed this to have happened to armies: then also they produce nourishments[2] and impure sustenance [and] bad moistures in the body and so they expose things to rottenness.

But Hippocrates, Galen and Aristotle are not seen to concede that the hidden attraction of the stars causes these diseases, but merely that this air is changed by the atmosphere due to light and movement, to coldness, heat, dampness and dryness: and through the happening of these initial conditions, then all the remaining effects are produced: This is indeed maintained by Hippocrates in many places, but especially in the book on air, places and waters: by Aristotle, in book 2, *On Atmosphere*, and indeed by Galen, Section 1, Problem 2 in every place, where he speaks on the change or corruption of the air, not on account of vapours (?), but he always maintains it happens due to a fault in the initial conditions, denying

---

[1] I am not happy with the translation of this and the preceding 4 lines. The final part in square brackets is a very free and perhaps inaccurate rendering.

[2] The grammar here is defective. The translation here depends on *cibus* which is nominative being read as *cibos* which is accusative plural. No sense can be made of this sentence if *cibus* remains in the nominative. *cibus* = food, nourishment.

any hidden cause from the stars, as it can be shown to all who read his explanations, in Aphir.[3] in the book on human nature and in the book on diseases of the people. Hippocrates shows that there is no [more] divine significance in this than the nature of the air surrounding us. However, since Avicenna and most skilful astrologers have conceded these influences of the stars, they should not be entirely rejected.

For pestilential fevers, the cause is either vapours (airs) or moistures, atmospheres due to dryness [i.e. dry vapours?] are with difficulty destroyed [i.e. hardly harmed?] since they import the nature of fire which destroys all moisture which is the cause of rottenness, however, in principle, they take to themselves some infection but immediately they communicate it to moistures but if it is confined to infective vapours, it may kill more quickly, and it may not be broken up into excrements but only with sweat like other passing things.

Moistures are either bile or brown melancholia [black bile?], vomiting a dry tongue, a burning greatest around the heart or belly also delirium with bilious excrements denote bile.

Then originating causes indicate melancholy, such as sadness, anxiety, especially in time of war, then a vile manner and way of living, the high cost of provisions, when men are forced to eat root crops, beans, vegetables and other things producing that kind of melancholy: Hence as a matter of form that is 'pestilential hunger' [Greek] (famine), to these add accompanying symptoms, such as rage with a vehement passion, black marks breaking out everywhere, palpitation of the heart, then a boil with itchiness, the part is inflamed, showing a crusted ulcer as if induced by red-hot iron, gross and dried-up blood.

---

[3] I cannot identify Aphir. Could it be Averroes? This Islamic scholar wrote on medical matters and would have been familiar with the works of Galen.

Appendix C

Notes on pestilential fevers are found in Galen in the 3rd [book] *On Symptoms* from beating [stroking] and in the 6th [Book] *On Common Diseases*, section 1, opinion 3 and in Aetius, book 5, chapter 92 and Aegeneta, book 2, chapter 35 and in Avicenna, opinion 41, tract 4, chapter 1 which are reported for the changing nature of the body and the moistures [humours], so that you may hardly see that two [men] polluted with the same contagion will be marked with the same symptoms. A headache with accompanying sickness and a falling asleep torment some; irksome sleeplessness, vomiting of bile, frequent shaking, delirium [torment] others; others seem resting neither being held by a strong lassitude nor by a great vehemence, so that although sick they remain without a feeling of pain to such a degree that these fevers, on account of their superficiality, from the beginning deceive doctors who are most skilled: an unquenchable undesired thirst bears upon these |men], then with external coldness and internal heat; with a burning fever: Pustules break out on these, and boils and carbuncles on others, and buboes, a frequent and vehement stamping in others, in some [who are] feeble and listless (that is if languidus is in error for languidis - if not, languidus does not agree with anything), the tongue commonly being dry, gasping with a foul smell, and for those who look into the mouth sometimes the colour of erysipelas (this is not a Latin word but in Greek comprehends the colour red), sometimes that of herpes appears (herpis in Greek is a creeping vine), some urines are delivered disturbed and of a bluish colour, and others, more often than nature desires, are more watery and thinner, those of others are similar but less frequent than nature desires; with colour and thickness; now and then intensely bilious, merely becoming black with a most corrupt settling down. Now and then, sweatings may be very ill-smelling, bilious excrements of the bowel unpleasantly emit smells, it is obvious washings (?) and ejections of the bowel, sweats, spittles, pantings, on account of prominent putridness are of foul smell. For as a good odour indicated one condition, as evidenced in Theophrastus [Book] 5 on the causes of plants (young shoots), chapters 15 and 17. But putridness according to Aristotle

[Book] 4 *On Meteors* (?), is the corrupting in every single moist heat on account of its own natural warmth: for the innate heat of everything preserves the thing itself, something different destroys. The causes of putridness have thus been generally seen and the diseases they are accustomed to produce howsoever often; some of these, or all may happen together, it will be opportune to avoid them; sooner or later medicine is prepared. Since evils become more powerful after long delays. Therefore of air; a particular irregularity must be corrected with more frequent fires, as once Acron Agrigentius and Hippocrates are held to have done for the city of Athens; then the necessary thing is to get rid of as much as possible, by making stagnant waters flowable, by burying dead bodies, by cleansing streets, lanes and alleys of all foul impurity, by avoiding bad and impure foods, then choosing good water; that is, anything which lacks all strange property or flavour, for example, smell and colour which are pleasing to those who drink, of which the descent from the belly and the stomach is easy, quickly growing warm and cooling; boiling up everything which is easily boiled: mixed with no poisonous or slimy (muddy) particle, but which is seen to be clear and transparent, in summer icy cold, in winter quite lukewarm, when pestilence is raging[4], the windows of the house may be opened to the East and the North, indeed, they may be opened to the South and the West, the bedroom may be perfumed (fumigated) with frankincense, leaves of ...[5] and other things; which fumigation improves the air; hands may be washed with water mixed with a little vinegar, a little sponge soaked with vinegar, which often may be perfumed, and kept in a

---

[4] I cannot decipher the word beginning *gras* ... but it may be derived from the deponent verb *grassi* = 'to rage'. On this assumption I have made the translation.

[5] This is indecipherable. It could be *iurus* but that means 'broth'. It could be an abbreviation - and a number of words have been abbreviated in the text. If it is an abbreviation, it could be *urtica* = 'nettle'. The phrase could then be translated as 'leaves of nettle' which makes sense, but this is a hazardous guess.

little box, to be produced in the morning ...[6] from this choice (amber) the size of a nut.

[Here follows the prescription.]

But indeed external causes do not produce diseases unless concurring with internal [causes]. For inclemency of the air is, however, healthy, unless the body is full of evil humours; it may be made liable to putridness, it does not infect; therefore, the immediate cure may be to remove all internal causes: that this may be done, the following rules were to be observed.

[It is here that the text is 'prefixed' to that of *the Sanitatis Semita* itself].

---

[6] The rest of this sentence produces major difficulties in translation. *Odimant* is not the correct reading of this indecipherable word. I cannot relate it to any other Latin word. The literal meaning of what follows is unclear. *Elect.* is an abbreviation. It could be *electus* = 'choice' or *electrum* = 'amber'. Or, it could refer to an 'electuary', which is the pharmacological term for a medicinal powder, bound together with honey to form an acceptable pill, perhaps the size of a nut.

Appendix D

The genealogical identity of Mareon Greir

The enquiry into the genealogical identity, childhood, and pre-marriage background, of Mareon Greir, Dr MakLuire's second wife, began with the assumption that the fact that Sir Robert Greir of Lag, the acknowledged Chief of the Greirson/Greir family, was the principal witness at the baptism of Mareon Greir's first child, would be significant.

Also, as it would have been her second son (William), who would normally have been named after the maternal grandfather, the first possibility considered (for the identity of Mareon Greir's father) had been Sir William Greir[son] of Lag, Sir Robert's father, who had died in 1629 - and the possibility that Sir Robert had thus been Mareon's brother.[1] But this possibility had been quickly excluded by referring to the genealogical information contained in *The Lag Charters*.[2] Also, no other 'William Greir', both closely related to Sir Robert, and also of appropriate age to have been Mareon Greir's father, had been identifiable.

The next possibility considered had been that her first son, John, although named, primarily, and according to custom, after the paternal grandfather, John MakLuire in Nether Carmonoch, had been named, perforce, after her father also - in which case, her father would have been a 'John Greir'. However, a similar search, in the Lag Charters, for a 'John Greir' amongst Sir Robert's close relations who might, plausibly, have been Mareon's father had also been unsuccessful.

---

[1] SRO CC5/6/1, Testament, Sir William Greirson of Lag, 1629.

[2] A.L. Murray, ed., *The Lag Charters, 1400-1720: Sir Philip J. Hamilton-Grierson's Calendar*, Edinburgh: Scottish Record Society, 1958, Old Series, 88.

Appendix D

The Greirsons of Castelmaddie and the Carmonochs

At this juncture, because of the failure of these first two lines of enquiry, and because of Dr MakLuire's own roots in Kirkcudbrightshire, attention had turned to the Kirkcudbrightshire Greirson/Greir family who were related, although rather more distantly, to the Lairds of Lag. These were the Greirsons of Castelmaddie and the Carmonochs, who had been descended from the early Greirs of Lag and had originally been the Greirsons of Dalton (Daton), in Dumfriesshire (see fig.)

These Greirsons, after a Gilbert Greirson of Dalton had sold Dalton to a John Lindsay in 1552, had continued, quite properly (if to the confusion of some present-day commentators), to use the words 'of Dalton' as part of their surname, while being the proprietors, only, of Castelmaddie and the Carmonochs, in Kirkcudbrightshire.[3] Now, a John Greirson, second son of the aforementioned Gilbert, as part of a marriage settlement, in 1591, with John Maxwell of Butill Maynes, had arranged that these lands be diverted from his older son and heir (to whom they would normally have fallen, but who may have been mentally or physically incapacitated) to his younger son, Gilbert Greirson, on the occasion of the latter's marriage to John Maxwell's daughter, Agnes Maxwell.[4] However, in 1598, that younger son, Gilbert, had pre-deceased his father, John, by three years, leaving, as 'bairns' (i.e. under fourteen years of age) two sons, Gilbert and John (see fig.)[5].

These two 'bairns', Gilbert and John, losing their father in 1598, may have spent some of their early childhood at Dalmanasyde, Kirkcudbrightshire, with their widowed mother, Agnes Maxwell, who had been left Dalmanasyde

---

[3] Sir P.J. Hamilton-Grierson, 'Notes on Various Families of the Name of Grierson', transcribed J.R.H. Greeves, Dumfries County Council Library, 1948, p. 39.

[4] Ibid., p. 41.

[5] SRO CC8/8/35, Testament, Gilbert Greirson, 3 February 1601, p. 129.

by her deceased husband. But, if their mother was, perhaps, the Agnes Maxwell who, by 1609, was spouse to a James Hamilton of Threepwood, in the parish of Beith, they may later have been living, with her, close to Braidstane Castle, the Ayrshire seat of Sir Hugh Montgomery, at the time of that James Hamilton's death in that year.[6] Wherever they may have spent their childhood, it had seemed probable, however, that by the end of their schooldays they would have returned to the family lands of Castelmaddie and the Carmonochs.

Gilbert Greirson, the older of these two bairns, had been retoured heir to his father in 1615, seventeen years after his father's death and fourteen years after his grandfather's death.[7] Presumably becoming of age in that year, his birth would have been about 1594. He was the 'Gilbert Greirson of Castelmaddie' already referred to as having appealed, successfully, to the King against the horning of 1618 - which itself had followed the failure to 'give up' the testament of his tenant, the 'John MakLuire in Castelmaddie' who it has already been argued to have been Dr MakLuire's paternal grandfather, and who had died in 1617. This Gilbert Greirson had married an Annabel Chalmers, and had been the 'Gilbert Greirson of Castelmaddie' whose signature appears on the 1637 petition against the Service Book (see Chapter 2, fig. 4).[8] He had died in April 1641, without male issue, and his younger brother, John Greirson, had been retoured his heir in 1643 - becoming laird of Castelmaddie and the Carmonochs.[9] As Gilbert Greirson had habitually styled himself as 'of Castelmaddie' it had seemed probable that it had been Castelmaddie (after the death of his tenant, John MakLuire, there, in 1617), that he, as a 'bonnet laird', had

---

[6] J. Paterson, *History of the County of Ayr, with a genealogical account of the families of Ayrshire*, Ayr, 1847, I, p. 271.

[7] SRO C22/6, Retour, Gilbert Greirson, 10 October 1615, fol. 73.

[8] Hamilton-Grierson, 'Notes on Various Families of the Name of Grierson', p. 42.

[9] SRO C22/17, Retour, John Greir, 16 May 1643, fol.185v.

himself farmed, and that his younger brother, John, would have been assigned the tenancy of the chief of the three Carmonochs - the Mid Carmonoch which, as 'Carminnows', exists to this day.

The typescript 'Notes on Various Families of the Name Grierson', by Sir Philip J. Hamilton-Grierson, held at the Ewart Library, Dumfries, provided crucially important information about this younger brother and about the subsequent history of his lands. A main source for the information quoted by these 'Notes' had been papers of the Dalgoner Charter Chest. How this information had come to be, specifically, in the Dalgoner Charter Chest was explicable on the basis that, after the death of this John Greir in 1669, and of his son and heir (who had reverted to the style 'John Greirson of Castelmaddie'), two years later, in 1671, without male issue, the estates of Castelmaddie and the Carmonochs had, by agreement, on 26 May 1673, been divided between a rather distant claimant John Greirson of Dalgoner, and the Master of Cathcart.

Her father probably this John Greir, later 'of Castelmaddie'

This 'John Greirson', the younger of the two 'bairns', who was later to call himself 'John Greir', was the only contemporary 'John Greir' identified who could well have been Mareon Greir's father. There had been several reasons for confidence that he was indeed her father.

First, in choosing to modify his name from 'John Greirson' to 'John Greir', his name had become one of the two names ('John Greir' and 'William Greir') which had been deduced as the most probable for Mareon Greir's father.[10] Second, as the younger brother of Gilbert Greirson (who appeared to have been born about 1594) this John Greir would have been born some time later than that date; would have reached marriageable age (sixteen) some time later than 1610; and Mareon Greir, if his

[10] Ibid.

daughter, would therefore, by virtue of being born some time later than 1610, herself have reached marriageable age some time later than 1626. This had fitted in well with the subsequent arguments that her marriage to Dr MakLuire would have been in 1634.

Third, it had seemed not surprising if a daughter of this John Greir would have married Dr John MakLuire, son of the tenant in Nether Carmonoch of her father's family. Finally, no 'William Greir', to cast doubt upon this 'John Greir' being Mareon's father, had been identified.

Grounds for caution considered

However, there had been reasonable grounds for caution before accepting this provisional conclusion that Mareon Greir had been a daughter of this John Greir. In the first place, the Hamilton-Grierson 'Notes' at Dumfries say that, according to the 'Dalgoner Charter Chest, 15', this John Greir, dying in 1669, had been survived by his widow, by his son John, and by four daughters - *viz.*, Agnes, Beven, Sidney and Helen. The 'Notes' do not mention a Mareon. On the other hand, a retour at Kirkcudbright dated 17 October 1672, finding the above four daughters to be heirs portionary of Gilbert Greirson of Castelmaddie, their paternal uncle (the retour upon which the above statement would appear to have been based) had taken place one year after the death of John Greir's son, John, three years after John Greir's own death, and some five decades after the probable time of his marriage.[11] Consequently, it had seemed not improbable that there may have been other sons and daughters of this John Greir who may, in the meantime, have died, and who would not, therefore, have been mentioned in the 1672 retour.

There had, indeed, been a positive implication, in the retour of 1672, that there had existed one other daughter of this John Greir who had been older than the four survivors listed in that retour. This implication had lain in the fact

---

[11] SRO C22/21, Retour, daughters of John Greir, 17 October 1672, fol. 149.

that Agnes Greir, the first-mentioned of the four, and presumably the most senior of them, would surely have been named after Agnes Maxwell her paternal grandmother. If so, this Agnes Greir would most probably have been the second, rather than the first, daughter of John Greir - in this way implying that there had indeed been another, hitherto unaccounted-for, first daughter. If Mareon Greir had indeed been that first daughter, she would have been yet another daughter, in addition to the above-mentioned four, who survived her father - because it is known that she had not died until 1671.[12] The absence, nevertheless, of her name from the list of survivors of John Greir given in the Hamilton-Grierson 'Notes' would have been fully explicable by the known fact that she had died in 1671, while those named on the list had been daughters who were surviving at the time of the retour in the following year of 1672 rather than at the time of John Greir's death.

Also, an entry in the Edinburgh baptismal register:

> 25th February, 1636: to Andrew Greir, cordiner, and Elizabeth Cowstoun, a son named Johne. Witnesses, Mr Johne MakLure Doctor in Physick; James Hamiltonn, Reader at the College Kirk; David Kinloch, skinner; David Makgill, wreater[13]

had suggested that there had been at least one other son to this John Greir *viz.*, this Andrew Greir, at the baptism of whose first son Dr MakLuire had been the principal witness. As the child's name had been 'John', and as he had been the first son, he would presumably have been named after the paternal grandfather, whose name would therefore have indeed been 'John Greir'. This had indicated that Dr MakLuire would have been the principal

---

[12] H. Paton, ed., *Register of Interments in the Greyfriars Burying-ground, Edinburgh, 1658-1700*, Edinburgh: Scottish Record Society, 1902, Old Series, 26, 21 February 1671.

[13] SRO OPR 685 1/4, Edinburgh (Greyfriars) Register of Baptisms, 25 February 1636.

witness by virtue of having been the father's brother-in-law.

Yet another, and important, piece of confirmatory evidence that Mareon Greir's father had indeed been this John Greir had been found (after a long search), in the Christian name of his wife - Mareon's mother. In this connection it had been noted, as already mentioned, that whereas Mareon Greir's second daughter, Alison, had been named after the paternal grandmother, Alison Denholme, it would have been her first daughter, Helen (see Chapter 2, fig. 1), who would have been named after the maternal grandmother. It had been only after a search initially confined to public records (which had failed to discover the name of this John Greir's wife), that the opportunity of consulting the typescript Hamilton-Grierson 'Notes' in Dumfries had led to the discovery that his wife had indeed been a 'Helen'. Importantly, also, she had been a 'Helen Greirson'.[14]

A regrettable frustration

The source of all this information recorded in the Hamilton-Grierson 'Notes' had been given as the 'Dalgoner Charter Chest, 15'. It had therefore been hoped, by consulting item 15 in the Dalgoner Charter Chest papers, at the Scottish Record Office, where the Hamilton-Grierson Papers, including the Dalgoner Charter Chest Papers, are held, not only to verify the information but to enquire into two further possibilities.

The first of these had been that there might be fuller information about the identity of this 'Helen Greirson', wife of John Greir, which might reveal a closer relatedness than that of her husband, John Greir himself, to Sir Robert Greir of Lag, thus explaining more fully how the latter had come to be the principal witness at the baptism of the first child to Dr MakLuire and Mareon Greir - and grand-child to Mareon Greir's mother, Helen Greirson. The second

---

[14] Hamilton-Grierson, 'Notes on Various Families of the Name of Grierson', p. 44.

had been that of finding that the Christian name of the mother of Helen Greirson herself might have been 'Mareon' - which would have added still more confirmation that Mareon Greir, by virtue of having been a first daughter, and named after Helen Greirson's mother, would indeed have been the daughter of this Helen Greirson, John Greir's wife.

However, in 1985, it was explained that these Hamilton-Grierson Papers were in such a state of disarray that even the making of an inventory of them was anticipated to be a major, lengthy, and tedious task prior to which production to readers was not possible. This seems still, unfortunately, to be the case.

Conclusions

Despite that particular frustration, confidence was maintained that Mareon Greir, Dr MakLuire's second wife, was the daughter of the John Greir who, in 1627, was to emigrate from Mid Carmonoch to Ulster for a period of fifteen years, taking his little girl, Mareon, with him and, later, to return to Kirkcudbrightshire to succeed as the laird of Castelmaddie and the Carmonochs.[15]

---

[15] Ibid., p. 43.

Figure

The Griersons of Castelmaddie and the Carmonochs.

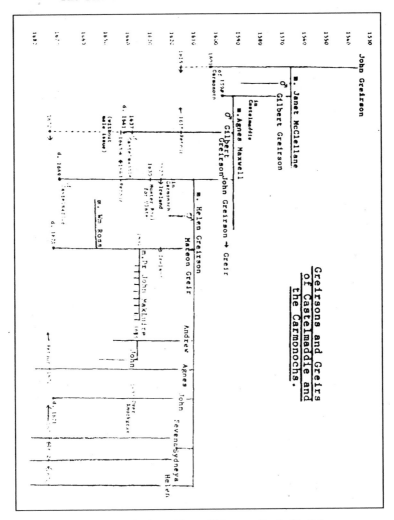

The deduced genealogical position of Mareon Greir, Dr John MakLuire's wife, amongst the Greirsons/Greirs of Castelmaddie and the Carmonochs.

Appendix E

Dr John MakLuire's issue

The lives of Dr MakLuire's nine children, although scarcely of relevance to the search for the full identity of Dr MakLuire himself are, perhaps, of some intrinsic interest.

It had become apparent that the first and the second of the three sons who had been named 'John', both dying in 1645, presumably of the plague of that year, had pre-deceased him. It appears that the uncertain number of his other children who survived him would all have still been 'bairns' - i.e. under the age of 14 - at the time of his death c1652. They were to acquire a step-father when their mother, Mareon Greir, married a William Ross, writer, in 1653.[1]

Their subsequent lives

Nothing was discovered about the lives of the two daughters, Helen (b.1638) and Alison (b.1639). Discoveries about William, James, Thomas, Hew, and John (the third to be so named) were as follows:

William, b.1640, the second son, may have been (if, in 1671, at the age of 31, he was still alive) the 'Mr' William McCluire, whose child is recorded as having died in that year.[2] However, no evidence of him having obtained a Master's degree to justify the appellation 'Mr' was found. It would appear that he was already deceased, and without male issue, by 1675 (see below), when he would have been aged 35.

---

[1] H. Paton, *The Register of Marriages for the Parish of Edinburgh 1595-1700*, Edinburgh: Scottish Record Society, 1905, Old Series, 27, p. 287.

[2] H. Paton, ed., *Register of Interments in the Greyfriars Burying-ground, Edinburgh, 1658-1700*, Edinburgh: Scottish Record Society, 1902, Old Series, 26, 21 February 1671.

James, b.1641. It would appear that he, also, was already deceased, and without male issue, by 1675 (see below) when he would have been aged 34.

Thomas, b.1643, matriculated at the University of Edinburgh in 1656 at the age of 13, and again in the following year.[3] He graduated MA in 1661, aged 18, and subsequently appears, in documents, as 'Mr Thomas McLure, writer in Edinburgh'.[4] It seems that he was to die on 8 April 1675, aged 32, two months after his younger brother Hew (see below) had died.[5] According to their common testament, these brothers had shared a house 'at Bow foot' in Edinburgh.

Hew, b.1644, matriculated at the University of Edinburgh in 1658 at the age of 14.[6] It seems that he did not graduate. In 1671, aged 27, he may have been the 'Hew McClure' from whom, jointly with Mareon Greir and Hugh Ross, two persons of the name Denholme had borrowed money - the deed being 'written by Hew McCluire', perhaps himself, but perhaps another 'Hew McCluire, writer', described, elsewhere as 'a bastard'.[7] He died, as mentioned above, two months before his brother, Thomas, on 15 February 1675, aged 31.[8]

John, b.1646, the third son to be given the name 'John' - and the youngest of the family - was probably, at the age of 14, the 'Johne McClure' who was in trouble through becoming involved in the 'bickering' between Leith and Edinburgh. An extract from the records of the burgh of Edinburgh dated 15 August 1660, reads as follows:

Compeired Mr Johne Home Master of the Grammar Schooll and compleind upon Johne

---

[3] List of Matriculating Students, University of Edinburgh, 1656.

[4] List of Graduates, University of Edinburgh, 1661.

[5] SRO CC8/8/75; Testament, Mr Thomas and Hew McCluires, 1675.

[6] List of Matriculating Students, University of Edinburgh, 1658.

[7] SRO RD4/23/340, Deed.

[8] SRO CC8/8/75; Testament, Mr Thomas and Hew McCluires, 1675.

Muschet and Johne McClure twa of Mr Thomas Blackburnes schollers for seduceing of the said Mr Johne his schollers to the bickering. The Councell appoynts the baillies to call for them and to tak such ordour with them as they sall sie caus.[9]

This John MakLuire, the youngest of Dr MakLuire's children, would have been of marriageable age in 1662 but there is no record of him having married in Edinburgh. He is mentioned in a Deed, dated 8 February 1669, in which he is specified as the son of Mareon Greir.[10] In 1675 he had been discerned the nearest of kin to his two older brothers, who had died in that year. This had implied that the still more senior brothers, William and James, were themselves already deceased, and without lawful male issue, by that year. In 1676, when this John MakLuire would have been aged 30, an Andrew Stewart is recorded as having received a sum from him and his mother, Mareon Greir.[11] It is, of course, possible that he married elsewhere than in Edinburgh. He is the only male survivor of his father and may have had descendants.

The improbability of the author's descent from Dr MakLuire

The factual information gleaned about the children of Dr John MakLuire had seemed to be of potential relevance to the possibility of Dr MakLuire having been an ancestor of the present author.

At the time of instituting the search for the identity of Dr MakLuire, it had just been established that the author's own earliest known-for-certain ancestor had been a David McClure (see fig. 1), flourishing at the end of the 1600s in the parish of Dailly, Ayrshire, and that he had probably

---

[9] M. Wood and R. Hannay, ed., *Extracts from the Records of the Burgh of Edinburgh 1655-1665*, Edinburgh: Scottish Burgh Records Society, 1940, p. 210.

[10] SRO RD4/23/263, Deed.

[11] SRO RD4/40/299, Deed.

been the same person as the David McClure (1656-1729), moving to, and dying in, the neighbouring parish of Barr, whose grave-stone is to be seen in the kirkyard there (fig. 2).

Now, the 'Doctor Makcleuir' newly discovered as the author of the 1630 petition to establish the Edinburgh College clearly had been flourishing only some two generations earlier than the author's ancestor, David McClure, and the prospect of finding him to be an even earlier ancestor had understandably held a certain fascination.

The David McCluire discovered to be the author's earliest known-for-certain ancestor (see fig 2), clearly could not himself have been a son of Dr MakLuire - having been born (in 1656) some four years after the latter's death. However, it had been thought, provisionally, that his father, who surely would have been born some time prior to 1640, could possibly have been a son, not recorded in the Edinburgh records.

Now, David McCluire, the certain ancestor of the present author, was probably the same David McCluire who, two years earlier than the baptism of his daughter, Jean McCluire (the author's ancestor), in the parish of Dailly, had had a child named Margaret baptised.[12] Also, it is recorded that that David McCluire's father, who had 'held up the child', had been a 'Hew McCluire'. It had seemed, therefore, if the two Davids in that baptismal register were indeed the same (as had seemed probable, but not certain, as it seems that there were two 'David McCluires' having children baptised in Dailly parish in the 1690s!) that that Hew McCluire may have been a still earlier ancestor of the present author.

This had raised the further possibility of this Hew McCluire, the presumed earlier ancestor of the present author, having been the unrecorded son of Dr MakLuire hypothesised above. If he was, he would certainly have

<hr>

[12] SRO OPR 585/1, New Daily Register of Baptisms, 20 November 1692.

been an illegitimate son, because Dr MakLuire's youngest son, John, in 1675, was discerned his only lawful descendant.[13] Here, the appearance in certain Edinburgh records of a 'Hew McCluire, 'write' (?either 'writer' or 'wright')', specified as 'a bastard', had raised the interesting possibility of this 'Hugh McCluire, a bastard', having been the Hew McCluire, possible earlier ancestor of the author. However, the 'Hugh McCluire, a bastard', was buried at Greyfriars on 26 March 1669 and could not, therefore, have been the grandfather in Dailly parish who held up the grandchild in 1692.[14]

Thus, while a legitimate descent of the present author from Dr MakLuire has to be ruled out, a particular illegitimate descent, through the Hew McCluire who 'held up' a grand-daughter in 1692, had also to be ruled out. While some other illegitimate descent of course remains theoretically possible, it is a possibility for which no evidence has been found.

---

[13] SRO CC8/8/75, Testament, Mr Thomas and Hew McCluires, 1675.

[14] Paton, *Register of Interments in the Greyfriars Burying-ground, Edinburgh*

Figure 1

David McClure, earliest known ancestor of the author.

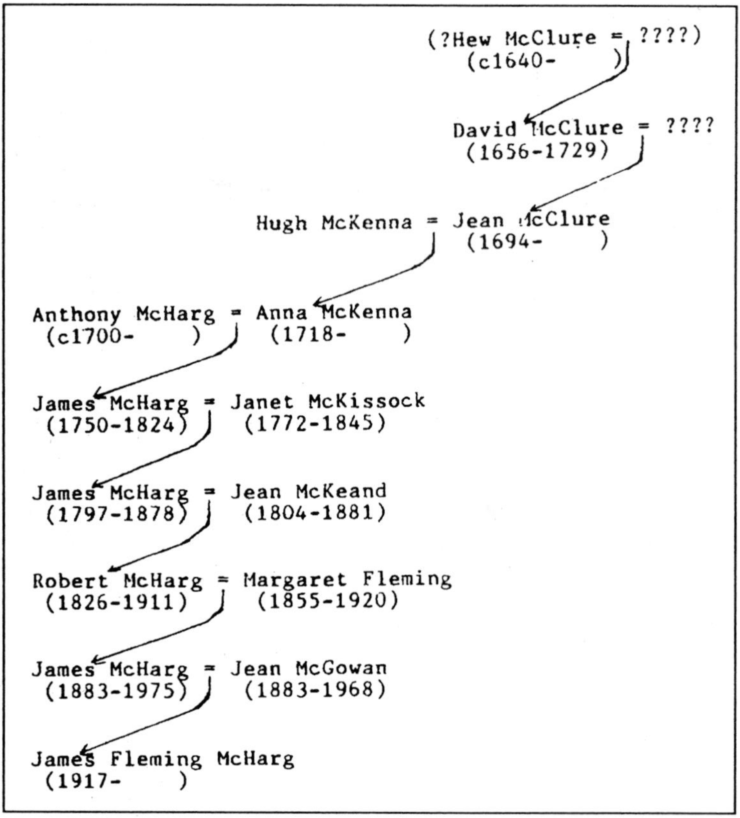

```
                                    (?Hew McClure = ????)
                                      (c1640-    )

                                    David McClure = ????
                                     (1656-1729)

                       Hugh McKenna = Jean McClure
                                       (1694-    )

          Anthony McHarg = Anna McKenna
            (c1700-   )    (1718-    )

          James McHarg = Janet McKissock
           (1750-1824)   (1772-1845)

          James McHarg = Jean McKeand
           (1797-1878)   (1804-1881)

          Robert McHarg = Margaret Fleming
           (1826-1911)    (1855-1920)

          James McHarg = Jean McGowan
           (1883-1975)   (1883-1968)

          James Fleming McHarg
           (1917-   )
```

Figure 2

The grave-stone at Barr, Ayrshire, of David McClure (1656-1729), probably the David McClure who is my earliest known-for-certain ancestor.

Transcription:

HEAR

LAYES • THE • COPS • OF
DAVID • McCLURE   WH
O • DYED   9 JANᵁ 1729
AGE   72 & ALSO   THE
CORPS • OF • JOHN • RIN
NNIE • HIS • SISTER • SO
N • ALSO HERELYESTH
E • CORPSOF • WILᴸIAMMᶜ
CLURE • IN DINGARVA
WHO   DYED   OCTOBER
??????????????????????????

INDEX

Index

Birds, susceptibility to air from mines 75, 76.
Bishops on the Privy Council 112.
Black Death 72; see also Plague.
Blair, J.S.G. 42, 43, 73.
Blawquhairn farm, Dr MakLuire's possible place of birth 23, 25;
    David MakLuire 1623 25; Adam Denholme 1637 25, 201.
Boyd, Robert, of Trochrig 62.
Braidstane Castle, parish of Beith 28.
Broad, William, of Aberdeen 72; his MD thesis not the first in
    Scotland 3.
Browne, Sir Thomas 145, 187.
Buckler, choice of the word by Dr MakLuire 103 *et seq.*
Buckler of Bodilie Health, The 5, 7, 70, 80, 81, 109.
Burdeous (Burdiehouse) 59, 189.
Caen University 58.
Cahors University 58.
Calderwood 72, 76.
Caledon, Earls of 57; Lands of, in Co. Tyrone 50.
Cambridge University 58, 72.
Carminnows 18.
Carmonoch, Upper or Over, Mid, Nether 18, 19.
Castlehill (Edinburgh) 58.
Channing, W, drawing of Galloway's Close 125.
Charles I, 1630 petition to 1, 109; his letter commending Dr
    MakLuire's petition 116; marginal labelling of the letter omitted
    from transcripts 120; Scottish Coronation 126, 154.
Charles II, establishing of Royal College of Physicians, Edinburgh 4;
    coronation at Scone 181.
Clancy, Michael, on the law of husband and wife 15.
Claneboye, Viscount, at Bangor 106, 141.
Columbus 185.
Comrie, J.D. 72, 183.
Copernicus 184.
Covenant of 1638 146.
Craig, Dr W.S., *History of the Royal College of Physicians of
    Edinburgh* omits mention of Dr MakLuire's petition 118; misleading
    statements about the 1630 attempt 120.
'Creditable persons', who supplied information about the young Hugh
    Montgomery's injury 168.
Cromwell, Oliver 180.

230

Curtis A.H. 188.
Dalgoner Charter Chest, not available for inspection 218, 221, 222.
Dalmanasyde 216.
Dalry, parish of 23-25.
Danzig, plague at 65.
De Motu Cordis 133.
Denholme, Adam, goldsmith in Edinburgh 200-201.
Denholme, Adam, in Blauquhairn 201.
Denholme, Alison 199, 200; Dr MakLuire's mother 11;
 mistranscription of name 12, 13; trial for adultery 14, 23.
Denholme, Katharine Panton, confusion with Alison Denholme 199.
Descartes R. 186.
Donaghadee 163.
Donnane, Alison, mistranscription of 'Dennane' (or Denholme) 12,
 13.
Douai, Counter Reformation centre 95, 146.
Douglas, William, fellow student 46.
Dysentery 79.
Edinburgh, the milk 2/3 water 58; Burgh Muir 65; Castlehill, 58;
 Arthur's Seat 50; King's Park 66; Burdeous (Burdiehouse) 59; Royal
 College of Physicians 1, 4, 109-120, 184; St Roque's Hospital 65;
 Sciennes Hospital 65.
Extent Roll for the Annuity Tax 122.
Fabricius 186, 190.
False pregnancy 189; see also Pseudocyesis.
Famine, in 1621 23 76.
Finlay, James, in Garrerie, trial for adultery 23.
Five Articles of Perth 146.
Flamborough Head 182.
Forensic psychiatry 171.
Franeker University 58.
Frankincence, for fumigation 78, 213.
Fraser, Francis, fellow student 45.
Froskan and Croattes, lands of 129, 141.
Galen 73-78.
Galileo Galilei 41, 186.
Galloway's Close, Dr MakLuire's house in 124; Channing's drawing
 125.
Garmouth on Spey 180.
Generall Practise of Medecine, The 5, 129, 184.

Index

Ross, William, writer, second husband of Mareon Greir 182.

Royal College of Physicians of Edinburgh, 1630 attempt to establish 1; established 1681 4; tercentenary celebrations 1, 7.

Royal remission of John MakLuire, Dr MakLuire's father 12.

St Andrews University, undergraduate teaching of medicine 42; doubts about early grants of MD 68-9.

St Leonard's College, University of St Andrews 39.

St John's Town of Dalry 25.

Sandie the souter 89.

Sandys, Patrick 73; birth 62; third Principal of Edinburgh University 62; carmen in praise of Dr MakLuire 62, 171.

Sanitatis Semita 5, 71; publication 1630 5, 69-70, 109.

Schaw, Mareon, in Craiginbae, trial for adultery 23-5.

Schevez W. 183.

Scott, James, fellow student 47; witness at baptism of Dr MakLuire's second daughter 47.

Scott, Mr William, Doctor in Physick, 59-60.

Scrymgeure, David, fellow student 46.

Scurvy 77.

Semita, choice of the word 103.

Servetus M 185.

Shaw, Elizabeth, wife of 1st Viscount Montgomery 32.

Sibbald, Dr George 111, 116-120; prime mover in 1617 attempt to establish RCPE 51, 111, 118-120, 171; carmen in praise of Dr MakLuire 41.

Sibbald, Sir Robert, unfinished manuscript History of RCPE 119; pseudonym 'Philiatreus' 129.

Skene G. 183.

Smart, Robert, Keeper of Muniments, St Andrews University 9.

Spencer, H.R. 188.

Spotswood, Sir Robert 'incendiarist' 172.

Spott, East Lothian 179.

Stars, causing disease 77.

Still G.F. 191.

Sympathie 133.

Taylor, John, London waterboatman 64.

Theophrastes 73.

Thistle, HMS 65.

Thome, Alexander, student at Edinburgh University 123.

Tobacco 93-4.